Manual of
Vegetation Analysis

MANUAL OF VEGETATION ANALYSIS

Stanley A. Cain

THE UNIVERSITY OF MICHIGAN

AND

G. M. de Oliveira Castro

INSTITUTO OSWALDO CRUZ, BRAZIL

(Facsimile of the 1959 edition)

HAFNER PUBLISHING COMPANY
NEW YORK
1971

581.526
C12m
78923
July 1972

Published by
HAFNER PUBLISHING COMPANY, INC.
866 Third Avenue
New York, N.Y. 10022

Library of Congress Catalog Card Number: 77-180016

Printed in U.S.A. by
NOBLE OFFSET PRINTERS, INC.
NEW YORK 3, N. Y.

CONTENTS

FIGURES

TABLES

PREFACE

THE *Manual of Vegetation Analysis* was prepared in first draft when the senior author was a member of the United Nations Technical Assistance Mission to Brazil, in 1955 and 1956. Employed by UNESCO as Expert in Ecology at the petition of the Musée Nacional, Rio de Janeiro, the first several months were spent on a research design for a study in human ecology of a small fishing village, Arraial do Cabo, that was just coming under the first impact of industrialization. The last several months of the period were spent with Dr. Castro, coauthor of the *Manual,* with the full coöperation of the Brazilian Serviço Nacional de Malaria.

Dr. Castro, whose permanent post is with the Instituto Oswaldo Cruz, a research institute specializing in tropical medicine, had for some years been "on loan" to the Serviço Nacional de Malaria. He had developed special interest in the structure and distribution of vegetation as it relates to medical ecology, that is, to the epidemiology of malaria, yellow fever, schistosomiasis, etc. We had become acquainted during the planning days for the study of the fishing village of Arraial do Cabo, Cabo Frio, so it was natural and logical to turn to him and the Serviço Nacional de Malaria for the purpose of making studies of Brazilian vegetation.

We became especially interested in the application of phytosociological concepts and methods, most of which had originated in the north temperate regions and had not yet been well tested under tropical conditions in Brazil. As time went on and we worked in various places from the Territory of Amapá in the north to the state of Rio Grande do Sul in the south, it occurred to us that our experiences would have more value for the Serviço Nacional de Malaria if we prepared a small manual of concepts and methods. It soon became clear to us that "a camel had got its head in the tent" as the manuscript continued to grow beyond the original intent and lose its provincial cast. Because the manuscript was being written in English, first drafts were made by the senior author, but they were read and discussed between us, sentence by sentence. Revisions and additions since 1956 are the sole responsibility of the senior author. As it turns out, the *Manual* is in no sense a study of Brazilian vegetation, but it does recognize the existence of the tropics and some of its problems, and that is something.

Since this preface is not being written by both of us, I will take this opportunity to express to Dr. Castro my appreciation of his scholarship, his interest in phytosociological matters when very few others in Brazil were interested in them, and, above all, for his warm friendliness that readily encompassed the idiosyncracies of his colleague and eased many a situation. And finally a word of appreciation to Doña Elza and Louise, his wife and mine, who saw us off to sometimes remote places with no more apparent qualms than if we were going to the office, I would like to say *piranhas* and *oncas* to the contrary. But bacilli, amebae, and mosquitoes are more to the truth.

S. A. C.

Ann Arbor, Michigan
April, 1959

ACKNOWLEDGMENTS

THE *Manual* project received the support of UNESCO and the cordial backing of M. Henri Laurentie, resident representative in Rio de Janeiro of the United Nations Technical Assistance Board, even though it was far removed from the initial interests that took me to Brazil. Dr. Manoel Ferreira, Director, Serviço Nacional de Malaria, was deeply interested in our work. He provided indispensable assistance, both personally and through the far-flung organization which he heads that has staff members in nearly every village and city in Brazil. The importance to our work of the travel facilities (plane, boat, and jeep) and local assistance he made available to us cannot be overemphasized in a country so large and, to a Norte Americano, often so perplexing. We are also indebted to the Conselho Nacional de Pesquisas, Rio de Janeiro, for financial assistance, and to Dr. Eloisa Alberta Torres, then Director, Musée Nacional, and Dr. Fernando Segadas Vianna, Botanist at the Musée, for office space, library facilities, friendly interest, and many aids at difficult times. Our deep appreciation and thanks go to all these persons. In a country with so vast a flora, not well known in many places, we found it possible to work efficiently only where there were local botanists and herbaria. They are mentioned at appropriate places in the text. Their generous assistance in the field and with our collections is gratefully acknowledged.

Several graduate students at the University of Michigan have read and discussed with me parts of the manuscript. Our appreciation goes to them although they remain nameless at this point.

Appreciation is here expressed to several publishers of copyrighted material for permission to use parts of it. Immediate and ultimate sources are cited at appropriate points in the text.

S. A. C.

Manual of
Vegetation Analysis

Chapter 1

INTRODUCTION

THE *Manual of Vegetation Analysis* contains many of the concepts of vegetation that have been developed by botanists and describes the basis for these concepts and the field techniques that have been found useful in developing and applying them. These range all the way from methods applicable to extensive studies of large areas of heterogeneous vegetation to others that are applicable to intensive investigations of small areas, single communities, and simple situations. Some methods are analytic, objective, and quantitative, and the concepts involved are precise and the data obtained are verifiable. Others which are qualitative and more subjective are likewise cogent. Some of the concepts and methods have stood the test of time and use in a variety of types of vegetation in many parts of the world. Others that have had wide acceptance and considerable usefulness are being weakened by the steady accumulation of objective data.

As Raunkiaer (337) has succinctly said, "Science consists in the recognition of similarity and dissimilarity so that the beginning and end of science is comparison. We must therefore reduce the materials yielded by our investigations to a state capable of comparison. In other words we must measure and count phenomena so as to be able to express them in numbers. I do not mean that we must always try to express ourselves in numerical formulae—far from it—but when scientific comparison has to be made, we should attain to numerical expression of phenomena, or to expression in terms of definite concepts which are as stable and unequivocal as numbers." What is desired in vegetation analysis is an accuracy of description and, where feasible, of measurement consonant with the required uses of the results. The

1

ultimate test of any methodology is its usefulness for the purposes at hand, including its relative efficiency.

The *Manual* has as its central objective the presentation and clarification of sociological techniques, not the explanation of ecological relations of vegetation. In a very real sense the two are not separable. Concepts of composition and structure of vegetation cannot be separated from the investigator's understanding of the vegetation with which he works, including his real knowledge of its ecology and his working hypotheses concerning it. Also, most morphological studies of vegetation are inevitably influenced by taxonomic (as well as physiological) concepts, that is, by the investigator's ideas concerning the association and the hierarchical relations of the various associations dealt with. This is true whether or not the investigator is strongly influenced by the concepts of succession and climax. Although we may set out to describe vegetation, morphological work being a logical antecedent to physiological-ecological work designed to explain it, concepts and methods relating to structure are inevitably influenced by concepts of actions and processes that occur in vegetation.

It seems to us that sound descriptions of vegetation—as objective and quantitative as possible, but at the same time compatible with the purposes—form concrete and enduring contributions to knowledge. On the other hand, ecological work done in the absence of adequate studies of the vegetation itself can have little meaning or usefulness. In the field of vegetation this is comparable to physiological work on organisms of unknown systematic position and genetic composition. No matter how precise the work, it matters little if the material on which it is done is unknown. We make no apology for a manual restricted to techniques and problems of the physical description of vegetation. Our present interest lies with the vegetation itself, not with its environment and the actions, reactions, and coactions.

We hope that this compendium from the literature, together with some of our experiences, understandings, interpretations, and evaluations, will be useful. At the same time, knowing that the *Manual* is neither complete nor perfectly representative of the concepts and methods of others, we trust that it will not become a guide to be slavishly followed. This is not intended to be a "cookbook" type of manual. First emphasis must be on concepts of vegetation, not on methods of gathering data or producing descriptions. The investigator has objectives. He is confronted by problems. He has concepts. His methodology must be related to these matters. Knowing what some of the methods are, the investigator must face his own problems and select or devise methods of vegetation analysis appropriate to his situation. He should ask himself a series of questions:

Why do a certain thing?

Why am I gathering these data?

What kinds of data result from my methods?

What objectivity and meaning do the data have?

What are the limitations of the methods?

Am I making the best use of my time and the resources at hand?

Under the circumstances and with the given objectives, should work be intensive, on one or a small group of stands, or should it be extensive?

Will the results have any general significance? Will they add to theory?

For example, Poore (327) asked himself, in a critical field study of phytosociological methods, "Is it possible, by describing sample plots in one of the various ways advocated by the sociologists, to build up abstract vegetation units which correspond with real, recognizable community types in the field?" Can one "form an opinion on the nature of the discontinuities and relationships between communities?" What is the "most valid and practicable method of characterizing such units, if distinguished?"

In most regions the history of vegetational studies starts with the employment of reconnaissance methods. This is in a sense the pioneer phase of vegetation analysis and has usually been done, especially in the past, by botanists thoroughly trained in taxonomy and often widely traveled in their own countries and in the world. On the basis of their observations, sharpened by long experience, they have judged the relative abundance of species, their relative dominance in their respective communities, their ecological amplitudes, their dynamic behavior, their relative exclusiveness to certain situations or associations, etc. They have observed the combinations of species, often in correlation with rather obvious natural situations or habitats, that formed obvious communities which reoccurred in suitable places over a more or less wide territory. Both the grosser aspects of physiognomy and some of its more subtle expressions have been perceived. As pointed out by Brown and Curtis (66), "In capable hands this method has produced results of highly significant value to our understanding of the vegetation of many regions of the world." It has given us the concept of plant association, with the tacit assumption of its objective reality in nature, and systems for the classification of vegetation units ranging from world formations correlated with major climatic areas to micro-associations correlated with relatively slight difference in habitat. It has produced systems of classification that are essentially floristic;

others in which physiognomy and life form predominate; some based on the development of vegetation and succession; and even systems that are based on physical environment and are only secondarily biological.

The reconnaissance method, despite its usefulness in the early stages of vegetation analysis, has certain important limitations. There never have been many persons whose comprehension of plants and the contributory sciences in the field of vegetation has been sufficient, whose experience has been broad and deep enough, whose observations have been astute enough, for their perceptions to stand up under later analysis by quantitative methods. But those who have been good have often been very good (Clements, Cockayne, Cowles, Diels, Drude, Engler, Grisebach, Hult, Kerner, Martius, Rübel, Schimper, Tansley, Warming, Willdenow, Wulff, *et al.*), even though some of their ideas must be discarded or reinterpreted. The principal difficulties of the reconnaissance method, however, lie in its highly personal nature and in the impossibility of using the results of the method to verify the community concepts upon which it is based (Brown and Curtis, 66). On the other hand, the method of quantitative measurement, when combined with valid sampling techniques, can be strictly objective and yield reproducible results. The first method is essentially practiced as an art; the latter method is scientific.

By the preceding discussion of methods we do not mean to imply that all vegetation analysis should be quantitative; there is always ample room for judgment and even for intuition. Many vegetational situations are so complicated, as to both composition and structure and the variable complex of interacting factors, that the analytic data yielded by the method of quantitative measurement pose a sometimes insuperable problem of valid integration or resynthesis. In the reconnaissance method the ecologist or plant geographer makes a rather subjective and intuitional integration of a myriad of factors to arrive at a conclusion that seems to fit the situation—to describe it, to give it a conceptual framework, to organize and classify it. Its contrast with the quantitative analytic method is perhaps analogous to the contrast between the phytometer method (Clements and Goldsmith, 129) and the usual techniques of plant physiology. The factors of the environment being so numerous and their effects on life processes in nature being modified by a change of state or condition of any one factor, the physiologist or ecologist is confronted by the extremely difficult problem of integrating data so that they have real meaning under natural conditions. However, any organism, by the fact of its successful life, has accomplished the automatic integration of the constantly changing environmental complex. This fact led Clements to the phytometer method, which involves the simple matter of determining relative measurement of different environments by the growth of a known strain of plants (such as *Helianthus annus*) in different habitats. A quantitative comparison of certain indices of growth of the phytometers provides a relative measure of the total environments of the different habitats. In principle, this is no different from the determination of site index in forestry by the measurement of the height of trees in a given period of time.

Chapter 2

FLORISTICS

FLORISTIC GEOGRAPHY

The phase of plant geography that studies the occurrence of kinds of plants in various parts of the world is *floristic geography*. The *flora* of an area is the total of all the kinds of plants that exist within the area. The term "flora" is also used as a title for botanical studies of an area in which primary attention is paid to the kinds of plants according to their genetic relationship. The floristic characterization of geographical regions is an ancient and honorable practice, as exemplified, for example, by Linnaeus' *Flora Lapponica* and Martius' *Flora Brasiliensis*. Taxonomists and geographers are still busy determining the natural occurrences of species, subspecies, genera, families, etc.

It early became apparent that plants are not indiscriminately distributed, but that each taxon has a definable area.[1] Furthermore, there are cases where the individual areas or ranges of several species are similar and together they thus constitute a type of *floristic area*. Such plants, common to and more or less confined within a given region, may be used to characterize a *floristic territory*. Other plants than those used to define it will occur within the territory, more or less extending through it, or beyond it. It is thus that one can speak of a "coastal plain flora," a "mountain flora," etc., because the areas of certain species are largely coincident with the topographic feature. A plant, the characteristic area of which is in a certain territory, may also occur outside of the territory. In its extraneous occurrence it is usually thought of as a representative of a "foreign" *floristic element*. For example, a given region might be a plateau lying between the sea and mountains, and its fiora might, and probably would, contain species characteris-

[1] A *taxon* is a taxonomic category of any rank, such as species, subspecies, or genus.

6

tic of other territories; thus the floristic elements represented would be such as the "coastal plain element," the "mountain element," etc., in addition to the species characteristic of the area. Certain problems involved here are discussed in more detail in *Foundations of Plant Geography* (Cain, 93).

All the concepts and terms discussed above have their counterparts in *faunistic geography*. Also, because both plants and animals sometimes show similar chorological phenomena, one can speak of *biotic territories, biotic elements,* etc.

VEGETATION

In the preceding section attention was given to natural floristic areas, and it is apparent that what was referred to are species and not their organization into communities. The point of view is changed when one considers the geography of natural areas established on a basis of plant communities. The vegetation of a region consists of all the examples of the different types of communities within the region. A *plant community* is an organized complex having a typical composition (floristic aspect) and structure (morphological aspect) that results from the interactions through time. It is not a mere aggregation of plants. We must recognize the distinction between the *stand,* or concrete example of a community, and the concept of community type. The former is a single, specific entity of aggregate character with limited spatial boundaries and a rather completely describable composition and structure. The latter is a conception of the *community type* based upon knowledge of a series of separate individual community stands which are more or less similar. One is the association individual, the *concrete association;* the other is the "association" *per se; the abstract association.* The concept of association as a classificatory unit has a complicated history (Carpenter, 112).

PLANT AND ANIMAL GEOGRAPHY

As we have seen from the preceding discussion, *plant geography* (phytogeography) includes both floristic and vegetational studies of areal patterns. Similarly, *animal geography* (zoogeography) includes both faunistic and community studies. *Biogeography,* naturally, combines knowledge of the geography of both plants and animals. *Ecology* is specifically the study of the interrelations between organisms and their environment; yet it is natural that the distinction between chorological phenomena and ecological or functional phenomena should often be blurred and that geographical studies include ecological data, and vice versa. In practice the distinction lies in emphasis, for each science would be sterile without the other. It is also clear that the isolation of plant from animal geography is artificial, but it is usually a practical necessity because of the lack of competence of most investigators to work equally with both plants and animals.

FLORISTIC SYSTEMS

The idea of floristic areas in the plant life of the world was an early development in botany that resulted as the geographical reports of travelers and the systematic studies of the ever-growing collections in herbaria became abundant. Natural floristic areas, characterized by the kinds of plants they contain, vary in size from very local ones (such as the flora of the Brazilian mountain, Itatiaia) to those that have a certain unity although they occur on two or three continents (such as the boreal flora).

Willdenow (418) believed that every major mountain mass had its peculiar flora and that there are as many chief phytogeographical kingdoms as there are primitive mountains. Schouw (362) delimited 18 floristic kingdoms to which he later added more. These kingdoms were in some cases divided into provinces, as shown in the following European example:

> Kingdom of Saxifragaceae and Musci (Alpine-Arctic flora)
> > Province of Carex (Arctic flora)
> > Province of Primulaceae and Phyteumae (Alpine flora, S. Europe)

Schouw felt the need for an objective basis in the establishment of floristic areas and he laid down the following rules: A kingdom must have (1) at least half its known species peculiar to it (i.e., *endemic*); (2) one-fourth of the genera endemic, or so prevalent that they do not represent another kingdom; and (3) some families that are endemic or reach their maximum development within the boundaries of the kingdom. Within a kingdom, provinces could be established for areas in which one-fourth of the species and at least some genera were endemic. Meyen (292) was not long in pointing out that Schouw had not found it possible to follow his own rules in the system of floristic kingdoms and provinces he erected.

Drude (169) set up the following hierarchy for the classification of floristic territories:

> Florenreichsgruppen
> Florenreichen

> Gebieten
> Bezirken
> Landschaften

Modern classifications of floristic territories, as represented by the opinions of Engler (180, 181), Rikli (346), Diels (165), Hayek (234), and others, all have considerable similarity and are well represented by the classification of Engler and Diels (185) in the 11th edition of the *Syllabus der Pflanzenfamilien*. In this system there are only four kingdoms for all terrestrial vegetation: I. Holarctic, II. Paleotropical, III. Neotropical, IV. Southern Oceanic. Subdivisions for North and South America are shown in Table 1.

TABLE 1. The floristic territories of the Americas according to the classification of Engler (184) or Engler and Diels (185)

I. Northern extratropical or boreal kingdom
  A. Arctic region
    1. Arctic province
      c. Subprovince of Bering Sea lands and western Alaska
      d. Subprovince of arctic North America and northern Labrador
      e. Subprovince of Greenland
  B. Subarctic or conifer region
    3. Subarctic American province
      a. Southern Alaskan subprovince
      b. Subprovince of Peace and Athabasca River lands
      c. Northern Ontario subprovince
      d. Quebec and Labrador subprovince
  H. Pacific North American region
    1. Pacific conifer province
      a. Northern subprovince
        (1) District of northern coastal forest
        (2) Cis-Cascadian forest district and Cascade Mountains
      b. Southern subprovince
        (1) California coastal forest district
        (2) Western Nevada forest and Sierra Nevada district
    2. Rocky Mountain province
      a. Northern subprovince
      b. Central subprovince
      c. Southern subprovince and transition to the chaparral-Sonoran province of the Central American xerophytic region
    3. Western American desert and steppe province
      a. Subprovince of transition to the chaparral-Sonoran province in the Gila and Mohave deserts
      b. Subprovince of the Great Basin
      c. Inner California subprovince
  I. Atlantic North American region
    1. Lake province
      a. Pinus strobus subprovince

TABLE 1—*(Continued)*

    b. Eastern transition subprovince with summer-green forest

  2. Province of Mississippi and Allegheny forests with the Allegheny Mountains

    a. Mississippi-Ohio-Tennessee subprovince

    b. Allegheny subprovince

    c. Pine-barrens subprovince

  3. Evergreen province of South Atlantic States

    a. Subprovince of coastal swamp conifers

    b. Mixed forest subprovince

    c. Prairie-woodland subprovince

    d. Northern pine forest subprovince

  4. Prairie province

    a. Northern subprovince

    b. Central subprovince

    c. Southern subprovince

III. Central and South American kingdom (neotropical kingdom)

  A. Middle American xerophytic region

    1. Chaparral province

    2. Sonoran province

    3. Province of Mexican highlands

  B. Tropical American region

    1. Province of tropical America and tropical southernmost California

      a. South-Californian subprovince

      b. Mexican subprovince

      c. Yucatán subprovince

      d. Guatemalan subprovince

    2. West Indian province

      a. South Florida, Bahama Island, and Bermuda subprovince

      b. Cuba subprovince

      c. Jamaica subprovince

      d. Santo Domingo subprovince

      e. Puerto Rico subprovince

      f. Lesser Antilles subprovince

    3. Subequatorial Andean province

      a. Nicaragua-Costa Rican subprovince

      b. Colombian subprovince

      c. Ecuadorian subprovince

      d. Eastern Peruvian subprovince

    4. Cis-equatorial savanna province (non-Andean Venezuela and the highlands of the Guianas and Trinidad)

    5. Amazonian or hylaean province

    6. South Brazilian province

      a. East Brazilian deciduous forest subprovince

      b. Caatinga subprovince

      c. Campos subprovince

      d. South Brazilian Araucaria subprovince

      e. Subprovince of the island of South Trinidad

  C. Andean region

    1. Northern and middle high Andean province

      a. Northern Andean subprovince

      b. Tucumán subprovince

TABLE 1—*(Continued)*
- c. Middle Andean subprovince
- d. Subprovince of north Chile to 30½° S. latitude
2. Argentinian province
  - a. Gran Chaco subprovince
  - b. Espinale subprovince
  - c. Pampas subprovince
3. Andean-Patagonian province
4. Chilean province from 30½ to 37° S. latitude

IV. Southern (high oceanic) kingdom
  A. Austral-antarctic region of South America
  1. Western forest province from 37 to 54° S. latitude
  2. Eastern non-forest province

One of the recent systems of floristic areas of the world is that of Good (218). He has erected 37 regions (or provinces) that are set up along lines of floristic coincidence and over which certain historical phenomena have left their stamp. These regions are illustrated in Figure 1. They are arranged into kingdoms and the kingdoms into subkingdoms in the following list:

Boreal

1. Arctic and subarctic
2. Euro-Siberian
3. Sino-Japanese
4. West and central Asiatic
5. Mediterranean
6. Macronesian transition
7. Atlantic North American
8. Pacific North American

Paleotropical
African

9. African-Indian desert
10. Sudanese park steppe
11. Northeastern African transition
12. West African forest
13. East African steppe
14. South African steppe
15. East African island
16. Ascension and St. Helena

Indomalayan

17. Indian
18. Continental southeastern Asiatic
19. Malayan Archipelago

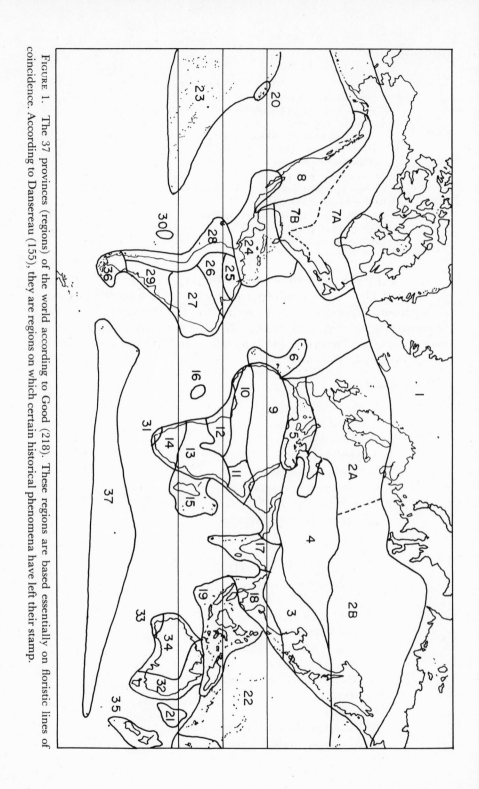

FIGURE 1. The 37 provinces (regions) of the world according to Good (218). These regions are based essentially on floristic lines of coincidence. According to Dansereau (155), they are regions on which certain historical phenomena have left their stamp.

Polynesian
   20. Hawaiian
   21. New Caledonian
   22. Melanesian and Micronesian
   23. Polynesian
Neotropical
   24. Caribbean
   25. Venezuela-Guiana
   26. Amazonian
   27. South Brazilian
   28. Andine
   29. Pampas
   30. Juan Fernandez
South African
   31. Cape
Australian
   32. North and east Australian
   33. Southwestern Australian
   34. Central Australian
Antarctic
   35. New Zealand
   36. Patagonian
   37. South temperate oceanic islands

PROBLEMS AND METHODS

Although several suggestions have been brought forward for quantifying the characteristics of floristic areas, none seems to have been practical. Floristic territories are characterized by the elements that are endemic to them or by other species, genera, etc., that predominate there. The difficulties are that the actual limits of range, even of the endemics, are seldom coincident, and predominance in a certain area is only relative and hard to be precise about.

The only technique that reduces the usually large element of subjectivity in the designation of floristic territories is one that has been developed by Gaussen (207), Lam (268), and Raup (339). The first step is the preparation of as accurate spot maps for each species of the flora as the available collections permit. Next the area of a species is delimited by a line drawn around the peripheral spots locating known occurrence. In doing this no assumptions should be made concerning the probable area of a species based upon topographic, climate, geologic, or soil boundaries, for the mapping should be as objective as possible and depend solely upon floristic data. Finally, outlines having been prepared of the areas of the species, they are superposed on a single map; or if the number of species is large, those whose real limits suggest a certain floristic boundary (as a result of coincidence of specific area boundaries in a certain place) are placed together on one composite map, and those determining other boundaries on other maps. If this procedure is faithfully followed, all species of a flora will be employed; this is quite a different matter from the usual subjective selection of certain species thought to "characterize" a floral territory.

Another problem presents itself. The above method makes no provision for delineation of area boundaries on the basis of relative abundance of a species within the various parts of its total range. For example, in Brazil *Araucaria* has its principal occurrence in an area from northern Rio Grande do Sul to Paraná, but the total area would have to include *Araucaria* almost as far south as Pelotas and as far north as the Montiqueira Mountains.

Finally, such boundaries of a floristic territory as can be deduced from the coincidence of boundaries of species have an embarrassing way of coinciding with sharp ecological barriers, such as abrupt changes in topography or soil and steep climatic gradients, and so are not purely floristic, although contrived from floristic data.

FLORISTIC-SOCIOLOGICAL TERRITORIES

Following the floristic divisions of Engler, Flahault, Diels, etc., Braun-Blanquet (58) recognized regional territories of six ranks based on a combination of floristic and vegetational characteristics. For the latter he used his concept of the plant association, and of the classification of associations into groups of higher rank on a basis of relationships revealed by significant species, especially those of high fidelity.

Region. The region is the most comprehensive unit. It is characterized by numerous well-defined climax communities. It has endemic families, tribes, genera, sections, etc. The unity of the region is shown by species of high sociological importance that occur throughout or nearly throughout it. Examples: The Euro-Siberic-North American region; the Mediterranean region; the Capetown region.

Province. The province is a subdivision of the region characterized by at least one distinctive climax community, and by various edaphic communities. It has endemic species and genera, and other genera that are only slightly represented in neighboring provinces. Examples: Central European, Illyrian, and circumboreal provinces.

Sector. An area of a province without any peculiar climax community of high sociological rank, such as an alliance. The special climatic or edaphic communities and geographical variants of the province are usually without endemic genera, but often have notable endemic species. Examples: North European, Carpathian, Alpine, Baltic, north Atlantic sectors.

Subsector. The subsector is less clearly marked by communities and has only microendemics. Subsectors are usually marked by peculiar geographical "races" of more widely distributed communities, and by communities and species which are lacking in adjacent areas. Examples: North, central, and south Alpine subsectors; mountains of south central Germany.

District. The district is characterized by communities and species which are rare or lacking in adjacent areas. Examples: District of the low plains of the Upper Rhine; the *Ilex* and *Erica cinerea* districts of the European north Atlantic sector.

Subdistrict. The lowest of synchorological units, the subdistrict is characterized by the mere dominance or suppression of edaphic or biotic communities, and by the presence or absence of distinctive species. Example: The precinct of the Schaffhausen basin of Hegau, of the Upper Danube.

The application of the major ones of these territories to Europe is shown in Figure 2, classified as follows:

I. Euro-Sibiric-North American region
   Atlantic province
     1. British sector
     2. North Atlantic sector
     3. Aquitanian sector
     4. Pyrenees sector
     5. Iberian sector
   Central European province
     6. Baltic sector
     7. Alpine sector
     8. Carpathian sector
     9. Pannonian sector
   Illyrian province
II. Mediterranean region
   Western Mediterranean province
   Eastern Mediterranean province
III. Aralo-Caspian region

Braun-Blanquet's floristic-sociological system of territories is based upon several criteria in which rank in the classification of species and

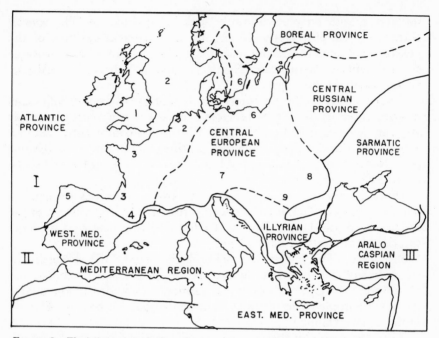

FIGURE 2.   Floristic-sociological territories of Europe according to Braun-Blanquet (58).

of communities more or less parallels rank in the hierarchy of territories. The criteria are as follows:

1. The presence of unique or almost unique communities; their
taxonomic, ecological, and floristic specialization. This refers to the
degree of organization of communities and their relations to the climax.

2. The presence of extensions of foreign vegetational elements in the
territory.

3. The dominance, suppression, or absence of certain communities
or ecological units (such as formations, synusiae, etc.).

4. The taxonomic position, number, and degree of ecological
specialization of endemic or nearly endemic species.

5. The presence of less minutely localized, disjunct species, and the
dominance, suppression, or absence of certain species or races.

Braun-Blanquet is careful to state that universal rules for the systematic evaluation of floristic characteristics of communities (and territories) cannot be laid down, as in systematic botany, in which one
or another morphological character must take a leading place as a criterion of relationship. It is logical that the above system combines
floristic and sociological phenomena, for in his concept of the association the fidelity of species is of supreme diagnostic importance. The

summation of floristic characteristics determines the classification of both communities and territories; and in doubtful cases the summation of all the floristic, ecological, syngenetic, and synchorological characteristics must be decisive, according to Braun-Blanquet. In practice this blending of floristic and sociological characteristics in subdividing the earth into territories does not fail also to reckon with topographic, climatic, and edaphic features, not only as they exist at the present, but as their historical conditions find expression in contemporary geographical patterns.

EXTRANEOUS FLORISTIC ELEMENTS

Any natural floristic territory of even moderate size, defined by any criteria at hand, will be found to contain not only the intraneous elements but also extraneous elements of several kinds. For any area, the *intraneous floristic elements* are either endemic to the area or range beyond it in *all* directions; i.e., within the area they are not at or near the limits of their distribution unless they are endemic. *Extraneous floristic elements* are those occuring in a given region but whose main areas of occurrence are elsewhere, and are at or near one limit of range in the area under consideration. This type of treatment was indicated by Cowles (140) and developed for the Great Smoky Mountains woody flora by Cain (79), Table 2.

As early as 1819 Winch (422) produced the first plant geographical study in England by classifying 2176 species of plants occurring in three

TABLE 2. Geographical affinities of the woody flora of the Great Smoky Mountains of eastern Tennessee (Cain, 79)

Elements	Number of Species	Per-centage
I. Intraneous elements	172	69.0
A. Eastern North America	89	36.0
B. Southeastern North America	27	11.0
C. Southern Appalachian Mountains	26	10.0
D. Endemic essentially to the Great Smoky Mountains	30	12.0
II. Extraneous elements	76	31.0
A. Northeastern United States	37	15.0
B. Southeastern Canada	17	7.0
C. Canadian transcontinental	9	3.6
D. Southern, Piedmont, etc.	9	3.6
E. Southwestern	4	1.6
Total	248	100.0

counties on the basis of such characteristics as whether they reached northern or southern limits in the district. Rare plants were grouped according to whether they were "native" of Switzerland or Lapland, or both, or of some other place. Maritime plants were subdivided according to whether they were confined to coastal areas, or extended from sea level to 650 m. altitude, or were disjunct from the coast to the high mountains. All in all, Winch was close to the concept of floral element, which was first introduced formally into plant geography by H. Christ (117). Originally the concept of floristic element had only a geographical significance, but Engler (180, 182) modified it to indicate center of origin and direction of migration. Braun-Blanquet (55, 56) favored restoring the term to its original purely geographical significance, but with the recognized floristic elements based on the formal phytogeographical regions as determined by Flahault. Heimans (236), working with the flora of The Netherlands, concluded that the only practical method is to define the elements of the native flora of an area in relation to that area itself, and not to some supposed universal system of floristic territories. This resulted in Heimans' proposing such simple and straightforward definitions as: "The boreal element of our flora contains the native plant species the center of whose area lies distinctly north of us, so that they reach or approach their southern limit *here* with us."

For any floristic territory the study of the extraneous elements is primarily an aid to understanding the historical development of the flora and the vegetation of the area. When a species or a group of related or even unrelated species occurs in a certain floristic territory but has its principal occurrence elsewhere, it has always seemed logical to assume that the area of the species has been extended by migration from the principal region to that in which its occurrence is extraneous. For example, no one suspects certain rather large tropical groups as having a temperate origin because of a few temperate representatives, as in *Diospyros, Phoradendron,* and *Tripsacum;* rather, quite the contrary. This point is well illustrated by a quotation from Merrill (291):

When a genus is described from material collected in a certain place and is known only from that region for many years, we more or less automatically accept it as a group characteristic of that region. If a representative of it is later found in another area, we are apt to consider it as an extraneous entity there. *Eucalyptus* is such a genus. It is tremendously developed in Australia, has a few species in New Guinea, and one which extends to the Bismarck Archipelago, the Moluccas, Celebes, and the Philippines. We are justified in accepting it as an Australian element in the other regions. The same is true of the few phyllodinous species of *Acacia* outside of Australia.

Extraneous elements of a flora lead naturally to speculation about the historical development of the flora. It is well understood that the territory occupied by members of a species population can only be expanded along migratory highways. A *migratory highway* consists of a sufficiently continuous series of habitats suitable for the species under question. For example, for species of a gallery forest the conditions along the stream and its lowland provide the suitable continuity of habitats for its migration; for a mountain species the habitats of a mountain system provide a highway for migration.

Extraneous elements in a floristic territory do not necessarily have continuous areas connecting them with the centers of their mass distribution; they are sometimes represented by disjunct subareas. In any case, the extraneous floristic elements of a territory are often contradictory in the sense that some of them are northern and others southern in their affinities, and still others are related to more humid or drier regions. The student of floristic geography is thus faced with problems of the history of the flora.

These problems and their relative importance can be posed by a geographical analysis of a flora, as in Table 2 (Cain, 79) dealing with the woody vegetation of the Great Smoky Mountains. The value of a statistical treatment of the problem can be illustrated by a conventionalized situation. Let us assume a floristic territory in the United States so located that to the north lies the flora of the Great Lakes *Pinus strobus* subprovince (see Table 1) and the still more northern subarctic American conifer province; to the south lies the Mississippi-Ohio-Tennessee subprovince; to the west lies the prairie province; and to the east is the Allegheny subprovince. In such a situation it is colder to the north, warmer to the south, moister to the east, and drier to the west than it generally is in the floristic territory which is under speculation and which might be in Indiana, Ohio, or southern Michigan. If such a territory contains extraneous floristic elements characteristic of regions north, south, east, and west—as it does—their presence in the territory must be due to past conditions that were different from present ones. It is not possible to suppose at any one time conditions suitable for the simultaneous migration of plants from the colder north and the warmer south, or from the moister east and the drier west. (This does not preclude the shrinking of area resulting in a relic vegetational enclave and the simultaneous convergence of the prevailing flora on it from all directions. This sort of situation could occur,

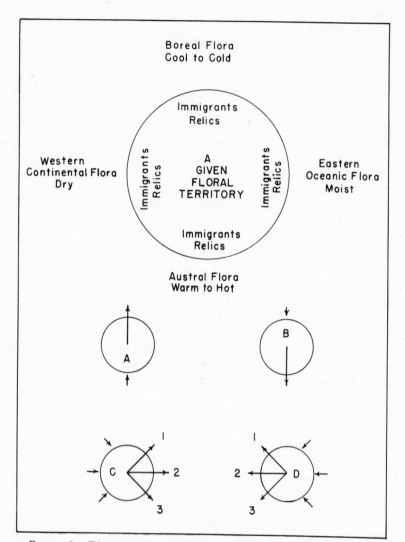

FIGURE 3. Diagram of a hypothetical floristic situation in east-central United States illustrating the historical origin of extraneous floristic elements in a given territory, with the production of immigrants and relics as a result of various climatic changes at different times in the past. If there had been a climatic shift toward warmer temperature, there would have been a north-ward migration as shown in A, with immigrants entering from the south and the preexisting vegetation leaving behind relics as it retreats northward. The converse is shown in B. C shows the effects of increased dryness; D the converse. C1 represents a change to warmer and drier; C2 is simple drying; C3 is a change to cooler and drier, bringing into the given territory, respectively, southern, central, and northern prairie province species.

for example, with reduction of topographic relief and consequent amelioration of the microclimate of hilltops. In such a case the geographical scale is quite different from the larger movements referred to above.) At a given time when conditions are such that migration from the south toward the north is possible, the territory we are speculating about could receive immigrants from the south and would lose much of its former northern element, but it would not lose all of it, for relics would be left behind in suitable places. The diagrams in Figure 3 show the directions of migration under the pressure of climatic changes of different sorts. It is on such a basis as this, although this is not the only one, that historical explanations for diverse floristic elements in a territory must be sought. As Hultén (243) wrote, "It is just the stations found outside the compact area that are likely to be the most valuable ones, which can give a clue as to how the development has taken place. They are so to speak 'the living fossils' of the species in question."

Hultén (243) developed the concept of *equiformal progressive areas* in his studies of arctic and boreal plant distributions. The chief feature of comparatively recent areas is their concentricity around the place from which the flora has radiated. The plants that have equiformal areas of different sizes have radiated from the same center; and if enough species areas are compared, centers of dispersal can be convincingly suggested.

In a study of characteristics of natural areas, Cain (96) treats some floristic as well as vegetational problems, and *Foundations of Plant Geography* (Cain, 93) has a section of ten chapters on areography. The present *Manual* has no special concern with floristic matters *per se;* investigators particularly interested in them should refer to the above book, or to Willis (420), Gleason (211), Wulff (425), Good (218), Dansereau (155), Darlington (157), etc., where such topics as topography of area, shape of area, size of area, margin of area, relic areas, continuous and disjunct areas, vicarious areas, centers of origin, frequency, variation, dispersal, etc., are discussed.

THE BIOTIC PROVINCE

Vestal (403) introduced the term *biotic province* for a territory that is characterized by the biological *tout ensemble,* showing a correspondence between the distribution of particular animals and vegetation. Vestal proposed two criteria for the determination of a biotic province: (1) similarity of range among animals of ecological similarity, whatever their systematic relationship, and (2) closeness of correspondence of area between particular animals and vegetation "provinces."

It is seen that the biome concept of Clements and Shelford (130) was foreshadowed by Vestal, for he was concerned not only with floristic and faunistic areas, but also with ecology and community structure. He also recognized the central difficulty in biological subdivisions of the earth's surface, for he stated that there is greater uniformity of the collection of species when the area under consideration is restricted and the conditions are uniform, than when the area is large and heterogeneous.

Dice (161), can be credited with systematizing his own studies and those of others in the formal description of 29 biotic provinces of North America. He leaned upon ecological matters, rather than on the more simple floristic and faunistic boundaries, giving heavy weight to topography, soil, and climate in the determination of provinces.

Each province covers a considerable and continuous area and is characterized by the occurrence of one or more important ecological associations that differ, at least in proportional area covered, from the associations of adjacent provinces. In general, biotic provinces are also characterized by peculiarities of vegetation type, ecological climax, flora, fauna, climate, physiography, and soil. . . . The limits of geographic range of species and races of plants and animals are not fully satisfactory criteria for determining the boundaries of biotic provinces. . . . The classification of biotic provinces should be based upon the distinctness and distribution of the various ecological associations. . . . Each biotic province is characterized usually by a single climax association. . . .

Both Vestal and Dice recognized the difficulties in applying their complex criteria in an objective manner. Many authors, facing these difficulties, have defined biotic provinces in terms of limited groups of organisms rather than the biological *tout ensemble*. For example, Burt (73) used the distribution of recent mammals, and Blair (45) used terrestrial vertebrates correlated with vegetation. Mello-Leitão (289), using only the scorpion fauna, divided South America into nine provinces that compared favorably with eleven districts proposed earlier by Cabrera and Yepes (78) on the basis of their studies of mammals. He conservatively refers to these regions as *provincias escorpiologicas,* rather than "biotic," and uses physiographic as well as faunistic phenomena (Figure 4). For a fauna of 207 species in 26 genera and 6 families, the method is illustrated in the following translation:

The province Caribe is limited on the west by the river Magdalena, which separates it from the province Incasica, and on the south by the confluence of the Parima, Roraima and Tumuc-Humac mountains, and comprises the eastern part of Colombia, Venezuela, and the Guianas. There occur in it a diplocéntrid (*Diplocéntrus grundlachi*), chactids of the genera *Broteochactas* and *Chactas,* butids of the genus *Centruroides,* and *Tityus* of the group *T. trinitatis* (with fusion of the ventral caudal crests). . . .

The province Hiléa or Amazónica is the least limited of the zoological provinces, comprising all of the valleys (basins) of the Amazonas and the Madeira, limited on the south by the line shown across the forests and savannas, and on the east by the monotonous forests of the cocales. Here

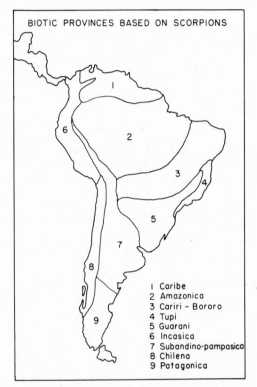

FIGURE 4.   Biotic provinces of South America based solely on scorpions. Mello-Leitão (289) intended them only to be *provincias escorpiologicas.*

are encountered an escorpiōnido *(Opisthacanthus cayaporum), Tityus,* spotted and black, chactids of the genera *Broteas* and *Acanthothraustes* and, in the western limit of the Marañon, *Chactas.* Failing to occur are Vejóvids and Botriúrids. . . .

Most publications putting forward a scheme of biotic provinces do not present the reader with more than the conclusions of the author; hence for a critical study of proposed boundaries one must have recourse to taxonomic monographs and the collections in museums. Reasons for compromise with the demands of biotic provinces are clear. Good distributional data and satisfactory taxonomic monographs usually exist, in any given region, for only a relatively small part of the biota; furthermore, the specialists in certain groups are often prin-

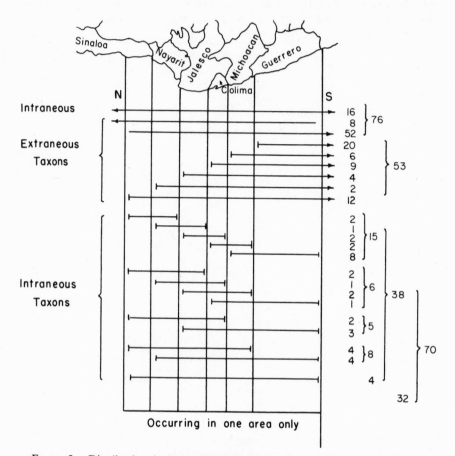

FIGURE 5.   Distributional relationships of the taxons (species and subspecies) of reptiles and amphibia in the Nayarit-Guerrero biotic province of arid tropical southern Mexico. This diagram is a revision of Figure 1 and other data in Peters (316).

cipally responsible for the adequacy of the data in their group and hence are the only ones who feel sufficiently confident to define biotic provinces.

We are indebted to one such specialist, Peters (316), for a critical study of a long-recognized biotic province. Peters has analyzed the distribution of 150 species and subspecies of reptiles and amphibia in the Nayarit-Guerrero Province in the southern arid tropical zone of Mexico (Figure 5). This province consists of five states and the southern part of Sinaloa. The six geographical units used for analyzing the distribution are all about the same size, except for the state of Colima; its addition to the state on either side would not significantly change the results.

Among the taxons (species and subspecies) endemic to the province, 32 are known from single areas usually as a result of a few specimens from type localities; 15 occur in two of the areas; 6 in three; 5 in four; 8 in five; and 4 in all six of the geographical subdivisions. Furthermore, as shown in Figure 5, all contiguous combinations are represented. To complete the intraneous fauna, we must add the 16 entities that range to both the north and the south of the Nayarit-Guerrero province. Of the extraneous entities, 8 reach southern limits in the province and 53 reach northern limits there. For this southern element, progressing from south to north, 20 taxons reach their northern limits in Guerrero; 6 in Michoacan; 9 in Colima; 4 in Jalesco; 2 in Nayarit; and 12 in southern Sinaloa. These data show that faunal breaks are not significantly greater at the boundaries of the so-called Nayarit-Guerrero province than they are within it; and, further, the geographical units used are themselves artificial or nonbiotic and ranges do not coincide within states any more than they do within the province. Peters reaches the following conclusions:

1. It seems unlikely that any plan to describe biotic provinces on a statistical or empirical basis will be uniformly successful.

2. Satisfactory boundaries for biotic provinces seem to occur only where there are strong physiographic breaks, i.e., where there are abrupt changes in the environmental complex; otherwise species are added gradually and others drop out gradually as one progresses across a territory. (He compares this situation by analogy with genetic clines.)

In spite of the results of his own analysis, Peters cannot reject the concept of objective reality for the biotic province—based merely on biotic data. He says the concept still has considerable value to biogeographers in analyzing distributional problems.

Chapter 3

THE COMMUNITY

Community is a generic term of convenience which is employed to designate sociological units of any degree of extent and complexity from the simplest synusia to the most complex phytocoenosis. Alechin (7) said that a plant community is a complex of plant species which has a definite structure and is composed of ecologically and phenologically different elements (*Schichtung* in time and space), which, moreover—in spite of its dynamism—forms a persevering system depicting botanically the physicogeographical relations and the history of the region. Despite the breadth of the term "community," there are both upper and lower limits. At the large end of the scale is the formation (or biome, if animals are given consideration). There is no unit larger than the formation, if the various continental examples of a formation are considered to compose it, as in the case of the rain-forest formation in Asia, Europe, and America. At the lower limit there are plant groupings that are excluded from the concept of community because they lack integration of their parts. This is made clear by Alechin. He gave the following classification of plant groupings:

   I. Open groupings
  II. Closed groupings; with competition
     1. Settlements; *Siedlungen*, without social integration
     2. Pure stands; populations of single species
       a. Temporary
       b. More or less permanent or enduring
     3. Communities
       a. With essentially stable equilibrium; climax
         (1) Unsaturated; without a full complement of societies
            or synusiae

(2) Saturated
b. With flowing equilibrium; successional
c. Dearranged equilibrium, usually because of some persistent biotic factor such as heavy grazing, or other factor such as recurrent fire

From the following series of statements we can see that there is considerable consensus as to the nature of communities, even though opinions vary concerning the exact criteria for community classificatory
units. For example, Wangerin (407) claimed that the basis of the
community lies in the floristic assemblage, but that the correlated
ecology is important. Braun-Blanquet (58) claimed that the community life of plants rests on universal and ever-present competition for
the necessities of life. Without physiological interference the characteristic floristic assemblages of communities would be without organization—there would be composition without structure. Clements (127)
emphasized the same point, that competition is a universal characteristic of all plant communities and is absent only in the initial stages of
succession when the pioneers are still isolated. Tansley (383) wrote:
"It is precisely this mass action, together with the actions due to the
close and often delicate interlocking of the functions of the constituent
organisms, which gives coherence to the aggregation, forces us to call
it a unit, justifies us in considering it an organic entity, and makes it
reasonable to speak of the development of that entity." Gleason (214)
points out that since its first recognition the community has always
been a geographical unit, occupying space and having boundaries.
Moreover, a community exhibits a certain degree of uniformity in
composition and structure within the area, for without such uniformity both extent and boundary lose all significance. This applies to
boundary in time as well as in space—there must be a beginning and
an end. Gleason states that the cause of this uniformity is twofold.
"The first [cause] is the existence over a considerable area of an environment which is itself uniform. . . . The second is the existence
throughout the area of a uniform type of physiological interference."
Whereas the manifestation of a community is distinctly areal, characterized by uniformity, extent, and boundary, the real cause is not
areal but lies in the competition of interacting spheres of physiological influence.

In conclusion we may say that a *community* is a sociological unit of
any rank, occupying a territory and having a characteristic composition and structure. It should be clear that this term, as used thus far,
refers to individual, concrete entities or stands that have objective

reality in nature. There is also, of course, the *community type*, a concept arrived at synthetically by knowledge of several different similar stands. (See also Alechin, 6; Cain, 89; Dansereau, 155, etc.)

As we have seen, each type of community is described as having a characteristic composition and structure; and if we follow Alechin we will not admit to the rank of community either open groupings without competition or closed groupings of single species. We have already dealt with the matter of composition, in part, in the discussion of floristics; but there remains the question of the specific assemblage both in single stands of a community and in the several stands that are known to constitute a community type. These relevés may be based on observation of whole stands or on samples of the stands. The presence or absence of certain species is of great importance in many of the concepts that are described below.

One of the characteristics of a community is its physiognomy, the way it appears. Physiognomy is largely a product of the predominant life forms of the organisms composing the community; but it also results in part from groupings of patterns of occurrence of the various life forms and in part from lesser morphological features such as leaf size. One of the most conspicuous features of most communities is the grouping of similar life forms into synusiae. A *synusia* is a social aggregate consisting of one or a few closely related life forms occurring together and having a similar ecology. *Stratification* of communities, by their synusiae that occur as horizontal layers (strata), is often readily apparent. There are, however, many other synusiae than those that form layers. The subdivision of the space occupied by a complex community into subspaces occupied by synusiae is not only an aerial phenomenon; there is also a subterranean stratification of the roots, rhizomes, etc., of vascular plants and of microscopic and larger organisms that live within the soil. The total complex of synusiae that simultaneously occupy the same terrain is called a *phytocoenosis;* this is the usual concept of community. In a sense, the synusiae are to the phytocoenosis what organs are to an organism; i.e., they are structural units that are themselves more or less complex. Although the phytocoenosis has areal extent and boundaries, as emphasized by Gleason (214), its principal organizing forces operate essentially vertically and have only slight horizontal influence. In nature the most severe competition occurs among the members of a given specific population, for they have nearly identical life requirements. It follows that competition among individuals of a synusia is relatively severe because of the similarity of life form and ecological requirements of its different members. Finally, among the different synusiae of a phytocoenosis there are different degrees of competition for the necessities of life inasmuch as the synusiae occupy different subdivisions of the total space of the phytocoenosis. In a rather loose sense of the term, there may even be cooperation among certain synusiae, for a tall layer may cause a modification of the general atmospheric conditions that results in the microhabitat necessary for the existence of a lower layer, or lower layers may produce conditions necessary for the germination of seeds of plants that ultimately reach higher layers.

We have elsewhere described briefly various kinds of sampling methods and some of their uses. To understand the problem of community description fully, we should consider briefly various analytic and synthetic concepts. Of the *analytic concepts,* pertaining to a single stand, some are *quantitative* (such as number, area, and frequency) and others are essentially *qualitative* (such as sociability, vitality, periodicity, and dynamic behavior).

Among the quantitative analytic concepts, *number* may be expressed as *abundance,* in which actual counts are not made, but for which each species is estimated as belonging to one of a limited number of abundance classes, usually five or six. When actual counts are made of the plants on sample units, the data can be expressed as *density,* usually the average number of individuals per unit area of the sample. If the sample units are randomly located within the stand, these density data may be attributed to the whole area of the community with definable limits of accuracy.

All individual plants ramify through and more or less occupy a certain volume of space from which they receive water, nutrients, air, illumination, etc. Also, two or more individuals often are interlaced and to a certain extent share a given space. For such reasons, volume measurements are seldom made or even estimates attempted for whole plants, although usable volume of wood in trees is often computed. But such phenomena are of real importance in the phytocoenosis, for they seem to be correlated with *dominance,* the relative degree to which a kind of plant predominates in competition for limited supplies of the necessities of life. Not only are there different degrees of dominance, there are different kinds of *dominants.* In the usual sense, the *dominant* plant or plants (codominants) are the predominant ones in the controlling synusia of the phytocoenosis. In a forest, for example, this is the uppermost tree stratum, which most strongly characterizes the physiognomy and exerts the greatest control over the community as a whole. In a tree-dotted savanna the trees belong to the tallest stratum; but because of its incompleteness, dominance of the community is found in the grass-dominated field layer. As an actual fact, however, one or a small number of species are usually dominant in each synusia of the complex community. Dominance generally arises from competitive ability, the ability to preempt space, and is a function, in major part, of size and numbers together. Because volume is so difficult to measure, and the actual physiology of competition so little known, dominance is usually expressed as coverage. For creeping plants, prostrate on the substratum, the concept of *coverage* is obvious—the relative amount of ground covered by the supraterrestrial parts. For most plants, however, it is necessary to imagine a vertical projection of the mass onto the ground area as if a shadow were being cast by direct overhead illumination. Coverage is usually estimated by means of a limited number of cover classes, but in some cases it is feasible to make measurements. For a variety of reasons, total cover does not bear a direct relationship to total leaf and stem areas. Cover provided by the various layers of a complex community may exceed 100 percent, and there will still be patches of ground that receive direct sun flecks; but on the other hand, much of the illumination of the foliage on the lower layers comes from light that has already filtered through or been reflected from the leaves on the upper layers.

In plant sociology the term "frequency" is used in a different sense from its customary mathematical meaning. *Frequency* refers to the portion of the units of a sample in which at least one plant of a species is present. For example, if a sample of a stand consists of 100 sample units, each 1 sq. m., and if one or more plants of a given species grows in 57 of these quadrats, the species will have a *frequency index* (or percentage occurrence) of 57. It is a common characteristic of communities to have a large number of species whose frequency index is small, and a considerable number of species of high frequency. The latter are not necessarily the dominants. It is readily apparent that frequency is only partially a function of size and number, for it is also affected by dispersion. Data concerning number and cover are not necessarily biased because of the size of the sample units, but frequency is strongly influenced by quadrat size because of the species-area relationship that exists in all communities.

Among the *qualitative analytic concepts* we class sociability, vitality, periodicity, and dynamic behavior of the species of a community. Although data concerning these attributes of plants can be given partial quantification, in the strictest sense they usually are not counted, measured, or weighed.

Sociability of plants refers to the degree to which they normally are aggregated in nature. Although many factors affecting the dispersal of plant propagules are haphazard in their action and there is a large element of chance, and although some factors are unidirectional in operation and none is purposeful, the results of dispersal are seldom a strictly random pattern of occurrence of individuals of a kind. Most organisms in nature have an average spacing through their communities for which the ratio to the average spacing expected for a random dispersion is less than unity; i.e., the plants are more or less clumped or contagiously distributed. In plant sociology, sociability is estimated for each species according to a limited number of classes. Some investigators consider a certain degree of sociability to be a characteristic of a species; but others believe that sociability is, in part at least, a highly variable product of forces within or acting upon the community. The causes of clumping are to be sought in vegetative reproduction, peculiarities or inadequacies of dispersal mechanisms, and spotty heterogeneity of microhabitats.

The concept of *vitality* of a species as it exists in a community refers to its ability to complete its normal life cycle. Some species in some communities are of low vitality in the sense that they remain vegetative, being unable to flower and set seed. A fully vital flowering plant sets seed in normal amount.

Periodic phenomena characterize all organisms; they may be correlated with external phenomena such as daylight and darkness or the orderly progression of the annual seasons. In plant sociology *periodicity* usually refers to the periods of the year during which a plant is vegetatively active, flowering, fruiting, bearing leaves, germinating seeds, etc. Because many species of a community or a synusia may have coincident rhythms of periodicity, most communities exhibit different aspects at different times. *Aspection* is essentially the phenomenon of changing physiognomy. For example, the broad-leaf, summer-green forests of eastern North America, Europe, and Asia show strong aspection because of their leafless condition during the cold winter and their often heavy canopy of fresh green leaves in the summer. This same formation shows a strong vernal aspect produced to a considerable extent by flowering geophytic herbs that complete their life cycles in the spring before the full shade of the forest canopy has developed.

Finally, among the qualitative characteristics of plants that can be analyzed for concrete stands is dynamic behavior. Most communities of the plant world are not in a climactic condition of relative equilibrium, but with time they undergo progressive, or sometimes retrogressive, change. The various kinds of plants in a community exhibit different degrees of *dynamic behavior* in the intensity with which their presence, life processes, and products affect other organisms and modify the environment of the community. The role played by some species is constructive or consolidating, whereas others are destructive to the long continuance of the community. Dynamic behavior is usually ascribed to one of a limited number of classes according to the functions of the species with respect to the integrity of the community.

The *synthetic concepts* refer to a community type, not to an individual stand that is an example of the community, or to species that characterize different communities. In a technical sense, *presence* is the presence or absence of individuals of a species in the various stands of a community type. Each stand has a certain assemblage of species; the various stands whereby the concept of community type is created have similar but not identical assemblages of species. Presence of a species is usually expressed as the proportion of the total stands that contain the species. For example, species lists are prepared for each of ten similar stands on the basis of the entire area of each stand; it is found that many species, usually the more important ones as measured by abundance, coverage, fidelity, etc., are present in 90 to 100 percent of the stands. Others are present in various numbers of stands, many more or less insignificant species being present in one or a few stands.

However comparable they may be in many respects, stands usually differ greatly in area, and because of the species-area relationship the larger stands tend to have the larger species lists. To obviate this difficulty, species lists that are based on samples of the same size are prepared for each stand. The comparative data thus obtained are called constancy. *Constancy* is the percentage occurrence of a species on samples of the same size in various stands of a community type. The basis for constancy lists may be a single minimal-area quadrat in each stand, or it may be equivalent series of subsamples from each stand, i.e., the same plots used for frequency data. For some plant sociologists the species that are *constant-dominants,* i.e., those with a high degree of both constancy and dominance, are most important in characterizing communities.

The final synthetic concept referring to the community type is fidelity. *Fidelity* is the degree of exclusiveness that a species shows in a given region with respect to a given community type. For some plant sociologists, particularly those of the Braun-Blanquet school, species with a high degree of exclusiveness that do not occur in any importance in any other community type (at least in the region) are the best species for characterizing a community type, even though they may not be dominants.

The preceding characteristics of communities and the various methods of community analysis will be examined in greater detail in succeeding sections of the *Manual,* where examples will be given and the problems associated with the concepts and methods will be explored.

THE SYNUSIAL STRUCTURE OF VEGETATION

The division of a complex community into layers is the most noticeable characteristic of its physiognomy, the synusiae of the phytocoenosis. Formal recognition of the importance of layers in the structure of vegetation goes back at least to Hult (242). Gams (204) was the first to propose organizing both plant and animal life on a basis of life-form groups which he termed *synusiae.* Lippmaa (272, 273, 274, 275) was the first to propose the classification of vegetation into *unions,* which he considered to be *unistratal plant associations,* more or less independent of one another. This dismemberment of the "association" was disapproved by the Amsterdam International Botanical Congress, and the name settled on for such "communities" is "union" (Sirgo, 368). Cain and Penfound (99) and Cain and Sharp (100) were among the first investigators other than Lippmaa and his colleagues to apply the method.

Because of the impressiveness of the dominant synusia of a complex community, much ecological work has superficially paid attention only to that layer or overemphasized it. In much of forestry, because of its extensive generalized nature and the obvious commercial pressures, one often "cannot see the forest for the trees," but the classical work of the Finnish forester Cajander (105, 106) on forest types was based on the characteristic ground vegetation which provided indicators of *site quality* independent of the arborescent overstory. Cajander held that similar ground vegetation characterized biologically equivalent sites.

Naturally enough, forest phytocoenoses present the most complicated structure, at least among terrestrial communities; and among forest-dominated communities those of hot humid climates tend to contain more synusia, with temperate forests of mesophytic situations next, and dry or cold-climate forests the simplest. Temperate oak forests often contain three layers based on phanerophytes, three of herbaceous plants, and a ground layer of nonvascular cryptogams, as well as certain nonlayered synusiae (Alechin, 7). Lippmaa (273) found the European *Ulmus-Acer-Tilia* association to consist of five layered synusiae and six vertically distributed corticolous communities of bryophytes and lichens. Cain and Penfound (99) found that the red maple swamp forest association of central Long Island had the following organization:

Aceretum rubri—the red maple swamp forest association
- Acer rubrum union—the single arborescent layer
- Clethro-Azalea union—the tall frutescent layer
- Rubus hispidus union—the herb-low shrub field layer
- Unifolium canadense union—a low herbaceous synusia of drier sites
- Spathyema foetida union—a herbaceous synusia of wetter sites
- Homomallium adnatum union—a cryptogamic synusia on trees
- Dicranum montanum union—a cryptogamic synusia on peat
- Several other bryophytic unions of special biotopes

We are indebted to Richards (344) for the most comprehensive treatment of tropical rain forest. At first rain forest appears as a bewildering chaos of vegetation in which every available space is filled, but a closer study shows a limited number of synusiae with a discernible arrangement in space. Richards claims that the structure of the primary rain forest is essentially the same wherever it occurs, because although the species are numerous and differ with geographical region, those of corresponding synusiae are alike in life form and physiognomy. He gives the following classification of synusiae of the tropical rain forest:

A. Autotrophic plants (with chlorophyll)
  1. Mechanically independent plants
     a. Trees and shrubs: arranged in a number of layers
     b. Herbs: arranged in a number of layers
  2. Mechanically dependent plants
     a. Climbers: ascending to different heights
     b. Stranglers
     c. Epiphytes: with different height ranges, including semi-parasites
        (1) Vascular epiphytes
        (2) Cryptogamic epiphytes
B. Heterotrophic plants (without chlorophyll)
  1. Saprophytes
  2. Parasites

Inasmuch as the synusia is a group of plants with similar life form, making similar demands on a similar habitat (filling the same niche), we can see the rationale for Richards' classification in which each synusia represents a different method of succeeding in the struggle for food. Some students of tropical rain forest claim that genuine strata do not exist (Mildbraed, 294; Chevalier, 115). Even though some species have maximum mature heights that fall into groups, strata are not apparent because the whole space is filled with *transgressives,* trees of various ages and heights that have not reached their maxima. Because of the often insuperable difficulties of direct observation, Davis and Richards (159) constructed profile diagrams to scale, based on felled strips. This and subsequent studies have shown that most normal primary rain forests consist of three tree strata, a layer of shrubs and giant herbs, and a layer of low herbs and undershrubs. One difficulty, besides that of direct observation, is the fact that each layer may be continuous or discontinuous, but seldom if ever are all layers continuous at any one station. The characteristic discontinuity of layers, together with the ever-present transgressives, gives tropical rain forest its uneven and cluttered appearance, in contrast to that of temperate forests. Furthermore, most rain forest has been seen only from the outside, either from above by airplane, or from the side along rivers and road cuts, internal visibility often being limited both vertically and horizontally. It is only from a freshly cut cross section of the forest that its characteristic structure can be analyzed, for old edges have their own structure as a result of a quick response to increased light.

Although mixed forests, very rich in species and without the dominance of one or a few species in the superior stratum, are most abundant, single-dominant rain forests are now known on all three continents (Richards, 344), and they too consist of three arborescent layers. They differ from mixed forests in their greater continuity and evenness of height, especially of the top layer.

Although most investigators consider the organic unit of vegetation to be the complete complex that occupies a given terrain (the phytocoenosis), some still say (Egler, 177) that "more than one community may exist on the same site at the same time (layer communities) or at different times (seasonal communities)." We prefer, however, to accept the reasoning of Gleason (214) against assigning full community status to layers because the dynamic bonds of the phytocoenosis are essentially vertical, binding the several synusiae together, whereas the lateral relations within any one synusia are relatively weak. Synusiae have some essential individuality and integrity, but they are not truly independent of one another. The fact remains, however, that in the analysis of vegetation not only must synusiae be recognized where they exist, but the statistical requirements of sampling usually necessitate separate investigations of each synusia (Cain, 87, 89).

The preceding points are well illustrated in Roach's work (347) on the vegetation of a small lava-flow region in Oregon, which he classifies as follows:

I. Aceretum circinati lavosum association
    Acer circinatum union (frutescent synusia)
    Cryptogrammo-Penstemon union (herbaceous synusia)
    Rhacomitrium patens union (bryophytic synusia of the ground layer)

II. Pseudotsugeto-Abietum lasiocarpae association
    Pseudotsuga-Abies union (arborescent synusia)
    Acer circinatum union (frutescent synusia)
    Sedum oregonense union (herbaceous synusia)
    Rhacomitrium patens union (bryophytic synusia)

III. Pseudotsugeto-Abietum grandis association
    Pseudotsugeto-Abies union (arborescent synusia)
    Castanopsis chrysophylla union (frutescent synusia)
    Chimphila umbellata union (herbaceous synusia)
    Rhacomitrium patens union (bryophytic synusia)

IV. Pinetum contorti lapillosum association
    Pinus contorta union (arborescent synusia)
    Ceanothus velutinus union (frutescent synusia)
    Carexeto-Penstemon union (herbaceous synusia)
    Polytrichum juniperinum union (bryophytic synusia)

V. Caxereto-Vaccinietum occidentalis association
    Salix union (frutescent synusia; alternating stand)
    Vaccinium occidentalis union (frutescent synusia; alternating stand)
    Carex sitchensis union (herbaceous synusia)

VI. Pseudotsugetum taxifoliae tsugosum association—the climax
    Pseudotsugeto-Tsuga union (arborescent synusia)
    Roseto-Vaccinium union (frutescent synusia)
    Linnaeto-Cornus union (herbaceous synusia)

Roach adapted the size of the sampling unit to the stature and complexity of the synusia. The number of units in a sample was arbitrary but adequate to portray correctly the disposition and arrangement of the species. For the arboreal strata he used 100 sq. m. quadrats; for the frutescent strata 16 sq. m. quadrats; for the herbaceous strata 1 sq. m. quadrats; and for the bryophytic ground layer 0.25 sq. m. quadrats. In each association the quadrats were laid out in nested sets; in three separate stands at 100-m. intervals along transects; i.e., each quadrat of a set was contained within the next larger one. In the climax association he used 12 quadrat sets; in the four subclimax associations 50 quadrat sets; and in the bog association 16 quadrat sets, for a total of 858 quadrats. If we refer now to the next section on the use of synusiae in classifying vegetation, we can understand that Roach's success in synusial organization of vegetation was due largely to the relatively few species in the vegetation of the recent lava flow and to the sharply controlling habitat factor involved.

THE USE OF SYNUSIAE IN CLASSIFYING VEGETATION. Any close observer of vegetation would notice that different stands of vegetation may have one or more layers in common, whereas other layers are different. Hult (242) was probably the first botanist to make use of this fact in classifying communities. His *Pineta polymorpha*, for example, had *Pinus silvestris* dominant in the tree layer. This was the *combining stand. Alternating stands* (layers) included *Vaccinium myrtillus* and *Hylocomium* in one case and *Calluna culgaris* and *Cladina* in another. In Hult's *Pineta-Betuleta Vagantia* the combining stand was the ground layer of Hypnaceae and the alternating stands were dominated by *Pinus* or *Betula*. Altogether Hult described sixteen such *twin formations,* as he called them.

The Russian plant sociologists found Hult's concept useful and developed and expanded the method (Keller, 253; Sukachev, 380; Katz, 252; Alechin, 8). Katz developed the idea of *homologous series* of twin associations which have significance with respect to both the structure and the ecology of vegetation. This can be illustrated by the following series of twin associations that, in addition to the species for which the associations are named, have a high constancy of plants characteristic of (1) mineral forest soils, *Vaccinium myrtillus, V, vitis-idaea, Hylocomium schreberi* or (2) moister decomposed peat, *Ledum palustre* and *Vaccinium uliginosum.*

1. Pinus silvestris—Ledum palustre—Sphagnum recurvatum association
Pinus silvestris—Cassandra calyculata—Sp. recurvatum association
Pinus silvestris—Eriophorum vaginatum—Sp. recurvatum association

The homologous series is the same except for the fact that the ground layer is dominated by *Sphagnum medium.*

2. Pinus silvestris—Ledum palustre—Sphagnum medium association

Pinus silvestris—Cassandra calyculata—Sp. medium association

Pinus silvestris—Eriophorum vaginatum—Sp. medium association

These two sets of twin associations constitute a homologous series. The tree layer, with its *Pinus silvestris* dominance, is combining for the homologous series; *Sphagnum recurvatum (S. angustifolium)* is combining for the twin associations of drier, more mineralized sites; and *Sphagnum medium* is combining for the associations of moister peat sites. The alterating layer in both cases is dominated by *Ledum, Cassandra,* or *Eriophorum.*

In Table 3 from the work of Katz we see that the organization of

TABLE 3.   Homologous Series of twin associations (Katz, 252)

A	B	C
1. Calluna vulgaris— Sphagnum fuscum association	Eriophorum vaginatum— Sphagnum fuscum association	
2. Calluna vulgaris— Sphagnum rubellum association	Eriophorum vaginatum— Sphagnum rubellum association	
3. Calluna vulgaris— Sphagnum magellanicum association	Eriophorum vaginatum— Sphagnum magellanicum association	Scheuchzeria palustris— Sphagnum magellanicum association
4. Calluna vulgaris— Sphagnum balticum association	Eriophorum vaginatum— Sphagnum balticum association	Scheuchzeria palustris— Sphagnum balticum association
5.	Eriophorum vaginatum— Sphagnum dusenii association	Scheuchzeria palustris— Sphagnum dusenii association
6.	Eriophorum vaginatum— Sphagnum cuspidatum association	Scheuchzeria palustris— Sphagnum cuspidatum association

rather closely related communities into twin and homologous series, based on combining and alternating synusiae, reveals for each association its floristic and ecological relationships, for there is a consistency between the two. In the table hydrophily increases from top to bottom and from left to right: thus the *Calluna vulgaris—Sphagnum fuscum* association is characteristic of the driest sites of the series, and the *Scheuchzeria palustris—Sphagnum cuspidatum* association is characteristic of the wettest sites. This table also illustrates that twin series can be made up in different ways for the same set of communities. In the vertical columns of the table (A, B, C) *Calluna, Eriophorum,* and *Scheuchzeria* form the combining stands in their respective series; the alternating stands are composed of different species of *Sphagnum.* In the horizontal columns (1 through 6) the species of *Sphagnum* form the various combining stands and the alternation occurs in the superior stratum. Communities corresponding to positions C1 and C2 in the table have not been found, probably because the sites are too dry for *Scheuchzeria;* contrariwise, communities for positions A5 and A6 are not known, probably because sites suitable for these species of *Sphagnum* are too wet for *Calluna vulgaris.*

Our comment on this system is that, although it has been shown to be functional for northern Eurasia, it is often not practical for other types of regions. Our reasons are as follows: In the north the flora is not rich in ecologically equivalent species and general living conditions are comparatively rigorous. This results in two phenomena that simplify vegetation and permit such organizations of it as that just described. When a flora is poor in species, constant-dominants are rather common for each synusia of a phytocoenosis because these species do not have to meet effective competition from ecologically equivalent species. Furthermore, the balance is so delicate that a relatively slight shift in intensity of one important factor of the environmental complex leads, more often than not, to a new constant-dominant in one or more of the synusiae. In mesophytic temperate forest regions, and especially in floristically rich tropical regions, where there are many more layers than the three which Katz dealt with, the possible combinations of synusiae are enormous.

Cain (89) on the basis of data for the red spruce association *(Piceetum rubentis)* of the Great Smoky Mountains (Cain, 85) has shown that slavishly following such a system results in a *reductio ad absurdum.* This forest has five layers, and the superior arborescent layer is the combining stand, in Katz's terminology. It would be possible to describe four alternating stands in each of the lower layers, as shown in the list below. Each of the species listed is known to be locally dominant in one place or another in the association, but the author was not familiar enough with their ecology (or presumptuous enough) to propose formally the separate layer societies listed in Table 3. The names are presented here as an illustration of the potential nomenclatural and systematic maze that would be created by such a procedure.

Piceetum rubentis association (superior arborescent stratum)
   I. Inferior arborescent stratum
     1. Abies fraseri layer society
     2. Betula allegheniensis layer society
     3. Sorbus (Pyrus) americana layer society
     4. Prunus pensylvanica layer society
  II. Frutescent stratum (shrub layer)
     1. Rhododendron carolinianum layer society
     2. Rhododendron catawbiense layer society
     3. Hugeria erythrocarpa layer society
     4. Menziesia pilosa layer society
 III. Herbaceous stratum (field layer)
     1. Oxalis montana layer society
     2. Dryopteris dilatata layer society
     3. Aster acuminatus layer society
     4. Clintonia borealis layer society
  IV. Cryptogamic stratum (soil layer of mosses and lichens)
     1. Hylocomium splendens layer society
     2. Rhytidiadelphus triquetrus layer society
     3. Polytrichum ohiense layer society
     4. Cladonia squamosa layer society

Holding strictly to the subalpine region of *Picea rubens* dominance, and assuming all possible combinations of the societies as alternating stands, would result in 256 different named phytocoenoses. Furthermore, using when possible only generic names of the dominants in each layer for the construction of the association name, we would have such titles as Picea-Abies-Rhododendron catawbiense-Oxalis-Hylocomium association; Picea-Abies-Rhododendron catawbiense-Oxalis-Rhytidiadelphus association; Picea-Betula-Hugeria-Clintonia-Polytrichum association, etc. If we were dealing with an alliance, which we will call the Piceion, with four alternating stands in the superior arborescent layer, in addition to the complexity described above we could have 1024 twin associations.

In conclusion it seems apparent that the use of such a system of vegetation classification and the elevation of the various synusial combinations to the status of named associations can be relegated to regions whose floras are poor in species tnd where environmenal conditions are critically limiting (see Roach, 347). On the other hand, the close student of community structure anywhere should be alert for the indicator value of a change in dominance in any layer. This may lead to knowledge of the localized occurrence of pests or of vectors of pathogens, to the recognition of site quality of interest in agriculture or forestry, or to a better understanding of the biology of any interesting organism, either plant or animal.

Chapter 4

MAJOR VEGETATION TYPES OF THE WORLD, with the Tropical Rain Forest as an Example

ECOLOGISTS and geographers have two ever-present problems: (1) the analysis and delimitation of concrete individual communities, and (2) their classification into progressively more inclusive groups according to their similarities. In the first problem the student of vegetation must decide what the diagnostic characteristics of a community are and then determine, on the ground, the limits of the stand of the community. To state the problem another way, the investigator must decide how much variation in composition and structure, with particular attention to the characteristics he has selected as diagnostic, can be allowed within the stand. He faces the same problem when he moves from the analytic to the synthetic approach. In comparing different stands of similar vegetation, he must again decide how much variation is permitted (or how much similarity is required) among examples of communities for them to be grouped together in synthesizing the concept of community type. Accepting the objective reality of concrete individual stands of vegetation and the feasibility of grouping similar stands as examples of a type of vegetation, we can accept the "association" as the unit of vegetation for the present discussion. Unless his studies are extremely provincial, the student of vegetation is then confronted with the second problem. He must classify his units, or associations, into a hierarchy of groups in order to produce a system for handling multitudinous and complex data and to enhance the understanding of relationships. At one end of such a hierarchy are the vegetational units, the associations; at the other end are the major world vegetation types, usually called the formations. The former are extremely numerous; the latter are relatively few.

It is only natural that different investigators have "solved" the above problems in different ways in accordance with their various interests, predilections, detailed and generalized knowledge and assumptions. Also, and of paramount importance, the natural phenomena with which they are concerned have different degrees of objective reality in nature. Associations have been compared with species, and the various categories of vegetational classification with the higher taxons of plant systematics; but the individuals in an association do not have the discreteness of the individuals in a species. Furthermore, the associations of any higher category, as well as the individual stands of an association, do not have in general the genetic relationships of the floristic taxons, although related associations may have been segregated through time (Braun, 53, 54).

The *Manual* is concerned primarily with the analysis of smaller units of vegetation—stands and associations—and attempts no detailed treatment of vegetational classification. It does, however, seem useful to us to pay some attention to the major classificatory unit, the formation. For this purpose we selected a single formation, the tropical rain forest, as an example. The treatment here is of necessity in strong contrast to that presented in the rest of the *Manual*. We commence with a brief review of some historical attempts at classifying world vegetation types and proceed to a series of topics that collectively give a description of the rain-forest formation.

Giving major importance to water balance in climatic and edaphic ecology, Warming (409) erected four major categories of vegetation:

> Hydrophytenvereine
> Xerophytenvereine
> Halophytenvereine
> Mesophytenvereine

Schimper (360) made a basic division between climatically and edaphically controlled formations, as follows:

> Climatisch bedingte Formationen
> Gehölz

Grasflur
Wüste
Edaphische bedingte Formationen
Durch Bodenwasser bedingt
    Galeriewälder
    Sümpfe
Offene edaphische Formationen
    Felsformationen
    Sandfluren

Drude (170) produced a more elaborate system of world formations:

A. Geschlossene Landformationen
    I. Wälder
        1. Äquatoriale Regenwälder
        2. Monsunwälder
        3. Savannen- und Dornwälder
        4. Subtropisch-temperierte Regenwälder
        5. Hartlaubgehölze
        6. Sommergrüne Laubwälder
        7. Nadelwälder
    II. Niederholzformationen aus Gebüsch und Gesträuch
        1. Immergrüner Busch
        2. Lichtes Niederholz
        3. Dornbusch
        4. Gebirgsniederholz
        5. Heidegesträuche
        6. Immergrünes Alpengesträuch
        7. Niedergestrecktes Zwerggesträuch
    III. Grasfluren
        a. Bei genügender und stetiger Bodenfeuchtigkeit
        1. Wiesen
        2. Torfwiesen und Grünlandsmoore
        3. Prärien und Hochgrasfluren
        4. Savannen
        b. Bei im Sommer ungenügender Bodenfeuchtigkeit
        5. Grastriften
        6. Grassteppen
    IV. Staudenmatten, Moos- und Flechtenformationen
B. Offene Landformationen
    V. Wüstensteppen und Wüsten
    VI. Fels- und Gratformationen, Geröll- und Schotterbestände

C. Aquatische Formationen
   VII. Litoralformationen von Halophyten
   VIII. Susswasserformationen der Seen, Flüsse, Bäche
     1. Alluvionen, Ufersümpfe und Ufergebüsche
     2. Flach- und Seichtwasserbestände, Röhrichte
     3. Tiefwasserbestände, Limnoplankton

Brockmann-Jerosch and Rübel (64) published a classification of world formations which Rübel (353) revised as a basis for his famous *Pflanzengesellschaften der Erde*. This system reflects the influence of Briquet (62), DuRietz (172), and Vierhapper (404), as well as older efforts at classifying world vegetation.

Lignosa

Pluviilignosa
   1. Pluviisilvae—Regenwälder—rain forest
   2. Pluviifruticeta—Regengebüsche—rain bush
Laurilignosa
   3. Laurisilvae—Lorbeerwälder—laurel forest
   4. Laurifruticeta—Lorbeergebüsche—laurel bush
Durilignosa
   5. Durisilvae—Hartlaubwälder—broad-leaf sclerophyll forest
   6. Durifruticeta—Hartlaubgebüsche—broad-leaf   sclerophyll bush
Ericilignosa
   7. Ericifruticeta—Echte Heiden—true heath
Aestilignosa
   8. Aestisilvae—Sommerwälder—broad-leaf summer-green forest
   9. Aestifruticeta—Sommergebüsche—summer-green bush
Hiemilignosa
   10. Hiemisilvae—Regengrüne Wälder-Monsoon or rain-green forest
   11. Hiemifruticeta—Regengrüne Gebüsche—monsoon bush
Aciculilignosa
   12. Aciculisilvae—Nadelwälder—narrow-leaf sclerophyll forest
   13. Aciculifruticeta—Nadelgebüsche—needle-leaf bush

Herbosa

Terriherbosa
   14. Duriherbosa—Hartwiesen,   Steppenwiesen—prairie   and steppe
   15. Sempervirentiherbosa—Immergrüne   Wiesen—Evergreen grassland

16. Altherbosa—Hochstaudenwiesen—tall herbaceous vegetation
Aquiherbosa
17. Emersiherbosa—Sumpfweisen—marsh or aquatic grassland
18. Submersiherbosa—Submerse   Wasserwiesen—submerged
aquatic vegetation
19. Sphagniherbosa—Hochmoor—Sphagnum or high moor

Deserta

20. Siccideserta—Trockeneinöden—dry desert
21. Frigorideserta—Kälteeinöden—cold desert or tundra
22. Litorideserta—Strandsteppen—strand grassland
23. Mobilideserta—Wandereinöden—dunes vegetation
24. Rupideserta—Felsfluren—vegetation of screes, talus, etc.
25. Saxideserta—Stein- und Holzfluren—vegetation of rocks, tree
trunks, etc.

Special Groups

26. Phytoplankton—free aquatic organisms, mostly microscopic
27. Phytoedaphon—terrestrial organisms, mostly microscopic and
subterranean

How can we understand a formation? How can we find out and communicate the nature of the tropical rain forest as an example of a world formation? If the delineation is in too general terms, the representation will be merely approximate and only parts of the truth will be revealed; yet any description must have its limitations. Confronted with a myriad details, can we gain a sense of unity in variety? It is the nature of science to be analytic, but there must also be synthesis. Specialization must go hand in hand with generalization; the common and the prevailing must be considered with the rare and the extreme. Luxuriance must be set beside impoverishment.

Just as a literary description may convey more meaning of some particular manifestation of weather and climate which one has not personally experienced than would a book full of instrumental data, so a vivid description of tropical rain forest may have its place in introducing us to more precise considerations. This purpose can be served by a rather lengthy quotation from *The Naturalist in Nicaragua* by Thomas Belt (36).

As soon as we passed Pital we entered the great forest, the black margin of which we had seen for many miles, that extends from this point to the

Atlantic. . . . On each side of the road great trees towered up, carrying their crowns out of sight amongst a canopy of foliage; lianas wound round every trunk and hung from every bough, passing from tree to tree, and entangling the giants in a great network of coiling cables, as the serpents did Laocoön, the simile being strengthened by the fact that many of the trees are really strangled in the winding folds. Sometimes a tree appears covered with beautiful flowers, which do not belong to it, but to one of the lianas that twines through its branches and sends down great rope-like stems to the ground. Climbing ferns and vanilla cling to the trunks, and a thousand epiphytes perch themselves on the branches. Amongst these are great arums that send down aerial roots, tough and strong, and universally used instead of cordage by the natives. Amongst the undergrowth several species of small palms, varying in height from two to fifteen feet, are common; and now and then magnificent tree ferns, sending off their feathery crowns twenty feet from the ground, delight the sight with their graceful elegance. Great broad-leaved heliconiae, leathery melastomae, and succulent-stemmed, lop-sided leaved begonias are abundant, and typical of tropical American forests. No less so are the cecropia trees, with their white stems and large palmated leaves standing up like great candelabra. Sometimes the ground is carpeted with large flowers, yellow, pink, or white, that have fallen from some invisible tree-top above, or the air is filled with a delicious perfume, for the source of which one seeks in vain, as the flowers that cause it are far overhead out of sight, lost in the great overshadowing crown of verdure. Numerous babbling brooks intersect the forest, with moss-covered stones and fern-clad nooks. . . . Unlike the plains and savannas we crossed yesterday, where the ground is parched up in the dry season, the Atlantic forest, bathed in the rains distilled from the north-east trades, is ever verdant. Perennial moisture reigns in the soil, perennial summer in the air, and vegetation luxuriates in ceaseless activity and verdure, all the year round. Unknown are the autumn tints, the bright browns and yellows of English woods, much less the crimsons, purples, and yellows of Canada, where the dying foliage rivals, nay, excells the expiring dolphin in splendour. Unknown the cold sleep of winter; unknown the lovely awakening of vegetation at the first gentle touch of spring. A ceaseless round of ever-active life weaves the forest scenery of the tropics into one monotonous whole, of which the component parts exhibit in detail untold variety and beauty.

TYPES OF TROPICAL VEGETATION

Schimper (360) clearly showed that within the tropics vegetation is extremely varied and the principal types are closely under the control of the amount and seasonal distribution of precipitation. Tropical *deserts* lie mostly near the limits of the tropical region and are allied to the more extensive temperate deserts. Natural tropical *grassland* oc-

48	MANUAL OF VEGETATION ANALYSIS

curs chiefly as *savanna,* but sometimes as treeless *steppes.*[1] Tropical tree-dominated vegetation falls into four groups according to physiognomy and climate; these are defined by Schimper as follows: *Rain forest* is evergreen, hygrophilous, rich in woody lianas and in herbaceous and woody epiphytes, and often more than 30 m. tall. As the rainfall distribution shifts so as to produce a more or less pronounced dry season, rain forest shows transition to *monsoon forest,* which is more or less completely deciduous with drought. It is usually less high and less rich in woody epiphytes than rain forest, although it is often rich in lianas and herbaceous epiphytes. *Savanna forest* is of still lower stature and more completely leafless during the dry season, and the trees are often arranged in a parklike pattern with intermediate grassland. It has a distinct xerophilous cast and is poor in lianas, epiphytes, and underbrush, although rich in herbaceous plants, particularly grass. *Thorn forest* is rich in thorny trees, shrubs, and vines and in other ways has a xerophilous cast. It usually has no epiphytes and is poor in herbs, especially grass.

MacMillan (282) pointed out that floristic differences along a parallel of latitude increase inversely with latitude. In the vast extent of the holarctic floral kingdom there is more floristic unity among temperate and northern parts of Asia, Europe, and America than between the neo- and paleotropical kingdoms, and what is true of the flora is similarly true of the physiognomy of vegetation; but even within the tropics there is more similarity in an east-west direction than there is along a meridian.

It is not the purpose of this chapter to consider all types of tropical vegetation, but to focus attention primarily on rain forest as an example of vegetation analysis applied to a world formation. Nor is it the intention to examine in detail the similarities and differences among the rain-forest formations in the various parts of the world, although they have more physiognomic than floristic characters in common.

Several classifications of tropical communities have been published that can be compared with Schimper: Warming (409), Shantz and Marbut (366), Chipp (116), Stamp (374), Burtt-Davy (77), Barbour (24), etc. A recent compendium on forest resources of the world edited by Haden-Guest (226) contains several regional chapters of interest to biogeographers as well as foresters. Chapters of special importance for tropical forests are "Middle America" by Holdridge, "South America" by Barbour, "Tropical Africa" by Aubreville, "India" by Chaturvedi, and "Southeast Asia" by Sewandono.

[1] Historically and properly, "steppe" should not be applied to tropical grasslands.

The recent classification by Beard (32), pertaining to climax vegetation in America, will be considered. In addition to the vegetal optimum of rain forest, Beard established five formations: the seasonal formations, the dry evergreen formations, the montane formations, the swamp formations, and the marsh or seasonal swamp formations. The formations of these series are arranged in the following sequence, with the applicable terminology of Schimper, as correlated by Beard, in parentheses:

A. Rain forest (tropical rain forest)
B. Seasonal formations
    1. Evergreen seasonal forest (monsoon)
    2. Semi-evergreen seasonal forest (monsoon)
    3. Deciduous seasonal forest (?savanna forest)
    4. Thorn woodland (thorn forest)
    5. Cactus scrub (tropical desert)
    6. Desert (tropical desert)
C. Dry evergreen formations
    1. Xeromorphic rain forest (Beard used the adjective "xerophytic.")
    2. Littoral woodland (littoral woodland)
D. Montane formations
    1. Lower montane rain forest (subtropical rain forest)
    2. Montane rain forest (temperate rain forest)
    3. Palm brake
    4. Elfin woodland (elfin woodland)
    5. Frost wood
    6. Mountain pine forest
    7. Bamboo brake
    8. Paramo (alpine grassland)
    9. Tundra (alpine desert)
E. Swamp formations
    1. Swamp forest (fresh-water swamp forest)
    2. Palm swamp (fresh-water swamp forest)
    3. Herbaceous swamp
    4. Mangrove woodland (mangrove woodland)
F. Marsh or seasonal swamp formations
    1. Marsh forest (fresh-water swamp)
    2. Marsh woodland (fresh-water swamp)
    3. Palm marsh
    4. Savanna (savanna, grass steppe, meadow)

It seems to us that Beard's classification of tropical American climax vegetation has the great virtue of not slavishly following a preconceived hierarchy. It is an attempt to deal with the actualities of the vegetation on a tripartite basis (cf. Richards, Tansley, and Watt 345). The classification begins with floristic groups or associations (which are very numerous and are not given in the preceding outline). The associations are then arranged into formations on the basis of physiognomy, and are finally placed in series according to habitat.

The term association is applied to the largest possible community which has consistent dominants in the highest closed stratum, of either the same or allied species. Associations thus defined usually occupy a considerable total area, and studies in any one locality probably deal only with one or a few faciations or lociations of the association type. The association is closely related to a local environmental complex which causes it to exhibit certain structural and life-form features. More than one facies of an association and more than one association of a formation may occur in a single area when the environmental differences are sufficient to affect the floristic composition of the communities without more than slightly modifying the basic structure and life-form composition of the vegetation. Also, associations that have different floristic compositions may exhibit strong similarities in structure and life form because of the action of essentially similar habitats upon different regional floras.

The associations are thus bound into formations primarily on a physiognomic basis. The formation is determined by what Beard calls the "characteristic essential habitat," by which is meant a broader and less closely defined environmental complex than those determining associations. Beard's use of the term "formation" is essentially like that of Grisebach (222), who proposed it, and from which there have been many departures. (For the complicated and confusing variations in the usage of such terms as "formation," see Carpenter's *Ecological Glossary,* 112; and DuRietz, 173).

Finally, the formations are simply and naturally arranged in a small number of formation series on the basis of closely related series of habitats. The classificatory hierarchy is thus seen to be formed by floristic units grouped into physiognomic categories and finally into large environmental groups. The vegetation itself plays a preeminent role. Considerations of microenvironment and of succession and climax, often assumed rather than demonstrated, are placed in a secondary position.

Although there is a basic truth in the primary causal sequence, climate-vegetation-soil, which Clements (128) has so strongly emphasized, it is also true, as Beard says, that "the mutual effects of all the environmental factors and the vegetation are inextricably interrelated [to] form one *ecosystem,* as Tansley [383] has defined it. It would be of considerable advantage, at any rate in tropical studies, if the idea of analyzing the habitat into its factors could be discarded in favor of viewing the local habitat of any given community as a complex, in the form of broadly conceived moisture relations." (See also Evans 189, for a discussion of ecosystem.)

As popularly conceived, and as discussed in general terms in portions of this chapter, rain forest is often treated broadly. In much of the literature it is impossible to be sure just what phase of humid tropical vegetation is being discussed, and often several types are described together without sharp differentiation. This is an inevitable state in the early study of complex vegetation. Refinements are possible only with increased knowledge which results from more observations, more detailed local studies, improved techniques of study (such as sample-plot analysis and profile diagrams), and more realistic and less theoretical methods of classifying and interrelating the data of communities.

Instead of attempting descriptions and definitions of all the tropical formations, we shall consider briefly only the communities recognized by Beard which are most closely related to true rain forest and which have been included by many students in the more broadly conceived rain-forest community.

OPTIMUM FORMATION SERIES OR TRUE RAIN FOREST. The type of vegetation known as true rain forest is arranged in three or four layers of woody plants, but the uppermost layer of "outstanding" or "emergent" trees may not occur, as in the rain forest of French Guiana (Benoist 37). The dominant trees usually have long clean trunks which are 20 to 30 m. to the first branches. The crowns are comparatively small. Such deciduous elements as may occur are completely unimportant in the vegetation as a whole. Although compound leaves may be abundant in the upper strata, simple leaves of mesophyll size (see our discussion of Raunkiaerian leaf-size classes) are usually dominant in all tree layers. Buttressing, the presence of palms and tree ferns, and an abundance of lianas are not diagnostic but may occur in varying degrees; and special features such as stilt roots, pneumatophores, thorns and spines, cauliflory, and low-growing epiphytes are of no particular significance for the type, although they may be present in varying degree. The true rain forest is the high forest of the constantly humid tropics.

EVERGREEN SEASONAL FOREST, AND SEMI-EVERGREEN SEASONAL FOREST

(Monsoon Forest).   Where temperature is constantly moderate to high, available moisture becomes the most important vegetation determinant among the climatic elements, and in general the total amount of annual precipitation is of far less significance than its seasonal distribution. There are, of course, all degrees of gradation from true rain forest, where there is no period of inadequacy of moisture, to the typical monsoonal cycle of wet and dry seasons; and the vegetation shows a corresponding series of gradations as the dry season becomes more pronounced and protracted.

The evergreen seasonal forest has many characteristics of true rain forest, but there is a conspicuous and important deciduous element in the superior canopy, approaching one-fourth of the species, although the lower layers are completely evergreen. The crown is lower and the tree trunks branch lower than in true rain forest. Ground vegetation, palms, lianas, epiphytes, and tree buttresses are often abundant.

In semi-evergreen seasonal forest the dominant stratum is mostly deciduous and the second story is mostly evergreen. The whole forest is lower than in the preceding types, the maximum height being 20 to 25 m. The deciduous habit is somewhat facultative, for it is more complete and of longer duration in drier years.

Xeromorphic Rain Forest.   The xeromorphic rain forest may occur in areas where the precipitation is as great and as well distributed as in some types of true rain forest, but where, because of constantly high temperatures and evaporation rates and well-drained and well-aerated soils, there is a constant insufficiency of water for the luxuriant growth of true rain forest. Such forests may have a canopy at 20 m. and emergent trees up to 30 m. high. Although the forest is strictly evergreen, the majority of the species have xeromorphic foliage instead of the prevailingly hygrophilous leaf anatomy of the rain forest proper.

Lower Montane and Montane or Temperate Rain Forest.   With increasing altitude in the tropics temperature eventually becomes important for vegetation. The first significant change is at the frost line which separates the lower levels that never experience frost from those above where colder temperatures are common. Other environmental conditions also change; precipitation often increases and then decreases with still greater altitudes, and wind increases, with consequent effects on humidity and cloudiness and on the quantity and quality of light. In some situations the atmosphere may be comparatively dry, whereas in others the humidity is so constantly high that there is development of the so-called mossy and cloud forests.

The lower montane rain forest has nearly always been classified as part of the true rain forest, but the tree strata are usually reduced to two and the maximum height is lower than in the rain forest proper. This is a widespread American formation that has been described by Gleason and Cook (215), Stehlé (376, 377, 378), Charter (113), Beard (31, 32), etc.

Montane rain forest is a world-wide formation (including vegetation often called temperate rain forest, cloud forest, moss forest, etc.) that grades into the elfin woodland of Schimper's description. It consists of two strata and may be as high as 20 m., but with short tree trunks because of the low branching. Bryophytic and lichen epiphytes are exceedingly abundant and may be accompanied by numerous epiphytic flowering plants. Leaves are simple, moderately large, and evergreen. The formation occurs in the warm temperate zone as well as in the tropics at altitudes from 700 to 3000 m., depending on the interaction of a number of factors. See the work by Shreve (367) on Jamaica, Pittier (325) on the Andes, Lam (267) on New Guinea, as well as papers cited above.

ASSOCIATIONS WITHIN THE TRUE RAIN FOREST

Although true rain forest is not as extensive as popularly supposed, it is nevertheless a world formation type with its distinctive representatives in the various suitable regions of the neo- and paleotropical kingdoms. Within this great vegetation which is under the primary control of climate, there are lesser communities or subdivisions of the formation series with various degrees of difference and extent which can be recognized on floristic, physiognomic, and edaphic bases. Successional series and climaxes in the sense of Clements occur in the rain forest, but it is not clear that the familiar uses of the terms "climax" and "association," as a floristic expression of the climax state, have anything like a universal applicability. There are some authors—for example, Gaussen (207)—who reason that the association as used by the Scandinavian ecologists is not even applicable in southern Europe, much less in the humid tropics. Careful modern ecological investigations, however, are showing that the association concept is applicable to true rain forest if the term is applied to floristically characterized communities that are mature, integrated, and comparatively stable. Such communities may with reasonableness be designated as climax associations, whether or not they are under the immediate control of edaphic conditions.

How many associations exist within the rain forest of a single region no one knows. Most commercial working of the rain forest yields little information on this question, and very few areas have received modern phytosociological study. For purposes of illustration we turn to the ex-

54 MANUAL OF VEGETATION ANALYSIS

cellent studies by the Oxford expedition on Moraballi Creek, British
Guiana (Davis and Richards, 159). These investigators recognized five
associations within this locality. They derived their quantitative data
from plots 400 ft. square (about 3.7 acres or 1.5 ha.) on which all woody
plants were felled, counted, measured, and identified. The five types
are briefly described below and some significant data are shown in
Table 4.

TABLE 4. Comparison of five associations of the true rain-forest formation of the
Moraballi Creek area, British Guiana (Data from Davis and Richards, 159)

| | Forest Associations | | | | |
	Mora Forest	Mora-bukea Forest	Mixed Forest	Green-heart Forest	Wallaba Forest
Dominants	Mora excelsa	Mora gonggrijpii	Licania nervosa Eschweilera spp.	Ocotea rodioei	Eperua falcata
Soil type	Fine silt	Heavy loam	Light loam	Sand	Light sand
Moisture percent at stickiness	47.5	49.1	28.1	20.1	nil
Illumination at forest floor as fraction of full sunlight	1/75	1/163	1/150	1/123	1/70
Saturation deficit of air within forest, mm. of Hg	1.04	1.48	1.86	. . .	3.68
Percentage which dominants are of all trees 16 in. d.b.h. and over	67.2	60.7	26.7	43.4	67.0
Trees per hectare over 4 in. d.b.h.	310	309	432	519	617
Trees per hectare over 16 in. d.b.h.	45	60	60	87	67
Number of species of trees per plot, with dia. 4 in. or over	60	71	91	95	74
Percentage of trees by individuals belonging to the Leguminosae	59	33	15	14	53
Buttressing of dominant species	Very strong	Strong	Slight	Very slight	None
Strongly buttressed subsidiary tree species	Abundant	Frequent	Occasional	Scarce	Rare

THE MORA FOREST.   The Mora forest association is dominated by a single tree, *Mora excelsa,* which constitutes over 67 percent of the trees which are 16 in. in diameter or over (4.5 ft. above the ground). Perhaps a word needs to be said about this species as the sole dominant of the association. In Scandinavian ecology a species is usually required to have a coverage of about 90 percent before it is said to dominate a consociation (single-dominant association). In American forestry a single species is usually required to occupy 80 percent or more of the superior stratum before the forest type is referred to as a consociation. In the more luxuriant tropical forests where the abundance of a single species in a community is comparatively rare, consociational limits are often set as low as 40 percent.

Davis and Richards found that the Mora forest occupies the lowest ground along creeks and rivers, much of it is liable to flooding, and the water table never sinks lower than about 0.5 m. below the soil surface. The number of tree species is moderate, about 60 species, and very strong buttressing is prevalent. Reproduction of *Mora* is much poorer in this association than in certain others of the area and the authors believe that this is one of the interesting cases where a species is dominant on a site that is less favorable for it than some other site. *Mora excelsa* is less adversely affected by the water-logged soil than are most of the other species of the mixed forest association with which it has to compete on better-drained sites.

THE MORABUKEA FOREST.   The Morabukea forest association is dominated by *Mora gonggrijpii,* a species that casts a much heavier shade than *Mora excelsa,* with the result that the Morabukea forest is gloomy and poor in development of herbaceous undergrowth. Tree reproduction is abundant and saprophytic societies are numerous. This association is never found on floodplains and usually occupies the lower slopes of low hills just above the Mora forest. Its site is damp but well drained. Large trees frequently are buttressed, but the phenomenon is less common than in the Mora forest.

THE MIXED FOREST.   The mixed forest is more typical of true rain forest as usually understood than are the preceding associations because it is not dominated by a single species. Davis and Richards found over 90 tree species on the single plot. *Licania nervosa* composed 11 percent of the superior layer and four species of *Eschweilera* together composed about 20 percent. This association is widely distributed within both the area and the region, and is one favored by the Indians for their primitive agricultural plots. It commonly occupies the upper slopes and tops of the lower hills, lying immediately above the Morabukea forest association.

THE GREENHEART FOREST. The greenheart forest association has a distinct although low dominance by *Ocotea rodioei* (43 percent), a species almost confined to British Guiana. Undergrowth is not abundant and vision through the forest is freer than in the other types, although the ground is littered with greenheart which long resists decay. This association occurs on the steeper slopes of the higher hills where the soil is brown sand, but it does not extend up to the hilltops with white sandy soil. By "higher hills" in this description is meant hills with local relief above the floodplain of 50 m. or more.

THE WALLABA FOREST. The wallaba forest association is dominated by *Eperua falcata*. There is a conspicuous admixture of deciduous trees, but the association is nevertheless predominantly evergreen and a true member of the rain-forest formation. It is found on the white, strongly leached, sandy soils of the higher hilltops (probably podzolized). It is at the opposite end of the ecological series from the *Mora excelsa* forest. Buttressing is rare or absent in this association; as a matter of fact, the phenomenon is progressively less common as the soils of the region are lighter and better drained.

These forest associations, the Mora—Morabukea—mixed—greenheart—wallaba, form a topographic sequence correlated with soil type and usually encountered from the creeks and floodplains over the low hills to the higher sandy hills and plateaus. The close correlation with soil is shown by the fact that when heavier soils are found on the low hilltops and loams on the slopes, the Morabukea and mixed forests exchange topographic positions. But the most striking correlation with soil type is that between the greenheart and wallaba associations. The occurrence of the white sands is always sharply limited and the boundary of the wallaba forest coincides exactly with its type of soil. A dramatic example of this phenomenon is reported by Wood (423) for the Bartica-Kaburi district:

In most cases it was possible to step in one stride from the white sand where the Greenheart never occurred to the brown soil where it did, generally at some point on the slopes down from the flat ridge to the creeks. The most striking instance was seen . . . where a nest of Akushi (leaf-cutting ants) had thrown up the soil over an area about 30 ft. square. On the upper half of the nest the soil was white, on the lower half brown, and the dividing line was sharp enough to lay a hand across. Two trees were growing out of the nest so close that a man would have to go sideways to pass between and they occurred one just on the white soil and the other just on the brown soil below. The upper tree was the last Wallaba and the lower tree the first Greenheart on that slope.

Each association is stable, mature, and integrated. The general prevailing climate is the same for all of this locality, so that the five forest types are climax in the usual sense of the word. The mixed forest occupies the most favorable site and is considered by Richards to epitomize the climatic climax. The greenheart and the Morabukea forests are perhaps lociations or variants of the mixed forest, taking an intermediate position between it and the Mora forest on the heaviest water-logged soils and the wallaba forest on the lightest, most leached soils. The last two associations he suggests may be considered as edaphic climaxes. Beard (32) thinks that the *Eschweilera-Licania* association, the mixed forest of Davis and Richards, may eventually be shown to be the principal rain-forest type in the whole Guiana region.

It is interesting at this point to consider the monoclimax hypothesis of Clements in relation to rain forest. The hypothesis holds that under a particular climatic regimen the reactions of the vegetation will overcome all soil differences and result in a single climatic community—the climax, in the strict and original sense. In the situation we have just examined there seem to be a number of facts that are contrary to this hypothesis. (1) According to the students of the area, there are no climatic differences sufficient to cause these five different forest associations. (2) The forests bear no known successional relationships to each other. (3) There is no evidence that they reflect a mixture of climatic types, some of which are relic, having resulted from vegetational migrations in the past under the compulsion of climatic changes; that is, that the wallaba is preclimax on drier sites and the Mora is postclimax on moister sites than the present climax of the area, the mixed forest association. (4) All the associations are very strongly correlated with soil types, as shown by their sharp boundaries and by topographic inversions when the corresponding soils are inverted. (5) No reactions of the vegetation of one type upon its soil are known that will change the soil type to that of another, thus permitting the spread of one type of vegetation at the expense of another.

The geologically slow process of base-leveling seems to provide the only factors that can change the essential existing pattern of the soils and forests under the prevailing climate (except, of course, the destructive activities of man).

Another technical point in the analysis of vegetation is the difficulty of correlating the published studies by different persons in the same or different regions. This can be illustrated by reference to the warm temperate rain forest in Tanganyika Territory, Africa, in which *Ocotea usambarensis, Podocarpus usambarensis, P. gracilior, P. falcata* (?), *Ficalhoa laurifolia, Pygaeum africanum, Olea hochstetteri, Clausena melioides,* and

Entandrophragma pygaeum (?) are important species. According to Pitt-Schenkel (326), this forest has the following synonomy:

Warm temperate rain forest	Pitt-Schenkel (326)
Hohenwälder (highlands forest)	Engler (183)
Temperate rain forest	Troup (393); Shantz and Marbut (366)
High forest and cloud forest as subdivisions of temperate rain forest	Shantz and Marbut (366)
Moist belt forest	Burtt-Davy (74)
Mountain forest	Chipp (116); Henkel (238)
Subtropical evergreen forest	Phillips (317); Snowden (372)
Upper tropical evergreen or rain forest	Phillips (318)
Subtropical rain forest	Phillips (318)
High mountain rain forest	Burtt-Davy (75)
Mountain rain forest	Rea (340); Tansley and Chipp (386)
Montane rain forest	Burtt-Davy (76)
Highland evergreen forest	Moreau (296)

COMPOSITION OF THE RAIN FOREST

Floristically the tropical kingdoms are characterized by the comparative absence of certain typical holarctic (arctotertiary) families such as Fagaceae, Betulaceae, Salicaceae, Ranunculaceae, Cruciferae, Saxifragaceae, Umbelliferae, etc.; only the Leguminosae, Compositae, and Gramineae are rich in both zones. There is an exclusive or rich occurrence in the tropics of such families as Marattiaceae, Cyatheaceae, Piperaceae, Anonaceae, Flacourtiaceae, Bignoniaceae, Theaceae, Dipterocarpaceae, Melastomaceae, Sapindaceae, Sapotaceae, Acanthaceae, Zingiberaceae, Malphigiaceae, Myrtaceae, Gesneraceae, Orchidaceae, Bromeliaceae, Araceae, Palmae, etc. (Hayek, 234). Some families are pantropical and others are exclusively or predominantly neo- or paleotropical. In comparison with the floras of higher latitudes, the flora of the tropics is very rich in species, especially in woody forms. This richness of flora in the forest formations of the tropics is generally attributed to the favorableness of the climate and to a long, uninterrupted evolutionary history.

Spruce (373), who spent many years in the Amazon valley about the middle of the nineteenth century, spoke of the apparent sameness of the vast Amazon forest which is due to some wide-ranging species, the constancy of many important genera through thousands of miles of rain forest, and especially the great structural similarity of this vegetation wherever met. But, he adds, this does not "preclude the possibility of the flora being wonderfully rich; for I have calculated that by moving a degree of either latitude or longitude I found about half of the species different."

The richness of the tropical vegetation in woody species can be illustrated by the findings of Warming (408) at Lagoa Santa, Minas Gerais, Brazil, where the very local forest studied contained about 400 tree species, including 30 Papilionaceae, 27 Myrtaceae, 23 Rubiaceae, 23 Lauraceae, 18 Artocarpaceae, 17 Euphorbiaceae, 15 Meliaceae, 12 Mimosaceae, 11 Anonaceae, etc. The importance of the Leguminosae (Papilionaceae, Mimosaceae, etc.) has already been illustrated by the study at Moraballi Creek, British Guiana, where the family made up more than half of the Mora and wallaba forests. In the paleotropics other families play a leading role as, for example, in the Philippine forests where the Diptocarpaceae are often dominant from sea level to an altitude of about 800 m.

Of special interest to persons familiar with the north temperate flora is the occurrence in the tropics of trees and tremendous woody vines in families known exclusively or mostly as herbs. In the words of Spruce (373), "There are grasses (bamboos) of 40, 60, or more feet in height, sometimes growing erect, sometimes tangled in thorny thickets, through which an elephant could not penetrate. Vervains forming spreading trees with digitate leaves like the horse-chestnut. Milkworts, stout woody climbers ascending to the tops of the highest trees. . . . Instead of your Periwinkles we have here handsome trees exuding a milk which is sometimes salutiferous, at others a most deadly poison. . . . Violets of the size of apple trees. Daisies (or what might seem daisies) borne on trees like Alders."

Graphic indications of the richness of tropical floras come from intensive studies of local areas and sample plots. At Lagoa Santa, Warming (408, and Warming and Graebner, 410) found on 3 sq. mi. about 2600 species of vascular plants and estimated the total number at 3000 species. Under the same general climate this area contains both campos cerrados (savanna) and rain forest, according to soil, topography, and water table. In the forest are about 400 species of trees and 1000 species of nonarboreal higher plants. In the campo there are about 80 species of trees and 650 nontree species. Chevalier (115) estimated for the Ivory Coast rain forest of Africa 300 to 400 species of large trees 20 to 50 m. high; 300 to 400 species of smaller trees and shrubs; 100 to 150 species of large woody vines; with 60 to 70 percent of the whole flora made up of woody species.

On 1200 sq. m. (about 0.3 acre) in the Philippines, Whitford (413) found 896 trees over 3 m. tall and representing 120 different species. In the Cameroons, West Africa, the Büsgen-Jentsch Expedition (Warming and Graebner, 410) found on 0.5-ha. plots (about 1.23 acres) from 260 to 323 trees of 66 to 91 different species. In the largest height class, 40 to 55 m. tall, they found 15 to 24 trees per plot of 6 to 21 different species. In later studies in the Cameroons, Mildbraed (294) employed 1.0-ha. plots for which the maximum was 72 large trees of 24 species on a plot.

In Table 5 we have gathered together some of the careful work on

TABLE 5.　Number of tree species 10 cm. in diameter and over on sample plots in tropical rain forest at various places

Vegetation	Place	Plot Size (Hectares)	Species	Author
Mora rain forest	British Guiana	1.5	60	Davis & Richards (159)
Morabukea rain forest	British Guiana	1.5	71	"　　"　　"　　"
Mixed rain forest	British Guiana	1.5	91	"　　"　　"　　"
Greenheart rain forest	British Guiana	1.5	95	"　　"　　"　　"
Wallaba rain forest	British Guiana	1.5	74	"　　"　　"　　"
Mixed rain forest	Sarawak, Borneo	1.5	98	Richards (342)
Mixed rain forest	Ivory Coast	1.4	74	Aubreville (21)
Mixed rain forest	Nigeria	1.5	70	Richards (343)
Mixed rain forest	Mauritius	1.0	52	Vaughn & Wiehe (400)
Terra firme rain forest	Pará, Brazil	1.0	87	Black, Dobzhansky, & Pavan (42)
Igapó rain forest	Pará, Brazil	1.0	60	"　　　"　　　"
Terra firme rain forest	Amazonas, Brazil	1.0	79	"　　　"　　　"
Terra firme rain forest	Pará, Brazil	3.5	179	Pires, Dobzhansky, & Black (320)
Terra firme rain forest	Pará, Brazil	2.0	173	Cain, *et al.* (103)

sample plots in tropical rain forest to indicate the constant richness of the formation in tree species. Black, Dobzhansky, and Pavan (42) and Pires, Dobzhansky, and Black (320), working recently in the Amazonian rain forest, have handled their sample-plot data in such a manner as to permit estimates of the probable total species in the local stands of associations with which they were working. They estimate for terra firme rain forest near Belém (Castanhal), where on 3.5 ha. there were 179 species of trees with diameters of 10 cm. or more, that the total local associational tree flora is probably about 250 species reaching such sizes. Their 1950 studies (see Table 5) resulted in estimates of total woody species in the local flora about double the number found on 1.0-ha. plots. Another way to consider the richness of the composition of tropical rain forest is to note that in some stands studied by sample plots every third tree, on the average, is a new species. Although such a ratio is high, it is common for every fifth to ninth tree, on the average, to be a new species.

Rain forest is not always excessively rich in woody species. The forest in the Luquillo Division of the Caribbean National Forest (Tropical For. Exp. Sta., 391) is similar to mixed rain forest elsewhere in tropical America. On the basis of 40 plots of 0.25 acre each, the Tabonuco type was found to have 73 species of trees, the Colorado type 51 species, and the palm type 63 species. Fanshawe (195) found that the *Alexa imperatricis* faciation of the *Eschweilera-Licania* association on a 5.2-acre plot had 86 species of trees over 15 ft. high. There were 52 species in the canopy, 22 species in the understory, and 12 species in the undergrowth. He estimated that the total woody flora of the faciation is probably 150 to 200 species. In the *Dicymbe altsonii* faciation of the same association he found 75 woody species on a plot 400 x 400 ft.

In Table 6 we have reproduced the tree species list from the Castanhal (Pará, Brazil) studies of Pires, Dobzhansky, and Black (320), identified from 3.5 ha. Here we find the following families represented by a considerable number of species: 30 Leguminosae, 22 Sapotaceae, 10 Apocynaceae, 8 Moraceae and Burseraceae. The Castanhal plot contained 1482 trees 10 cm. or over in diameter. The leading family is Lecythidaceae, with 275 trees (18.5 percent). The only other families with more than 50 trees on the plot were 230 Sapotaceae, 174 Leguminosae, and 168 Burseraceae. The leading species of the association, as sampled by the plot, is *Eschweilera krukovii* (Lecythidaceae) with 171 trees (11.5 percent). Other species of relative importance are *Eschweilera odora* with 86 trees (5.8 percent); *Micropholis guianensis* (Sapotaceae), 48 trees (3.2 percent); *Rinorea passoura* (Violaceae), 43 trees (2.9 percent); *Trichila smithi* (Meliaceae), 40 trees (2.7 percent); *Sterculia* sp? (Sterculiaceae), 39 trees (2.6 percent); *Protium polybotryum* (Burseraceae) and *Pouteria* sp? (Sapotaceae), 35 trees (2.3 percent); and *Protium* sp?, 33 trees (2.2 percent). Examination of herbarium sheets at the In-

stituto Agronômico do Norte, Belém, Pará, for subsequent determinations has resulted in a few slight changes in the published list which are
incorporated in our table.

TABLE 6.　Composition of terra firme rain forest near Castanhal, Pará, Brazil, based
on tree species 10 cm. in diameter or over on a plot of 3.5 hectares (Pires, Dobzhansky,
and Black, 320)

Scientific Name and Herbarium Number, Inst. Agron. Norte	Common Name	Number of Trees 10 cm. dia. and Over
Palmae		
Oenocarpus distichus Mart. (632)	Bacaba	3
Musaccae		
Ravenala guianensis (Endl.) Benth. (1320)	Sororoca	1
Moraceae		
Bagassa guianensis Aubl.	Tatajuba	1
Perebea laurifolia Tul	Mão de gato	1
Ogcodeia sp? (4095)		9
Helicostylis sp?	Mão de gato	9
Brosimum paraense Huber	Amapá	7
Coussapoa sp?		2
Cecropia bureaniana A. Richt.	Imbauba vermelha	5
C. obtusa Trec.	Imbauba branca	3
Proteaceae		
Proteaceae gen? (4180)		1
Olacaceae		
Liriosma sp?		10
Minquartia guianensis Aubl.	Acariquara	5
Heisteria sp? (4181)		1
Nyctaginaceae		
Neea sp? (4177)		7
Neea sp.? (4169)		2
Menispermaceae		
Abuta sp?		3
Anonaceae		
Guatteria elongata Benth.	Envira	1
Duguettia sp? (4171)		1
Anona sp? (4170)		1
Anona sp? (A. Silva 54)	Envira preta	7
Anonaceae gen? (4172)	Envira preta	4
Myristicaceae		
Iryanthera paraensis Huber	Ucuuba	7
Compsoneura sp?		1
Lauraceae		
Lauraceae gen? (4155)	Louro rosa	2

TABLE 6—(Continued)

Scientific Name and Herbarium Number, Inst. Agron. Norte	Common Name	Number of Trees 10 cm. dia. and Over
Lauraceae gen? (5 spec. nos. 4156–4160)	Louro	1–5
Rosaceae		
Licania sp? (4132)	Caripé	4
Licania sp? (4133)		1
Licania sp? (4134)	Pintadinho	17
Couepia hoffmanniana Kl. (4146)	Cariperana	26
Couepia sp? (4135)	Pajurá	2
Connaraceae		
Connarus angustifolius (Radlk.) Schellenb.	Barbatimão	1
Leguminosae		
Inga alba (Ew.) Willd.	Inga	1
I. brachystachys Ducke	Inga de sapo	6
I. capitata Desv.	Inga	8
I. fagifolia Willd.		1
I. heterophylla Willd.	Inga	11
I. ingoides (Richr.) Willd.	Inga	2
I. thibaudiana DC.	Inga	9
Enterlobium schomburgkii Benth.	Orelha de negro	4
Pithecolobium pedicellare (DC.) Benth.		8
P. cf. racemosum Ducke	Angelim pedra	11
P. trapezifolium (Vahl.) Benth.	Ingarana	4
Mimosa sp?	Rabo de camaleao	3
Stryphnodendron pulcherrimum (Willd.) Hochz.	Visgueeiro	2
Piptadenia psylostachya Benth.	Timborana	19
Parkia sp? (4128)		3
Dimorphandra multipora Ducke (4123) (D. pullei Am.)		1
Copaifera reticulata Ducke	Copaiba	1
Hymanaea sp?		2
Bauhinia altiscandens Ducke	Escada de jabotí	7
Cassia apoucouita Aubl.	Coração de negro	1
Vouacapoua americana Aubl.	Acapú	29
Sclerobium paraense Huber	Tachí	14
Diplotropis purpurea var. belemnense Ducke		1
Bowdichia nitida Spruce	Sucupira	5
Ormosia coutinhoi Ducke	Boiussú	1
O. nobilis Tul.	Pau de bixo	2
Poecilanthe effusa (Huber) Ducke	Tento	14
Platymiscium filipes Benth.		1
Hymenolobium excelsum Ducke	Angelim rajado	1

TABLE 6—*(Continued)*

Scientific Name and Herbarium Number, Inst. Argon. Norte	Common Name	Number of Trees 10 cm. dia. and Over
Andira retusa HBK	Mangabarana	2
Humiriaceae		
Vantanea cupularis Huber? (4143)	Uchirana	22
Vantanea sp? (4144)		2
Erythroxylaceae		
Erythroxylum sp?		2
Rutaceae		
Fagara juniperina Engl. (4176)	Tamanqueira	4
Euxylophora paraensis Huber	Pau amarelo	14
Simarubaceae		
Simaruba amara Aubl.	Marupá	1
Simaba cedron Planch.	Pau para tudo	13
Burseraceae		
Protium heptaphyllum (Aubl.) Marsh.	Breu branco	25
P. hostmannii Engl.	Breu	29
P. (= heptaphyllum?) (4121)	Breu branco	25
P. polybotryum Engl.		35
P. sagotianum Marsh.	Breu inhambú	7
Protium sp? (4118)	Breu sucuruba	33
Protium sp? (4119)		12
Protium sp? (4122)	Breu	2
Meliaceae		
Cedrela sp?	Cedro	1
Carapa guianensis Aubl.	Andiroba	3
Trichila smithi C. DC. (4149)		40
Malphigiaceae		
Byrsonima amazonica Griseb.	Murucí	11
Vochysiaceae		
Qualea albiflora Warm.	Quaruba	9
Erisma uncinatum Warm.	Quaruba	6
Euphorbiaceae		
Euphorbiaceae gen? (4184)		2
Rinorea guianensis Aubl.		7
Croton matourensis Aubl.	Caferana	1
Aparisthmium cordatum (Juss.) Baill.		3
Sagotia racemosa Baill.	Arataciuba	12
Sapium sp?	Murupita	2
Anacardiaceae		
Anacardium giganteum Engl.	Cajú-assú	1
Thyrsodium paraense Huber	Amaparana	2
Astronium sp? (4148)		1
Celastraceae		
Goupia glabra Aubl.	Cupiuba	7

TABLE 6—*(Continued)*

Scientific Name and Herbarium Number, Inst. Agron. Norte	Common Name	Number of Trees 10 cm. dia. and Over
Icacinaceae		
Dendrobangia boliviana Rusby		3
Icacinaceae gen? (4150)		1
Sapindaceae		
Talisia megaphylla Sagot.		3
Tiliaceae		
Sloanea porphyrocarpa Ducke		2
Sloanea sp? (4165)	Urucurana	2
Apeiba petouma Aubl.	Pente de macaco	15
Bombacaceae		
Bombax longipedicellatum Ducke		1
Sterculiaceae		
Theobroma subincanum Mart.	Cupuí	6
Sterculia sp?	Tacacá	39
Caryocaraceae		
Caryocar glabrum Aubl.	Piquiarana	5
Quiinaceae		
Quiina obovata Tul.		1
Touroulia guianensis Aubl.		1
Lacunaria crenata (Tul.) A. C. Smith		5
L. jenmani (Oliv.) Ducke		1
Guttiferae		
Clusia grandiflora Splitg.	Apuí	3
Tovomita sp?		1
Symphonia globulifera L.F.	Anani	6
Violaceae		
Rinorea passoura O. Ktze.		43
Leonia glycycarpa R. et P.	Envira de sapo	9
Flacourtiaceae		
Casearia javitensis H.B.R.		2
C. sylvestris Ew?		1
Thymelaceae		
Lophostoma calophylloides Meissn.		8
Lecythidaceae		
Lecythidaceae gen? (4179)		2
Lecythis sp?	Sapucaia	4
Eschweilera krukovii Smith	Atereua	171
E. odora (Poepp.) Miers	Matamatá	86
Couratari pulchra Sandw.	Tauarí	7
Holopyxidium jarana Ducke	Jarana	5
Combretaceae		
Terminalia amazonia (Gmel.) Excell.	Tanimbuca	7

TABLE 6—(Continued)

Scientific Name and Herbarium Number, Inst. Agron. Norte	Common Name	Number of Trees 10 cm. dia. and Over
Myrtaceae		
Myrcia deflexa DC.		2
Myrtaceae gen? (4151)	Murta	1
Myrtaceae gen? (4152)	Murta	4
Myrtaceae gen? (4153)		3
Myrtaceae gen? (4154)	Murta	5
Melastomaceae		
Mouriria huberi Cogn.		2
M. nervosa Pilger		2
M. plasschaerlii Pulle		4
Miconia guianensis Aubl.	Buchuchú	15
Araliaceae		
Didymopanax morototoni (Aubl.) D. & P.	Morototó	4
Sapotaceae		
Pouteria egregia Sandw.	Abiurana	9
P. engleri Eyma (4096)	Abiurana	7
P. glomerata Radlk. (4107)	Abiurana	13
P. reticulata (Engl.) Eyma (F. 24889)	Abiurana	8
P. decussata (Ducke) Baheim. (4102)	Abiurana	1
Pouteria sp? (4101)	Abiurana	14
Pouteria sp? (4103)	Abiurana	13
Pouteria sp? (4104)	Abiurana	17
Pouteria sp? (4105)	Abiurana	35
Pouteria sp. (4106)	Abiurana	2
Pouteria sp? (4108)	Abiurana	1
Micropholis sp? (4113)		1
M. acutangula (Ducke) Eyma (= Sideroxylum)		24
M. guianensis (A.DC.) Pierre	Mangabarana	48
Pradosia huberi Ducke	Guajará bolacha	1
P. praealta Ducke	Casca doce	3
Manilkara amazonica Standley	Maparajuba	5
Sapotaceae gen? (4098)	Abiurana	1
Sapotaceae gen? (4099)	Abiurana	1
Sapotaceae gen? (4109)	Abiurana	14
Sapotaceae gen? (4111)	Abiurana	8
Sapotaceae gen? (4114)	Abiurana	4
Ebenaceae		
Diospyros melinoni (Hiern.) A. C. Smith		7
Apocynaceae		
Rauwolfia paraensis Ducke		1
Ambelania tenuifolia Muell.	Pepino	3
Lacmellia aculeata (Ducke) Monach.	Pau de colher	11
Parahancornia amapa Ducke	Amapá	2

TABLE 6—(*Continued*)

Scientific Name and Herbarium Number, Inst. Agron. Norte	Common Name	Number of Trees 10 cm. dia. and Over
Couma guianensis Aubl.	Sorva	1
Plumeria sp?	Sucuuba	1
Aspidosperma desmanthum Benth.	Araracanga	5
A. nitidum Benth.	Carapanauba	6
Geissospermum sp? (F. 23576)	Acariquararana	2
Geissospermum sp?	Acariquararana	1
Boraginaceae		
Cordia foeldiana Huber	Frejó	1
C. scabrida Mart.?		1
Verbenaceae		
Vitex triflora Vahl.	Tarumán	1
Bignoniaceae		
Tabebuia sp?	Pau d'arco	3
Rubiaceae		
Amaioua guianensis Aubl.	Puruirana	4
Chimarrhis turbinata DC.	Pau de remo	5

Gachot, *et al.* (203), in an FAO report on forest development in the Amazon valley, points out that although considerable botanical work has been done it has been mostly concerned with floristics and little is known about the actual composition of stands. Currently the FAO is making extensive study of forest composition, but detailed results have not been published. Gachot quotes a count by Artur de Miranda Bastos in the forests of Santa Maria de Vila-Noca, Amapá, in which there are 891 trees per hectare: 767 trees 15 to 30 cm. in diameter, and 124 trees 30 cm. and over in diameter, having a total of about 400 cu. m. of volume. In all, 46 species were enumerated, of which the following were highest in number and volume:

Angelim, Hymonolobium sp?	5 trees yielding 20.0 cu. m. per ha.
Angelim amarelo, Hymonolobium (sp?)	4 trees yielding 18.5 cu. m. per ha.
Caraipe, Licania sp?	10 trees yielding 13.6 cu. m. per ha.
Acapu, Voucapoua americana	11 trees yielding 12.9 cu. m. per ha.
Capiuba, Goupia glabra	6 trees yielding 12.4 cu. m. per ha.
Tauari, Couratari sp?	3 trees yielding 10.4 cu. m. per ha.
Tachi preto, Tachigalia sp?	5 trees yielding 9.4 cu. m. per ha.
Matamata, Eschweilera sp?	9 trees yielding 9.2 cu. m. per ha.

While on a trip up the Rio Capim, arranged by the Serviço Nacional de Malaria, we were able to make a brief study in the vicinity of Igapó Putirita, Pará. Here, with the aid of a mateiro (local, native woodsman), we made species lists for small contiguous samples of terra firme (50 trees), restinga (59 trees), and varzea (51 trees). Terra firme is the primeval rain forest of the upland; varzea is floodplain subject to annual inundation; and restinga (in local terminology) is intermediate in site. Our results are shown in Table 7. From the table we find that the ratio of species to trees is very high (1.4 to 2.4) and, further, that there are very few species in common to these kinds of rain forest which are all within a few hundred meters of each other. Terra firme and restinga, with a total of 57 species, have only 9.6 percent in common; restinga and varzea, with a total of 56 species, have only 3.8 percent in common.[2]

The usual procedure for work in tropical rain forest (except for specialists with long experience) consists of three steps: (1) A mateiro is used in the woods for identification and provision of common names. (2) Common names are checked against such published lists (of Le Cointe, 270) as may exist that give their scientific equivalents. (3) Collected material, in critical cases, is checked in the herbarium and the literature. As a matter of fact, all work going on in the Amazon, for example, finds the use of mateiros indispensable. A skillful mateiro will be consistent in his identifications and frank in failing to name unknown and doubtful species. A different mateiro in the same region may use some different common names, and in a different region the same common name may refer to a wholly different species.

Some workers claim that the only accurate way to inventory completely a sample plot in tropical rain forest is to cut down all the trees and shrubs and vines, although in recent Amazonian work the trees have been successfully handled with the assistance of experienced native woodsmen and the collection of doubtful specimens by tree climbers. These are, however, relatively open forests and not the popular conception of "jungle" which is only found in second growth, along stream banks, etc. The tremendous task of making sample-plot studies in tropical rain forest, and the large number of woody plants that may occur in a small area, are strikingly revealed in the account of an investigation by Burkill (Chipp, 116) on 30-year-old secondary forest on the island of Singapore. The original plan called for a study of 2 acres; but the plot was reduced to ⅓ acre from which the woody

[2] On the 2-ha. plot at Mucambo, Instituto Agronômico do Norte, Belém, the ratio of trees to species is 7 to 1. It is clear that comparisons must be made of tracts of similar area if they are to be valid as suggestions of richness of flora. Even in the richest floras, the ratio goes down as larger areas are studied.

TABLE 7. Small samples from terra firme, restinga, and varzea locies of the tropical rain forest at Igapó Putirita, Rio Capim, Pará, Brazil

	Terra firme	Restinga	Varzea
Couratari guianensis Mart. (? = pulchra)—Tauarí (Lecythidaceae)	1	..	..
Manilkara sp?—Maparajúba (Sapotaceae)	6	..	..
Manilkara huberi (Ducke) Standley—Massarandúba (Sapotaceae)	3	2	..
Goupia glabra Aubl.—Cupiúba (Celastraceae)	1	2	..
Holopyxidium jarana (Huber) Ducke (= Eschweilera)—Jarana (Lecythidaceae)	2	..	..
Eschweilera matá-matá Huber—Matá matá (Lecythidaceae)	9	3	3
Bombax sp?—Mamorâna (Bombacaceae) [Cf. B. spruceanum (Dcsne) Ducke?]	1	..	..
Euphorbiaceae gen?	1	..	..
Theobroma sp? (Cf. T. speciosa Spreng.) Sterculiaceae	1	..	..
Family?	1	..	..
Protium hepataphyllum (Aubl.) March—Breu (Burseraceae) (? = P. nodulosum Swart.)	4	1	..
Piptodenia suaveolens (DC.) Benth.—Timbórâna (Leguminosae)	6	4	..
Apeiba tibourbou Aubl.—Pênte de macáco (Tiliaceae)	3	..	..
Andira retusa HBK.—Mangarâna (Leguminosae)	1	..	..
Caryocar villosum (Aubl.) Pers.—Piquiá (Caryocaraceae)	1	..	..
Pseudochimarris turbinata (DC.) Ducke- Pau de rêmo (Rubiaceae)	1	..	..
Peltogyne lecointei Ducke—Pau roxo (Leguminosae)	2	..	..
Couepia hoffmanniana Kl. (Licania scabra Hook.)— Caripé (Rosaceae)	2	..	..
Sapotaceae gen?	1	..	..
Fagara rhoifolia Lam.—Tamanqueira (Rutaceae)	1	..	..
Hymenaea sp?—Jutaí (Leguminosae)	1	..	..
Hebepetalum humiriifolium (Planch.) Jackson— Caférâna	1	..	..
Inga sp?—Inga da terra firme (Leguminosae)	..	1	..
Family?—Abio triangular	..	2	..
Sideroxylon aff. guianensis A. DC.—Mangabarana (Apocynaceae)	..	4	..
Macrolobium bifolium (Aubl.) Pers.—Ipé de terra firme (Leguminosae)	..	1	..
Anonaceae gen?—Envira pe d'anta	..	1	..
Ocotea laxiflora Mez.—Louro (Lauraceae)	..	1	..
Eschweilera sp?—Jatereu (Lecythidaceae)	..	3	..
Family?—Caa-ingá	..	1	..
Saccoglottis amazonica Mart.—Uchírana (Humiriaceae)	..	6	2
Family	..	1	..
Sapotaceae gen?	..	1	..

TABLE 7—(Continued)

	Terra firme	Restinga	Varzea
Sapotaceae gen?	..	1	..
Sclerolobium goeldianum Huber—Tachí (Leguminosae)	..	1	..
Qualea wittrockii Malm.—Mandioqueira (Vochysiaceae)	..	1	..
Family?	..	1	..
Protium sp?—Breu vermelho (Burseraceae)	..	2	..
Parinarium rodolphi Huber—Parinari (Rosaceae)	..	1	..
Rosaceae (?Couepia divaricata Huber)—Macucu	..	3	..
Leguminosae?—Coração de prequica	..	3	..
Connarus erianthus Benth.—Mão de gato (Connaraceae)	..	1	..
Hymenaea parviflora Huber—Jutaí-pororoca (Leguminosae)	..	1	..
?Ptychopetalum olacoides Benth.—Muira-puama (Olacaoeae) Mateira said "muirapu-rama"	..	1	..
Mapati-rana [like Pourouma cecropiaefolia Mart. (Moraceae)]	..	2	..
Family?	..	1	..
Coumarouna odorata Aubl.—Cumaru (Leguminosae)	..	1	..
Protium sp?—Breu mescla = Breu branco (Burseraceae)	..	1	..
Xylopia marginata? Mart.—Envira preta (Anonaceae)	..	1	..
Protium unifolium Engl.?—Breu branco (Burseraceae)	..	1	..
Family?	..	1	..
Melastomaceae gen?	..	1	..
Andira inermis HBK.—Cumarurana, Andira-uchi (Leguminosae)	..	..	3
Family?—Rim de paca	..	..	1
Family?—Anuera	..	..	3
Sapotaceae gen?	..	..	2
Family—Mouriria	..	..	1
Andripetalum spp. and Roupala spp.?—Louro-faia (Proteaceae)	..	..	2
Macrolobium chrysostachyum (Miq.) Benth.—Ipé de varzea (Leguminosae)	..	..	11
Family?—Fava-bolacha	..	..	2
Caryocar microcarpum Ducke—Piquia-rana da igapó (Caryocaraceae)	..	..	5
Rosaceae gen?	..	..	1
Pithecolobium unifoliatum Benth.—Ingarana (Leguminosae)	..	..	4
Calophyllum brasiliense Camb.—Jacaréuba (Gutiferae)	..	..	1
Schwartzia sp?—Saboeira (Leguminosae)	..	..	2
Rosaceae gen?	..	..	1
Family?	..	..	1
Family?	..	..	1

TABLE 7—(*Continued*)

	Terra firme	Restinga	Varzea
Anonaceae gen?—Envira	. .	. .	2
Anoera, if "Anauera" this may be Licania macrophylla Benth. (Rosaceae)	. .	. .	1
Number of trees	50	59	51
Number of species	22	35	21
Percentage of species in common:			
Terra firme and restinga	⊢—9.6%—⊣		
Restinga and varzea		⊢— 3.8%—⊣	
Terra firme and varzea	⊢————4.9%————⊣		

undergrowth less than 6 ft. high was first removed, sorted into species, and counted. Next the trees 6 to 18 ft. high were handled in the same way; and finally the larger trees were examined and measured. It was impossible to avoid injury to seedlings and smaller plants, so careful estimations were made on a basis of local counts. The somewhat staggering results for the ⅓ acre were:

> 378 trees over 18 ft. high
> 2,728 woody plants 2 to 18 ft. high
> 27,342 smaller plants, mostly woody seedlings
> 30,448 plants on about 1350 sq. m.

STRUCTURE OF THE RAIN FOREST

The term community is generic in that it is applicable to the whole range of plant aggregations, small or large, simple or complex, just as it is in human ecology where one can speak of rural, village, and urban communities, and in cities, furthermore, can consider smaller units such as neighborhoods that compose the larger one. Plant communities may be very simple, as when on rock surfaces only a single life form, crustose lichens, composes the whole vegetal cover; but in the vast majority of cases plant communities are complex in that their species are of two or more life forms, sometimes many, which have their own social organization and compose the synusiae or life form communities of the phytocoenosis or entire vegetal cover of a station. Forest vegetation is characteristically complex in structure, although certain cool temperate woods dominated by single, closely stocked species (certain woods of *Fagus, Pinus,* or *Picea*) may be as simple structurally as grassland or tundra; but tropical rain forests are usually the most complex of all vegetation types. The woody plants may be in three or even four layers—"forests upon forests," as Humboldt said—with numerous other life-form communities associated with them. The herbaceous and woody ground cover may be more or less rich, as may be the lianas, the herbaceous, woody, and bryophytic epiphytes, and various saprophytic and parasitic synusiae. Sometimes the rain forest, as Schimper says, may "display a dense mass of foliage from the ground up to the tops of the trees, through which we can only laboriously cut our way with a bill-hook; others are like immense, dark-columned halls, which afford a free passage and a clear outlook in all directions."

In temperate forests mature uneven-aged stands, whether of broad leaf, needle-leaf, or mixed composition, present a regular canopy. In contrast, tropical humid forests usually have a strikingly ragged appearance, with an uneven crown canopy from which project clumps or individual specimens of emergent trees that tower above their neighbors. There are many general pictures of this structure; Pittier's description (324) of Panama forests will be given as an example. He speaks of islands of emergent trees, reaching 175 ft. in height, with *Couroupita paraensis, Coumarouna panamensis,* and species of *Ficus* and *Lecythis.* The uppermost closed story contains species of *Copaifera, Virola, Lecythis, Brosimum, Pourouma;* the third level has species of *Alseis, Warscewiczia, Guatteria, Eschweilera, Brounea,* and many palms; and the shrub layer is very rich in Rubiaceae, Piperaceae, Melastomaceae, and dwarf palms. To these layers must be added the herbaceous flowering plants and ferns, the mosses, liverworts, lichens, and fern allies of the ground cover; and the lianas and epiphytes of all kinds.

By way of further illustration let us consider the more exact description of the rain forest of the Moraballi Creek area (Davis and Richards, 159), applicable in general to all five associations of the climax formation studied by these authors in British Guiana.

I. Plants not dependent on others for support
    A. Autotrophic or nutritionally independent plants
        1. *Outstanding (emergent) trees:* These are trees which, scattered through the forest and nowhere abundant, lift their whole crowns above the main canopy of the forest, and reach heights of 50 m.
        2. *The main canopy:* The trees of this layer have the bottom of their canopy at about 20 m. and the top is very uneven, averaging somewhat less than 30 m. The numerous component species can be divided into two partial layers at about 27 m.

3. *Undergrowth trees:* This stratum ends rather abruptly at about 13 m. and is principally 5 to 9 m. high.

4. *Small shrub-tall herb layer:* This synusia is about 1 to 1.5 m. tall and often consists of nothing but suppressed saplings of the trees.

5. *Small herb layer:* In this layer there are three different societies of herbs and seedlings of trees.

   a. *Light-tolerant society:* A community of various flowering herbs that occurs where the canopy allows the penetration to the ground of abundant sun flecks, or where it has been removed by wind-throw of trees and there is nearly full illumination.

   b. *Fern society:* A community of intermediate light relations, being able to stand sun flecks but not full light.

   c. The third ground society is the saprophytes.

B. *Society of saprophytes:* This community consists of nutritionally dependent flowering plants of the Murmanniaceae, Gentianaceae, Orchidaceae, etc., which grow where the shade is deepest and the humus thickest. Humus is usually not very abundant because of high oxidation and activity of microorganisms in the soil.

II. Climbing plants, lianas and bushropes

A. *Climbers reaching the canopy:* These often climb to the tops of the tallest trees, but are most abundant in the main canopy of the forest.

   1. *Typical lianas:* These are mostly twiners with massive woody stems and produce little or no foliage below the top of the canopy; they include species of *Bauhinia, Strychnos, Dioclea, Arrabidea,* etc.

   2. *Root climbers:* Lianas, mostly with slender stems, which reach only the lower part of the canopy, such as *Schlegelia violacea* and some Araceae.

   3. *Epiphytic trees and shrubs:* Plants in this group send down numerous and often massive roots to the ground, appearing like lianas, in the genera *Clusia, Ficus,* etc.

B. *Climbers on the undergrowth:* The members of this group are often herbaceous or semi-woody and include the scrambling palm (*Desmoncus* spp.), climbing ferns (*Lygodium* spp.), *Salpichlaena hookeriana, Carludovica coronata,* and species of *Smilax.*

C. *Small herbaceous climbers:* These plants do not reach above about 3 m., including plants such as *Trichomanes pedicellatum.*

III. Epiphytes
    A. Autotrophic epiphytes
        1. *Society of shade epiphytes:* This community is usually best developed up to about 14 m. above the ground, but may reach 20 m., growing on undergrowth and young canopy trees and even on heavy bushropes. Common members of the group are ferns such as *Hymenophyllum polycanthos, H. ciliatum, Hecistopteris pumila, Trichomanes* spp., stray Bromeliaceae, occasional orchids such as *Cheiradenia cuspidata,* and other plants such as *Peperomia emarginella.*
        2. *Society of sun epiphytes:* These plants grow in the center of the crowns and on the larger branches of the principal trees. The common families are Orchidaceae, Araceae, and Bromeliaceae; but there are many other families, including Piperaceae, Gesneriaceae, Cactaceae, Lentibulariaceae, and numerous ferns.
        3. *Society of extreme xeromorphic epiphytes:* These plants grow on the most exposed branches of the canopy and on the crowns of the emergent trees. Many of them are succulent or narrow-leaved. Included are *Rhipsalis* spp. (Cactaceae), narrow-leaved species of *Tillandsia* and *Aechmea* (Bromeliaceae), and some Orchidaceae.
    B. *Society of epiphytic parasites:* These plants are members of the Loranthaceae and occur in situations about like the habitat of the preceding society.

The preceding tabulation takes into consideration 16 communities (synusiae) of the rain-forest phytocoenosis, each of which can be given floristic, life form, and ecological characterization. Nor is this all. A still more intensive investigation of rain forest would include communities within the soil; the smaller cryptogams (algae, mosses, liverworts, lichens) on soil, rotten wood, tree bark, leaves, and rocks where they are exposed; and the special biocoenoses of the water-catching basins of clumped leaves of epiphytic and terrestrial Bromeliaceae, etc. Tropical rain forest is indeed structurally complicated!

Although gregariousness or high sociability, as understood among plants of higher latitudes, is exceptional in tropical rain forest, and although competition is most severe among highly social species and organisms generally with the same ecological requirements, the rain forest is certainly not without severe competition for space and living requirements. Although differences in humidity are not unimportant, the nutritional requirements as related to light occurrence in the forest and the light requirements of the species seem to be far more controlling in the development of forest structure. As to the universality of this structure we can do no better than quote Richards (344):

"As far as is known there is no climax community to which the term Tropical Rain forest can properly be applied in which all of these ecological groups are not present. There is also no region in the Rain forest which possesses local synusiae not found elsewhere. The variations in the plan or pattern of structure which are met with consist chiefly of differences in the relative strength with which various synusiae are represented by more species and individuals, and show a wider range of form, than in others. Similarly, some Rain forests are richer than others in climbers. The spatial arrangement of the synusiae . . . also varies to a greater or lesser extent.

In some stands of rain forest the typical three layers of forest trees are obvious, whereas in others they are not at all apparent. In old-growth or primary forest, where all age classes are present, layers are often difficult of ascertainment in temperate forests. In rain forest where woody species predominate, even in the ground layer, and where all-age transgressives are constantly present, the layers that exist because of differences in life form—that is, because of differences in mature height of species—are often obscure. A few investigators have plotted the number of trees in various height classes. The result is usually a continuous curve with no indication of frequency modes for certain height classes. Booberg (48) concluded that the layers usually described for rain forest in Java cannot be demonstrated. Davis and Richards (159) obtained such a continuous curve for rain forest in British Guiana. Vaughn and Wiehe (400) got a similar curve for the rain forest of Mauritius, even though the observer could see the strata. It can be concluded, then, that strata, if they really exist, must be demonstrated by a technique that distinguishes life-form groups from the transgressives. In a forest a *transgressive* is a young tree of a species occurring in the layers below its maximum potential development. In other words, it is on its way through the lower layers of the forest to its ultimate position as determined by its life form.

Because the direct observation of the stratification of rain forest is difficult, Davis and Richards (159) developed the profile diagram, a device that has since been widely used. The *profile diagram* consists of a scale drawing of actual trees along a narrow transect through the forest. The relative positions of trees, their diameters, heights, and crown masses, are all drawn to a convenient scale. With identification of the individual plants it becomes possible to distinguish the natural strata of the mature forest from the more or less numerous transgressives which usually confuse direct observation. Authors who construct profile diagrams usually fell all the trees on the strip to measure them.

SIZE AND FORM OF TREES

The fact that world records for height, diameter, and volume of trees are held by such temperate trees as *Sequoia, Sequoidendron, Agathis, Eucalyptus, Taxodium,* etc., does not detract from the magnificent development of trees in the tropical rain forest. Martius in *Flora Brasiliensis* mentions an Amazonian tree with a radius of 1368 Paris lines (a Paris line is $\frac{1}{12}$ pouse, 2.256 mm., 0.0888 in.), which seems to be a diameter of about 25 ft. It was said to be about 2736 years old. Spruce (373) measured a Brazil nut tree (*Bertholletia excelsa* HBK.) that was 42 ft. in circumference. It was unbuttressed and had about the same diameter 50 ft. above the ground; its first branch was at about 100 ft. Many large trees give the appearance of tremendous size because of the plank buttresses which may extend 20 to 30 ft. up the trunk and laterally at ground level for 15 ft. or more. Pittier (324) measured a *Lecythis* in Panama that was 5.3 ft. in diameter above the butt swell, 138 ft. to the base of the crown, and 175 ft. to its top. Schimper mentions a Malaysian specimen of *Althingia excelsa* that was 181 ft. tall; Mildbraed, an African *Desbordesia glaucescens* that was 175 ft. tall; Spruce, an Amazonian *Eriodendron* (silk-cotton tree) 165 ft. tall; and Davis and Richards, a British Guiana *Couratari pulchra* 142 ft., a *Mora gonggrijpii* 144 ft., and a *Terminalia tanibouca* 148 ft. tall. Although Spruce never saw them, he wrote that sawmill operators in the Amazon reported trees of 231 ft. in height, and Chevalier (115) cites similar exceptional specimens on the Ivory Coast of Africa. Richards (344) lists some large trees which he considers to be reliably measured (see Table 8); he

TABLE 8. Heights of exceptionally tall trees of the rain forest. Records gathered from various sources by Richards (344), and for the Amazon region by Ducke and Black (171)

Name	Locality	Height Meters	Feet
Koompassia excelsa	Sarawak, Borneo (Foxworthy)	84	275
Koompassia excelsa	Malay Peninsula (Foxworthy)	81	265
Koompassia excelsa	Sarawak (Beccari)	70	230
Eucalyptus deglupta	New Britain (Lane-Poole)	71	233
Agathis alba	Celebes (van der Koppel)	70	230
Entandrophragma cylindricum	Nigeria (Kennedy)	59	196
Desbordesia glaucescens	Cameroons (Mildbraed)	56	184
Dinizia excelsa	Brazil	55	180
Dinizia excelsa	Brazil, south of Gurupá	60	197
Cedrelinga catenaeformis	Brazil	49	161
Apuleia molaris	Brazil	43	141

concludes that the average height of taller trees in the rain forest is seldom over 150 to 180 ft., individual trees over 200 ft. are not uncommon, and considerably larger ones have been recorded. As interesting as these data are, it should be remembered that such trees are of the emergent stratum and no canopy is so high. In fact, we have been impressed in the rain forest of Pará by the tall but slender trunks of the trees, with diameters over 1 m. being relatively infrequent and the canopy often at heights between 30 and 40 m. This is less than the maximum heights of dominant temperate trees. For example, Cain has measured *Liriodendron tulipifera* (Magnoliaceae) 167 ft. high and *Picea* rubens (Coniferae) 145 ft. high in the Great Smoky Mountains, Tennessee; and Warming and Graebner (410) record *Picea excelsa* at Bialowies, near the Polish-Russian border, as 155 ft. tall.

As great as rain-forest trees may be in height and diameter, they are preponderantly of moderate dimensions; within the forest one is more impressed by the slender, columnar trunks that seldom branch until the region of the relatively small crown than by trees of dramatic size. This fact is well shown by sample plot studies in the *Eschweilera-Licania* association in British Guiana (Fanshawe, 195). In the *Alexa imperatricis* faciation Fanshawe found on 5.2 acres 105 trees per acre of 4 to 12 in. diameter, 36 trees per acre of 12 to 20 in. diameter, and only 5 trees per acre with diameters in excess of 20 in. In the *Dicymbe altsonii* faciation on a plot 400 × 400 ft. (3.67 acres) he found for the same diameter classes the following number of trees: 138, 27, and 13, respectively. Only about one-fourth of the species had trees in the largest-sized class. Table 9 gives specific data for the *Alexa* faciation.

All the common tree forms of temperate regions also occur in the rain forest, except the excurrent coniferous type of trunk; in addition there are such forms as palms, tree ferns, and the banana. There are also special developments that will be given more description, namely, stilt roots, the banyan form, and plank buttresses.

Some trees with stilt roots commence their lives as epiphytes, having germinated on stumps, logs, and in low tree crotches. With the decay of the substratum the tree is left standing on a series of trunklike "legs," and it is sometimes possible to stand erect among them with the regular trunk of the tree directly overhead. This habit occurs in several families and genera, such as *Tovomita, Musanga, Balanites, Duboscia, Clusia, Virola, Protium, Ficus,* and the palm *Acanthorrhiza*. This habit has an interesting although minor counterpart in certain humid temperate forests. For example, *Betula alleghaniensis,* in the Great Smoky Mountains (Cain, 91), is often seen standing on stilt roots, and may even produce roots from the main trunk that run from several feet high along the outside of the trunk to the ground.

TABLE 9. Density of trees by size classes, *Eschweilera-Licania* rain forest, *Alexa imperatricis* faciation, British Guiana (Fanshawe, 195)

Species	Diameter Classes in Inches		
	4–12	12–20	Over 20
Eschweilera sagotiana	170	83	6
Alexa imperatricis	68	36	9
Pentaclethra macroloba	37	9	..
Pouteria guianensis	27	12	1
Eschweilera alata	28	5	..
Eschweilera grata	30	3	..
Inga spp.	17	3	..
Hebepetalum humiriifolium	15	2	..
Eschweilera corrugata	14	1	..
Jacaranda copaia	10	2	1
Eschweilera decolorans	11	1	..
Pouteria venosa	6	4	..
Trattinickia demerarae	8	2	..
Diplotropis purpurea	5	3	1
Sterculia rugosa	5	3	..
Sloanea guianensis	8	..	..
Pouteria minutiflora	8	..	..
Goupia glabra	4	1	2
Minquartia guianensis	5	1	..
Maytenus myrsinoides	5	1	..
Clathrotropis brachipetala	6	..	..
Chrysophyllum sanguinolentum	3	2	..
Parinari campestris	3	..	1
Pithecolobium japunba	..	2	1
Himatanthus bracteatus	4	..	..
Sterculia pririens	4	..	..
Protium decandrum	4	..	..
Terminalia dichotoma	3	..	..
Aspidosperma oblongum	2	..	..
Additional species (24)	26	5	4
Total on 5.2 acres	536 (72%)	181 (24%)	26 (4%)
Total per acre	105	36	5

In some cases the roots from epiphytes so interlace and entwine about the host tree that a single ropy and perforated false trunk may be developed. The extreme development of this tendency is found in the banyan form, *Ficus religiosa* being an example, where all the principal branches put out aerial roots that form false trunks, and a single plant covering thousands of square feet stands on hundreds of stilts.

PLANK BUTTRESSES

Plank buttresses are so striking a feature of many rain forests, and there is so much confusion about them, that they deserve special attention in an analysis of the rain-forest formation. Humboldt, Wallace, Schomburgh, Bates, Belt, Warming, Schimper, and many other early and recent naturalists have described the phenomenon of comparatively thin, planklike structures that seem to rise from the principal lateral roots and extend varying distances up the trunks of trees. They are all more or less triangular. Some extend up the trunk for 20 to 30 ft. or more; others may be comparatively low but extend laterally from the base for 15 to 20 ft. or over.

Fanshawe (195) found buttressing to be common in the *Eschweilera-Licania* association in British Guiana. In the *Alexa imperatricis* faciation of this association—that is, typical lowland rain forest on lateritic red-yellow earths—he found that 25 percent of the canopy species had well-marked plank buttresses. In the *Dicymbe altsonii* faciation 12 percent of the trees are strongly buttressed and 88 percent are moderately buttressed to basally swollen, with few exceptions.

The development of buttresses is especially frequent in trees of the Bombacaceae, Leguminosae, Lecythidaceae, Moraceae, and Artocarpaceae. Some examples from British Guiana include *Mora excelsa, M. gonggrijpii, Eschweilera sagotiana, Peltogyne pubescens, Couratari pulchra, Terminalia tanibouca,* and species of *Bombax* and *Mimusops.* Examples from Africa include *Terminalia superba* and *Ceiba pentandra* from the Camaroons, and *Cynometra alexandri* from Uganda. In the West Indies high narrow buttresses occur in *Ceiba pentandra, Dipteryx odorata,* and *Glycoxylon grande;* and low broad ones in *Erythrina glauca* and *Parkia pendula,* according to Navez (299). In Panama, according to Pittier (324), the buttresses are tall and broad in *Ficus,* tall and narrow in *Sterculia,* low and broad in *Sloanea,* rounded and stout in *Mimusops,* and intricate in *Dimorphandra.* Figure 6 shows the "ground plan" of the plank buttresses of a *Ceiba pentandra* studied by Cain on the varzea rain forest of Rio Capim about 5 km. south of Capim, Pará, Brazil. Some planks extended up the trunk of the tree to a maximum height of about

10 m., at which point the cylindrical trunk was still about 2.5 m. in diameter. Planks radiated in all directions, some of them anastomosing; the longest reached 20 m. from the base of the trunk proper.

Such buttresses are often spoken of as roots and it is said that they rise along the trunk as the tree grows. It is therefore necessary to examine these phenomena a little more closely. In some cases the principal lateral roots may run over the soil surface for 10 to 15 m., as in *Caryocar nuciferum,* without the production of buttresses. This same

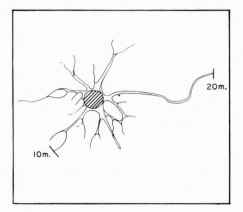

FIGURE 6.   Scale drawing of the "ground plan" of the plank-buttressed base of a *Ceiba pentandra* observed by the authors in the varzea rain forest near Capim, Pará.

phenomenon is shown by certain temperate trees in poorly drained sites, as, for example, *Fagus grandifolia* in acid flatwoods in southern Indiana. Also the development of moderate buttresses (but no real planks) is not uncommon among temperate trees on wet sites and floodplains, as in *Ulmus* spp. and *Taxodium distichum.* Petch (315) reports that roots may develop vertical flanges exactly like buttresses except that they are several feet removed from the trunk of the tree, and that in other cases (*Cauarium commune*) buttresslike flanges may develop from large branches 25 to 30 ft. above the ground and with no connection with roots. It is apparent, then, that these structures are not roots but are outgrowths of roots and stems which may or may not have a continuous development, and that an explanation of plank buttresses should likewise be applicable to the anomalous cases. These flanges result from extremely localized and highly pronounced eccentric growth which tends often to occur in a continuous but narrow zone from the principal roots up the stem.

Until comparatively recently the explanation of this phenomenon accepted by naturalists was represented by the following quotation from Bates (27):

The purpose of these structures is as obvious, at the first glance, as that of similar props of brickwork which support a high wall. . . . Their nature and their manner of growth are explained when a series of young trees of different ages is examined. It is then seen that they are roots which have raised themselves ridge-like out of the earth, growing rapidly upwards as the increasing height of the tree required augmented support. Thus they are plainly intended to sustain the massive crown and trunk in these crowded forests, where lateral growth of the roots in the earth is rendered difficult by the multitude of competitors.

Spruce noticed that large buttressed trees usually have a shallow root system and no taproot, and Schimper thought that the phenomenon was correlated with more or less water-logged soils. Navez pointed out, however, that buttresses also develop on some trees growing in thin rocky soils that are well drained. The most popular explanation of buttressing still is that it is a response to mechanical stresses on the part of shallow-rooted species; but this has been questioned by Francis (200) for Queensland, Petch (315) for Ceylon, Davis and Richards (159) for British Guiana, and others.

The following objections can be raised to the mechanical explanation of buttressing of the type here considered. (1) The development of buttresses is not correlated with size of the tree crown or with height. Some equally large trees, such as *Hylenaea courbaril* and *Bertholletia excelsa*, are completely without them. (2) There is usually no correlation between the orientation of the buttresses and the direction of the principal stresses produced by prevailing winds, although Navez (299) reports such a correlation for *Ceiba pentandra* in Cuba. (3) Buttresses appear in young trees under the canopy, but only in the trees whose life form permits them ultimately to reach the canopy. This objection is weakened by the fact that a functional structure not uncommonly appears earlier in the ontogeny than the time of its usefulness. (4) The height of buttressed tropical trees is little or no greater than that of unbuttressed temperate trees. Furthermore, the crowns of rain-forest trees may be so bound together by stout lianas that the stresses are shared. In fact, it is sometimes very difficult to fell a tree in rain forest without cutting many surrounding trees and bushropes. (5) The types of rain forest in which buttressed trees are best developed occur in the most protected topographical situations on floodplains and in sheltered valleys.

There would seem to be no doubt that buttresses add strength to shallow-rooted trees; but trees similar in all other respects on the same sites do not have such planks. Some species develop buttresses whatever the site, and others inherit the tendency and express it more or less according to the wetness of the site. Petch (315) has put forward the most interesting hypothesis but, unfortunately, it is not yet supported by experimental data. Noting that tropical trees often do not behave as a physiological unit, different branches of the same tree being in different stages of development (we have seen this in species of Bombacaceae and Lecythidaceae in Rio, Belém, and elsewhere), Petch supposed that the planks might be explained by narrow paths for conduction of water and solutes and soluble foods on certain radii of the tree coincident with principal roots, thus accounting for exaggerated radial growth along these lines. This needs careful experimentation.

CAULIFLORY

Cauliflory is the adventitious production of flowers and fruits on leafless woody stems. It is one of the characteristics of the rain-forest formation, for nowhere else is it a common phenomenon. It does occur in certain temperate Leguminosea (*Cercis, Gleditschia, Gymnocladus*), and is approached in short fruiting spurs on some fruit trees; but in the vast majority of species flowers are produced on leafy twigs from buds of the preceding season's growth in ordinary twigs. This system also prevails in the rain forest, but Mildbraed (293) has estimated that cauliflory nevertheless occurs in over a thousand species, and he lists nearly 300 cauliflorous species in Africa alone.

Schimper distinguished cauliflory on main stems only, on branches only, and on both trunks and branches. Mildbraed, however, has set up definitions of several types. (1) *Simple cauliflory* is the production of flowers anywhere on trunks, branches, and twigs resulting from the fact that buds remain active for an indefinite period of time. This type occurs in species of *Theobroma, Diospyros,* etc. (2) *Ramiflory* is the production of flowers on larger branches but not on the trunk, as in *Turraeanthus zenkeri* in Africa and species of *Polyanthia* in Borneo. (3) In *trunciflory* flowers are limited to the main stem of the tree, as in *Cola,* some *Diospyros,* and *Omphalocarpum procerum.* (4) *Basiflory* is the production of flowers only at the base of the trunk, as in the African *Uvariopsis sessiliflora* and the *Polyanthia flagellaris* of Borneo. (5) *Idiocladanthy* is the production of flowers on comparatively long leafless shoots from trunks or lower branches, as in *Couroupita guianensis* and *Annonidium mannii.* (6) *Flagelliflory* is the production of flowers on long whiplike branches which lie on the ground, as in *Paraphyadanthe flagelliflora.* The preceding account is based on Richards (344).

Cauliflory is fairly common in the Leguminosae, Sapotaceae, Myrtaceae, Moraceae, Anacardiaceae, Menispermaceae, Aristolochiaceae, and Flacourtiaceae. American genera with cauliflory include *Theobroma, Brownea, Grias, Gustavia, Quassia, Simaba, Talisia, Couroupita, Ficus, Swartzia, Crescentia, Aristolochia, Parkia, Couepia, Cynometra, Diospyros, Parmentiera, Artocarpus, Steculia,* etc. Sometimes the phenomenon produces very striking results, as in the custard apple *(Polyalthea* of Borneo, mentioned by Wallace, 406), which bears orange-red flowers about 3 in. in diameter and abundant enough to clothe the trunk of the tree, the foot-long fruits of *Pamentiera cereifera* of Ceylon, and the cannonball tree *(Couroupita)* of Panama.

Cauliflory is an inherited characteristic, strongly fixed in some species and somewhat variable in expression in others. Its essential limitation to rain forest, and there to trees of the lower strata, suggests some functional relationship to conditions within the rain forest, but we do not know of any experimental studies of the phenomenon that combine morphology, physiology, and ecology. Most of the "explanations," such as the thin bark of many tropical rain-forest trees, do not explain, and many of them are frankly teleological speculations.

LIANAS

Next to the trees themselves, the woody lianas are the most conspicuous feature of most rain forests. The forest often seems so full of them as to make it impossible to trace out the individual plants. They range from fine cordlike stems to gigantic bushropes that fill most of the native needs for cordage. They climb the trunks and branches to the tops of the tallest trees and hang in coiled festoons when their supports die and break away. Although no sharp distinction is possible between some weak-stemmed trees and half-climbing shrubs on the one hand and some climbing epiphytes on the other, large lianas have three important biological features: (1) an almost unlimited growth in length, (2) a strong capacity for conduction, and (3) a long life span.

Spruce (373) speaks of a specimen of *Schnella splendens* with flat, wavy, ribbonlike stems up to 12 in. broad and up to 300 ft. long. Schimper reports a measurement by Treub of a rattan palm *(Calamus)* that was incompletely pulled from the canopy but was nevertheless 790 ft. long. Wallace (406) says that the palms *Calamus* and *Desmoncus* reach lengths of nearly 1000 ft. No one knows the age lianas may attain; but the positions in which they are found, together with their methods of climbing, indicate that most of them which have reached the tops of the largest trees are as old as their supports, and in some instances they have apparently outlived more than one tree.

Schenck (357; see also Schimper, 360; Hayek, 234) recognized four main groups of lianas. (1) The *scramblers* are the least specialized in that they do not twine or have specially adapted organs. Here are included the unarmed shrubby climbers like *Coccoloba ochrealata* and *Ocotea declinatam,* little changed from ordinary shrubs except for their weak stems and elongated internodes; thorned climbers like *Bougainvillea spectabilis* and some species of the cactus *Cereus;* scramblers with prickles like the temperate *Galium* and *Rosa;* scrambling bamboos like *Arthrostachys capitata* and *Merostachys kunthiana;* palms like *Chamaedora desmoncoides, Oncocalamus, Ceratolobus,* and *Desmoncus;* and ferns like *Gleichenia dichotoma, Adiantum,* and *Selaginella* spp. (2) The *climbers with adventitious roots* occur in many families such as Piperaceae *(Piper nigrum),* Moraceae *(Ficus pumila),* Marcgraviaceae *(Marcgravia schimperiana),* Cactaceae *(Cereus flagelliformis),* Bignoniaceae *(Bignonia fruticosa),* Myrtaceae *(Metrosideros florida),* Melastomaceae *(Medinilla radicans),* Asclepidaceae *(Hoya macrophylla),* Araceae *(Pothos, Anthurium, Monstera),* Cyclanthaceae *(Carludovica),* Pandanaceae *(Freycinetia strobilacea),* Palmae *(Plectomia),* Orchidaceae *(Vanilla),* Filices *(Polybotrya osmundacea).* (3) The *twiners* include a very large number of forms in the rain forest. Some are slender-stemmed, others are large and ropelike, and still others are flat-stemmed or variously angled, fluted, and coiled. Schenk lists 105 genera in 46 families. (4) The *tendril climbers* include some sensitive and highly modified structures arising from leaves or various parts of leaves and twigs. Some tendrils may even retain their foliage-bearing capacity, or be associated with inflorescences.

EPIPHYTES

Vascular epiphytes are as characteristic of rain forests as lianas and account for much of the impression of luxuriance that such forests present. They are plants that live without any direct attachment to the soil; the vast majority of them are perched upon the trunks, branches, and even the leaves of other plants, but some are also saxicolous forms that grow directly upon rock surfaces. Since ordinary terrestrial plants depend upon soil for their water and mineral nutrients, and this source is denied epiphytes, they usually have special biological features that enable their peculiar modes of growth. Some epiphytes are without special features that withstand desiccation or store water, so they are restricted to constantly humid regions. At the other extreme are plants whose protoplasm seems able to endure more or less prolonged periods of comparative desiccation. Such plants are mostly small cryptogams (algae, mosses, liverworts, and lichens) that can grow on rock, bark, etc. There are also some pteridophytes that can likewise endure intensive drying. In between these extremes are various types of epiphytes that have structures enabling them to reduce transpiration and to obtain water quickly from rain and dew, and then store it. They are thus provided with stores of water, either within their tissues or as free water, which tide them over periods of high saturation deficit of the air. Although the adaptations of epiphytes are primarily to water needs, there are also obvious relations to illumination and mineral nutrients and dissemination that are connected with epiphytism. Saprophytes and parasites are excluded from the guild of epiphytes, even when they have no connection with the soil, but hemi-parasites are transitional and may be included or not as one chooses.

Schimper (359) published a well-known monograph on epiphytes in which he studied their occurrence in the plant kingdom as known at that time and described their types and adaptations. Considering only vascular plants, he found that among the Pteridophyta epiphytes occur in 2 families (Lycopodiaceae and Filices) and 21 genera. In the Monocotyledoneae there are 7 families and about 150 genera that include epiphytes. By far the largest epiphytic family is the Orchidaceae, with 119 genera with epiphytic species. In this family the Epidendreae (*Cattleya,* etc.) includes 39 epiphytic genera, the Vandeae (*Odontoglossum,* etc.) 77 genera, the Neotheae (*Vanilla*) 2 genera, and the Cypridedieae (Cypripedium) 1 genus. The other monocot family with many epiphytes is the Bromeliaceae which we discuss in detail later. In the Dicotyledoneae there are 26 families and 88 genera with epiphytes. Some of the important families are Melastomaceae, Ericaceae, Gesneraceae, Rubiaceae, Araceae, and Rutaceae. It is obvious that this habit has evolved separately in a great many phyletic lines. According to Schimper, it was likely that the epiphytic habit developed first in humid tropical situations and that further morphological and physiological modifications have permitted some descendants to penetrate drier types of vegetation. Pittendrigh, as we will show later, has come to an opposite conclusion which seems to us to be much more probable, that the xerophytism of epiphytes originated in desert and semi-desert conditions.

Epiphytes can be classified in various ways to reveal their characteristics. For example, they can be grouped according to their propagules (Schimper, 359) into (1) those with moderately heavy seeds, but with aids to dissemination such as wings, hairs, prickles, etc.; (2) those with gelatinous mesocarps that facilitate bird dissemination and attachment to the substratum; and (3) the largest group with spores or exceedingly minute seeds that are readily wind-disseminated and are also small enough to find lodgment in small crevices of the substratum. Epiphytes can also be classified according to their ecological position in the forest

(Davis and Richards, 159), primarily with respect to light exposure. Most basic classifications, however, are based jointly on morphology, water relations, and nutrition (Schimper, 360; Hayek, 234; Pittendrigh, 321). The following outline represents such a classification, after which we give the modern system for Bromeliaceae evolved by Pittendrigh.

I. *Facultative epiphytes:* These are plants that usually live on the soil but are also found on the trunks of rough-barked trees and sometimes on low branches. In such cases there is always found a more or less thick carpet of bryophytes and lichens within and under which there is an accumulation of leaf mold, humus, and dust. In such cases the distinction between epiphytes and terrestrial plants has largely disappeared, and it is only accidental that such plant are not growing on the ground. This phenomenon is not confined to rain forests, for it occurs also in humid temperate woods. For example, dozens of species of the forest floor can be seen behaving as "facultative epiphytes" in the moist cove hardwood forests of the Great Smoky Mountains, growing several feet up on the butts of soft-barked trees such as *Liriodendron* and *Tilia* and even in the crotches of branches as much as 20 ft. above the ground. Examples include such ferns as *Polypodium virginianum (P. polypodioides* is a true epiphyte) and *Cystopteris fragilis;* flowering plants such as *Circaea alipna, Oxalis montana, Viola blanda, Dentaria diphylla,* and *Arisaema quinatum;* and even woody plants such as *Kalmia latifolia, Leucothoe catesbaei,* and *Rhododendron maximum.* These shrubs, incidentally, belong to the Ericaceae, a family which provides many true epiphytes in the tropics.

II. *True epiphytes*

    A. *Holo-epiphytes:* These never have connection with the ground.

        1. *Proto-epiphytes:* This is a fairly heterogeneous group which includes plants that differ little from comparable terrestrial species except that their leaves are somewhat more xeromorphic, usually with thickened cuticle. In other cases the compactly arranged leaves and root clusters catch and hold some moisture and such nutrients as exist in rain water and are washed along the bark. The most modified members of this group have water-storage tissues and organs. Here are included many of the tuberous structures of Orchidaceae, Piperaceae, and Gesneraceae developed from leaves, petioles, and stems. One of the most interesting specializations is the development of a tissue called velamen in the cortex of roots. It has a structure somewhat analogous to that of *Sphagnum* leaves and is capable of quickly absorbing any moisture

that gets on the root surface. The water is taken up by means of the mechanical action of surface tension and subsequently enters the central cylinder of the root by diffusion through thin-walled cells of the endodermis. This feature is found in many epiphytic orchids and aroids, and their greatly elongated and numerous roots often form one of the conspicuous features of rain forest as they hang down like so many glistening cords.

2. *Nest epiphytes:* These are more efficient than proto-epiphytes in that the basal rosettes or nests of leaves are a good mechanism for catching and retaining humus and minerals as well as water. Instead of forming rosettes, the leaf bases of some types form individual pockets between themselves and the tree trunk.

3. *Cistern or tank epiphytes:* This type has a very reduced root system that functions only for anchorage, and the expanded and overlapping leaf bases form a water-catching basin. Leaves are often somewhat spoon-shaped at the base, and the tank that is formed may contain several liters of water in the larger forms. Such basins become the characteristic habitat of numerous protozoans, insects, worms, frogs, etc., and even hydrophytic plants such as *Utricularia,* which finds there numerous small creatures for its traps. It is probable that the tank epiphytes obtain nitrogenous materials from the decomposing organisms they contain.

4. The *Tilliandsia form:* This has the most completely reduced root system, for it functions only in the seedling stage. The entire shoot is covered with scales that serve to conserve water during dry times and to facilitate absorption during wet periods.

B. *Hemi-epiphytes:* These plants start life as true epiphytes, but roots sooner or later reach the ground and become organs of attachment, support, and absorption. In Schimper's classification this group includes both the stilt-root forms and the banyan type. *Clusia, Ficus, Anthurium, Philodendron, Carludovica,* etc., are among the genera with species of this type.

C. *Pseudo-epiphytes:* These plants are in a sense the reverse of the preceding type. They start life as terrestrial plants and continue as epiphytes as the roots and lower parts die and lose connection with the soil.

D. *Hemi-parasites:* Members of the Loranthaceae provide examples of hemi-parasites which obtain some nourishment through absorbing organs which penetrate the tissues of the host, and some by photosynthesis.

EPIPHYTISM IN THE BROMELIACEAE

The Bromeliaceae is a large family (over 1600 species) that is known for its epiphytism. Pittendrigh (321) has made a careful analysis of epiphytic types in the family, their ecology, and their relations to the *Anopheles*-malaria complex in Trinidad. Because of the importance of this family in rain forest, it is of interest to supplement our more general description of epiphytism with notes from this careful study. Although the Trinidad forest is usually considered true rain forest (Marshall, 284), Beard's wide study (34) of the American situation causes him to classify it as evergreen seasonal forest because the seasonal rainfall results in some seasonal leaf fall and a more open structure than is found in true rain forest.

The family as a whole has marked xerophytism with which are associated various absorbing systems of the leaves—in particular, absorbing scales that act as one-way valves, and tank formation by imbricated leaf bases. As Pittendrigh points out, the fundamental division in the family is between plants dependent upon their substratum for water and solutes and those that are independent of it, whether growing on rocks (saxicoles) or as epiphytes. From the evolutionary point, Pittendrigh rejects their development as epiphytes from plants of the moist forest floor, and concludes that their xerophytism was preadapted in desert and semi-desert situations. Four principal ecological types of bromeliads are recognized.

TYPE I. SOIL ROOT.   The soil-root type, represented by *Pitcairnia integrifolia* in Trinidad, has well-developed root systems, and soil constitutes the source of supply of water and mineral nutrients. Although leaves of Pitcairnioideae may have scales, there is no evidence that they are specialized absorption organs. Tanks are not formed by leaf bases.

TYPE II. TANK ROOT.   The tank-root type is a hitherto unrecognized type in which leaf bases retain rain water and dew. This water becomes rich in humic materials from decomposing vegetable and animal substance. In *Bromelia humilis,* which best represents the type, roots enter the ground only rarely, but a system of mycorrhizal axillary roots grows upward between the expanded and overlapping leaf bases, utilizing the entrapped water and nutrients. Other members of this type, *Bromelia karatas, B. chrysantha,* and *Ananas comosus,* are not exclusively dependent upon the interfoliar roots.

Type III. Tank-Absorbing Trichomes. The tank-absorbing tri-chome group contains the great majority of the bromeliads. The "tank" (term introduced by Schimper, 359) is better developed than in the preceding type, with the leaves rosulate and upright so that rain and falling leaves are effectively collected. Roots serve merely to anchor the plants, absorption occurring through epidermal scales. Some of these epiphytes attain tremendous size. *Glomeropitcairnia erectiflora* develops an inflorescence that may be 9 ft. high, the whole plant is too heavy for a man to lift, and its tank may have as much as 5 liters of free water. The tanks contain a microcosm or biocoenosis rich in microorganisms and larger forms—not only a sort of aquarium but also a terrarium of plants and animals living on the exposed humus of the tanks (Picado, 319). Pittendrigh recognizes several subtypes. (1) Species such as *Guzmania lingulata* depend wholly on the single tank. (2) Other species such as *Gravisia aquilega* produce nests as a re-sult of vigorous vegetative propagation, and additional humus en-trapped in the nests is utilized as well as that in the tanks. (3) Other species such as *Tillandsia monadelpha* have ephemeral tanks. (4) Finally, there are species associated with ants that may be regarded as myr-mecophilous. Some, such as *Aechmea mertensii* and *Araecoccus micranthus*, Pittendrigh has not seen except in ant gardens; others, such as *Witt-mackia lingulata, Tillandsia bulbosa*, and *T. flexuosa*, are not associated with ant gardens but are nevertheless myrmecophilous.

Type IV. Atmosphere-Absorbing Trichomes. In the atmosphere-absorbing trichomes the tank and absorbing roots are both lacking; in *Tillandsia usneoides* all roots are absent. Rain and dew are absorbed by scales that usually cover the entire plant, and the only source of mineral nutrients must be dust in the air. There is a suggestion that some species of his type have symbiotic fungi which may be nitrogen fixers, but this needs investigation. In Type IV Pittendrigh places (1) certain forms intermediate with Type III; (2) those that absorb wholly from the atmosphere, including rain types and dew types; and (3) those that are myrmecophilous.

The same author studied the occurrence of bromeliads in the forest and divided them into three main groups. (1) The *exposure group* con-sists of species that occur in the highest levels of the forest, concen-trated in the crowns of emergent and semi-emergent trees, with essen-tially complete exposure to the sky. In the forests studied, all members of this group were tank species (III), with no tendency to nest conditions. Under drier conditions the exposure group becomes pre-dominantly the atmospheric type (IV). (2) The *sun group* contains the largest number of species and is generally distributed through the upper canopy. These plants include both the pure tank type and the tank-nest type, and contain the species that attain the most massive growth. (3) The *shade-tolerant group* occurs predominantly in the lower levels of the forest, even near the ground, but they increase in density with increased illumination. Most of these are of the ephemeral tank type, containing only very small amounts of water. The nest type is absent, as it is in the exposure group.

Examples of the exposure group from Trinidad include *Catopsis sessiliflora, C. floribunda, Vriesia procera,* and *V. amazonica;* the sun group includes *Tillandsia fasciculata, T. bulbosa, Guzmania monostachia, Aechmea mertensii, A. nudicaulis,* and *Gravisia nudicaulis;* and the shade-tolerant group includes *Tillandsia anceps, T. monadelpha, Vriesia albiflora, V. simplex,* and *Guzmania lingulata.*

Many aspects of the biology of epiphytes remain to be worked on. It would be remarkable if some of the larger epiphytes could obtain sufficient quantities of mineral nutrients only from dust brought down by rain. They undoubtedly also reuse minerals from decomposed plant and animal remains trapped in their tanks and nests formed by leaf bases. A study by Curtis (143) of the nutrient supply of epiphytic orchids in Haiti showed a very low concentration of ions in the rain water collected on tree trunks, but with some surprising ratios. The ratio of NH_4 to NO_3 ions was 35 to 1; and of Mg to Ca, 7 to 1. The orchid *Pleurothallia racemiflora* had an osmotic concentration of the cell sap of 2.6 atm., which is a reflection of the low concentration of the water of the medium. Harris (230) gave an average of about 3 atm. for orchids in Jamaica. This may be compared with the average of about 10 atm. for herbs in the temperate zone and 15 atm. for herbs in the desert. Although the concentration of solutes is low, epiphytes may have access to a considerable volume of water. For example, Voth (405) attached cups to the stems of tropical trees in the rain forest of Panama and found that they collected from 2.5 to 7 times the quantity of rain water as was collected by rain gauges of equivalent area located near by in the open.

SOME MISCELLANEOUS FEATURES OF RAIN FOREST VEGETATION

The general impression one gets of the foliage of the rain forest is a massive display of glossy leaves intermixed with more or less feathery mimosa-like compound leaves. The majority of the trees of the canopy have leaves of the laurel type (lanceolate, ovate, oval), smooth, shining, entire, more or less leathery, and belonging to Raunkiaer's mesophyll leaf-size class. (See our section on leaf-size classes.) The leaflets of compound leaves are usually like the prevailing simple leaves but they average somewhat smaller. The general impression is of dark and monotonous foliage interrupted only by bursts of color which come with new leaves on some species. But closer examination shows that the foliage of the tropics is exceedingly varied in the undergrowth. Here occur the gigantic leaves of tree ferns, palms, and Musaceae, and the enormous palmate leaves of *Cecropia*. In exposed situations the leaves are generally more or less xeromorphic, but in the undergrowth occur all types of hygrophilous foliage, from the membraneous *Tricomanes* to the velvety *Begonia*. With atmospheric humidity so high in the lower layers of rain forest, many leaves have hydathodes (Haberlandt, 225) from which liquid water is exuded under root pressure. Also, whatever the significance, a remarkably large percentage of rain-forest canopy trees have leaves with drip points, a feature not common elsewhere, and surfaces that are not easily wetted. Leaves in the undergrowth are usually oriented at right angles to incident light, and leaves toward the top of the forest are usually arranged obliquely to the light. A common behavior affecting illumination of leaf surfaces is the almost daily wilting of leaves, with consequent dropping that effectively reduces their midday insolation. Many compound leaves have leaflets that fold up in bright light or are sensitive to touch and fold when spattered by rain (Mimosaceae). One cannot make much of such matters as adaptive behavior, however, since other species in the same situations do not have such devices.

In tropical forests that have no dry season the question of periodicity is an engaging one. Although the rain forest is predominantly evergreen, leaves are eventually shed. When one month is about like another, such periodicities as occur seem to be controlled by internal factors, or else the environmental "controls" are too subtle to have been detected. In some cases leaves are shed just previous to the flowering of the tree, and up until the day the leaves are dropped there is no browning or other indication of the imminence of their fall. New leaves usually appear within a few days after leaf fall, sometimes only one or two days, and their manner of appearance and their limpness are such as to suggest that they "flow out of the bud," only gradually becoming turgid and assuming normal coloring, form, and position. Some trees shed their leaves several times a year. Schimper (360) observed *Urostigma glabellum* to develop six sets of leaves in one year. At the other extreme are some species that have been observed to go a few years without a new set of leaves. It is very common in the rain forest for different trees of the same species to shed leaves at different times of the year (*Poinciana regina, Terminalia catappa, Paloquiana macrophyllum*); and in strong contrast to temperate trees, individuals often do not behave as a physiological unit. Some species are "ever-bearing" in the sense that they seem almost continually to be in flower and fruit. In other cases, different trees of the same species may at the same time be in different stages of development—some bare of leaves, others with old leaves or new leaves, some with flowers, etc. It is also not uncommon for different branches of the same tree to be in different stages of development. For example, in front of the Museu Nacional in Rio de Janeiro there is an avenue of a species of *Lecythis* which in September and October has some trees bare, others with new rose-purple foliage, and some in flower.

One other miscellaneous feature of rain forest is the abundance of myrmecophilous plants in some types. Ducke and Black (171) describe the extreme frequency of myrmecophilous plants as one of the most striking features of the Amazonian hylaea. Myrmecophilous families include Polypodiaceae, Araceae, Bromeliaceae, Orchidaceae, Piperaceae, Cactacea, Solanaceae, and Gesneriaceae; and species of such genera as *Pourouma, Triplaris, Hirtella, Inga, Tachigalia, Sclerobium, Pterocarpus, Picrolemma, Tococa, Myrmidone, Clidemia, Mayeta, Tachi, Remijia, Gleasonia,* and *Duroia,* which seem exclusively hylaean. Some of these "epiphytes" on ant nests have never been observed elsewhere. Ule (397) has described these ant gardens in the Amazon, and Ducke and Black (171) have produced the synopsis shown in Table 10.

TABLE 10.　A synopsis of the myrmecophilous plants observed in the Brazilian Amazonia (Ducke and Black, 171)

Type	Examples
I. Epiphytes on the nests of ants	
A. Not known except with ants	Coryanthes spp.
	Epidendrum spp.
	Marckea camponoti
	M. formicarum
	M. sessiliflora
	Ectozoma ulei
	Codonanthe sp.
B. Originated in ant nests, but survived after destruction of the nests	Marckea coccinea
	Codonanthe sp.

TABLE 10—*(Continued)*

Type	Examples
C. Often on ant nests; also elsewhere	Araceae
	Bromeliaceae
	Orchidaceae
	Gesneriaceae
	Peperomia
	Phyllocactus
	Ficus (? paraensis)
II. Trees or shrubs inhabited by ants	
A. Special accommodations for the ants	
1. Hollow stems or branches	Cecropia spp.
	Triplaris spp.
	Picrolemma
	Tachia
2. Inflated hollow tips of branches	Cordia nodosa
	Duroia spp.
3. Pockets on extremities of the petioles	Pourouma spp.
	Hirtella spp.
	Tococa spp.
	Myrmidone spp.
	Clidemia spp.
	Mayeta spp.
	Duroia spp.
4. Stipules sheltering ants	Remijia glomerata
	Gleasonia uaupensis
B. Cavities hollowed out by ants, later becoming inflated	
1. Hollow twigs	Inga cinnamomea
	Tachigalia spp.
	Sclerobium spp.
2. Hollow peduncles or axes of inflorescences	Pterocarpus ulei
	Platymiscium ulei
	Sapium sp.

Among the least-known features of rain forest are the rate of growth and the age of trees. Age cannot be determined by the simple expedient of counting annual rings of growth as for most temperate trees, either because rings are not formed or because they do not represent a year of

TABLE 11.   Rate of growth of trees of the rain forest, Luquillo Division, Caribbean National Forest (391)

Species	Number Measured	Mean Annual d.b.h. Growth (Inches)
Tabonuco Type (lower montane rain forest)		
Ormosia krugii Urban	41	0.26
Manilkara nitida (Sesse & Mac.) Dubard	40	0.20
Dacryodes excelsa Vahl.	131	0.18
Sloanea berteriana Choisy	61	0.18
Tabebuia pallida Miers	106	0.15
Linociera domingensis (Lam.) Knobl.	37	0.14
Didymopanax morototoni (Aubl.) Dcne.	54	0.13
Colorado Type (montane thicket rain forest)		
Micropholis chrysophylloides Pierre	139	0.07
Micropholis garcinifolia Pierre	231	0.04
Calycogonium squamulosum Cogn.	143	0.04
Ocotea spathulata Mez.	41	0.04
Magnolia splendens Urban	38	0.04

TABLE 12.   Estimated tree ages in virgin rain forest, Luquillo Division, Caribbean National Forest, based on three-year growth record (392)

Diameter at 4.5 ft. in Inches	Estimated Age in Years
2	90
4	125
6	135
8	160
10	190
12	220
16	265
20	300
24	335
30	380
40	460

growth. An approach to these questions has recently been made in the Caribbean National Forest. The Tenth Annual Report of the Tropical Forest Experiment Station (391) reported on growth rates of trees on five 1-acre plots on which each tree was tagged and remeasured after two or three years. The results (Table 11) range from 0.26 in. annual diameter growth for *Ormosia krugii* to 0.04 in. for *Magnolia splendens*. The Eleventh Annual Report of the Experiment Station (392) reported the estimated age of 639 trees in the upper canopy of the rain forest (Table 12). Both the comparatively slow rates of growth and the consequent great age of relatively small trees are somewhat surprising because of the presumably favorable growing conditions, at least climatically. The explanation lies apparently in the very intense competition for space, light, and sustenance.

THE TROPICAL RAIN-FOREST CLIMATE

Our concern in the *Manual* is with vegetation analysis, not with the environment *per se;* but as we have taken the tropical rain forest as an example of a world formation type and the problems involved in such an analysis, a very brief account of both the external climate and the internal microclimate of the rain forest is in order so as to round out the exposition.

THE EXTERNAL CLIMATE OF THE RAIN FOREST.   The tropical rainy climate constitutes Type *A* in Köppen's classification (258, 260). The temperature of the coldest month is not less than 64° F., and the mean annual temperature is usually between 70 and 80° F. The annual temperature range of the monthly means is small, sometimes as little as about 2°, and consequently is much less than the average daily range, which often is from 15 to 16° F. This situation has led to the figurative statement that "night is the winter of the tropics." The small annual range in temperature is due to the slight changes in day length and the position of the sun at the zenith. The strong daily change in temperature is due to the equal day and night periods during which heating and cooling occur. In tropical lowlands temperature apparently is never a limiting factor on biological activity, and only when sufficient altitude has been reach for frost to occur does temperature become really significant. In contrast, moisture conditions assume a tremendous importance in climatic modification in the tropics and in control of vegetation.

The Köppen system of climatology provides for the division of the *A* climate into moisture types; *f* indicates the absence of a dry season, and where *Af* climates occur there are true rain forests; *s* indicates that there is a summer period with relatively low rainfall; and *w* means that the dry period occurs during the "winter" of low sun. The *Aw* climate is separated from the *Af* type when the driest month has a precipitation of 60 mm. (2.4 in.) or less. There are intermediate conditions between these two types of climate, and the vegetation shows corresponding modifications. The monsoonal tendency toward alternating wet and dry seasons, when well developed, is designated as *Am*. With a strongly emphasized dry winter, rain forest cannot develop and the forest is more or less completely deciduous during the dry period, first in the upper layers and finally throughout the woody growth. The *As* climate scarcely occurs because the doldrums shift position with the sun, bringing heavy rain with high sun.

As Stamp (375) emphasized, rain forest does not pass into monsoon, nor woodland into savanna and grassland, merely by a reduction in total annual precipitation. In addition to total amount, the seasonal distribution of rain exerts a primary control. Also, soil has great influence on water availability and other conditions affecting forest development. There is some tendency to think of the prevailing climate of a tropical region as overcoming topography as an influent on vegetation, but this is no more true for rain forest than it is for vegetation types in temperate regions. Altitude, slope, and exposure have characteristic influences on winds, rain, and insolation.

Land and sea breezes are characteristic of tropical coasts because of the strong contrast in day and night temperatures over land and sea. In a sense, also, monsoon winds are a seasonal rather than a daily expression of the same phenomenon. Although the tropical sunshine is very intense, cloudiness averages much higher than for the mid-latitudes. For example, in the rain-forest region of Moraballi Creek, British Guiana, Davis and Richards (159) report the average daily sunshine as about 5.5 hrs., being 6.3 hrs. per day during the dry season and only 4.4 hrs. a day during the wet season. Mean annual humidity is between 80 and 90 percent for many rain-forest regions, but in the drier months it may average in the 60's. Twice a year the equatorial zone is under the calms and variable winds of the doldrums; alternating with them are the northeast and southeast trade winds; and at all seasons violent winds may accompany thermal convection thunderstorms. Certain rain-forest areas also lie in the path of tropical hurricanes which sometimes are terrifically destructive to vegetation.

THE INTERNAL RAIN-FOREST MICROCLIMATE. The interior of rain forest offers the most equable situations available to terrestrial plants and animals, according to Allee (12). He said, "The animals of the lower forest [Panama] ... would need only to avoid the higher temperature, light intensity, and lower humidity of the sun flecks in order to keep under conditions so constant that they must excite the envy of every experimental ecologist with experience in trying to control environmental factors for land animals in a laboratory." The uniformity of conditions dimishes upwards within the forest with rather abrupt changes after the undergrowth trees have been passed. The stratification of vegetation in the rain forest is partly in relation to this environmental stratification; but it must be remembered that general climate is of primary importance in permitting the luxuriance of life in the first place, and that the vegetation itself acts only as a modifying factor, producing still greater constancy of conditions.

Within the forest the light intensity may average very low—$\frac{1}{70}$ to $\frac{1}{150}$ or even $\frac{1}{400}$ of full sunlight. It is said, however, that the intensity of the tropical light permits growth and photosynthetic activity at lower fractions of full light than would be possible for comparable forms at higher latitudes. Allee reported that the free air movement of the trade winds was about 24 times that at the top of the rain forest (in Panama) and about 240 times that near the forest floor where the average air movement may be only about a mile a day. The high relative humidity, the low air movement, and the scarcity of sun flecks in deep for-

TABLE 13. Stratification of internal climatic factors of the rain forest, Moraballi Creek, British Guiana (Davis and Richards, 159)

Climatic Factors	Above the Herb Stratum 1.5 m.	Within the Canopy 20.0 m.	Within the Canopy 27.0 m.	Above the Canopy 33.0 m.
Dry, sunny days				
Temperature, °C.	26.7	29.7	30.3	30.6
Relative humidity, %	89.5	66.6	63.1	59.7
Saturation deficit, mm.	2.73	10.35	11.82	13.6
Temperature	27.6	30.5	30.8	29.7
Relative humidity	87.4	60.2	60.5	59.6
Saturation deficit	3.44	12.91	13.06	12.53
Temperature	27.6	29.6	30.3	30.3
Relative humidity	88.1	77.7	. . .	67.0
Saturation deficit	3.25	7.86	. . .	10.5
After showers				
Temperature	24.7	. . .	26.1	25.4
Relative humidity	95.7	. . .	84.7	85.2
Saturation deficit	0.99	. . .	3.85	3.56
Temperature	27.4	29.5	29.6	29.5
Relative humidity	87.9	73.1	69.7	70.0
Saturation deficit	4.43	8.25	9.31	9.08

These measurements were made during early afternoons in the dry season, October 13 to November 9. Although they do not represent absolute extremes, they are a fair sample of the stratification during the season when it is strongest.

TABLE 14.   Comparative data on evaporation from Livingston atmometers in rain forest and temperate montane and low-elevation forests

Average Daily Evaporation (Cu. cm.)	Place	Reference
	Mt. Maquiling, Luzon, Philippine Islands	Brown (68)
9.2	Crown of second-growth tree	
5.8	Beneath second-growth tree	
	Dipterocarp forest	
16.4	Top of dominant tree	
5.3	Crown of second-story tree	
2.7	Forest floor, on ridge	
1.5	Forest floor in ravine	
	Barro Colorado, Panama	Allee (12)
45.0	Over Gatun Lake	
15.2	Forest canopy	
7.3	Forest floor, peak of dry season	
	Cinchona Laboratory, Blue Mts., Jamaica	Brown (67)
8.2	Opening in the forest	
0.8	Under forest cover	
	Mt. LeConte, Tennessee, 6500-ft. elevation	Cain (80)
5.7	Under evergreen ericaceous shrub community	
2.3	Transition	
1.04	Under Picea-Abies "moss" forest	
	Woods on sand dunes, Indiana	Fuller (201)
22.3	Under Populus deltoides woods	
11.0	Under Quercus velutina woods	
10.4	Under Pinus banksiana woods	
8.8	Under Quercus borealis woods	
7.0	Under Fagus-Acer climax forest	

est combine to reduce the so-called evaporating power of the air to negligible amounts near the ground, and the temperature changes to so slight a degree that diurnal curves practically disappear. Allee reported a change within an entire week of only 78.4 to 81.3° F. on a thermometer 9 in. above the ground in rain forest; and evaporation from a standard Livingston atmometer may be as little as 1 cc. per day. Low evaporation can occur in other than tropical rain forest, as in the humid, cool-temperate conifer forests of the southern Appalachian Mountains or the Pacific Northwest of the United States.

Table 13, from Davis and Richards (159) shows the stratification of environment in rain forest, and Table 14 shows some comparative

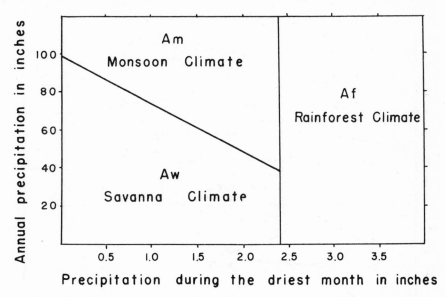

FIGURE 7. Precipitation relationships of tropical vegetation of Köppen *A* climates. (Diagram after Haurwitz and Austin, 232.)

data for atmometers. Figure 7, from Haurwitz and Austin (232), diagrams the Köppen *A* climates; and Figure 8 shows some comparative climagraphs.

RAIN FOREST OF THE AMAZON

Our discussion of the rain forest as an example of a world formation type has been general. A recent paper by Ducke and Black (171), dealing with the phytogeography (actually the floristics) of the Brazilian Amazon, permits us to consider this largest[3] and most famous rain forest more specifically. It is the hylaea of Humboldt and Bonpland, with natural limits of the Atlantic on the east and the Andes on the west; north and south it is replaced by floras of drier regions; and internally, especially eastward, it is interrupted by small to large areas

[3] Rain forest constitutes 93 percent of the vegetation, or about 3⅓ million sq. km. of the Amazon Basin.

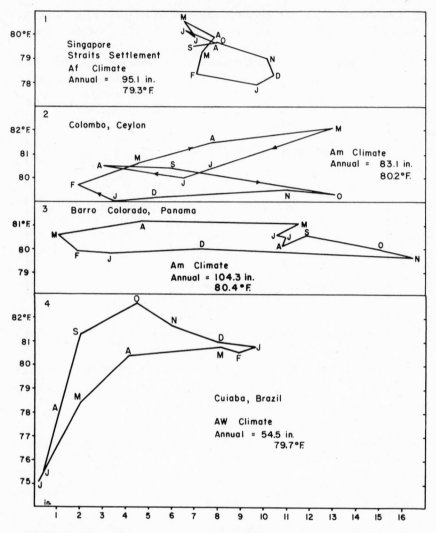

FIGURE 8.   Climagraphs (mean monthly precipitation and temperature) for tropical *A* climates of Köppen.

of nonrain forest vegetation known as campos, campinas, and caatinga. The hylaea is approximately coextensive with the area of the genus *Hevea,* generally well known because it contains the most important rubber-tree species. The hylaea is a region of high rainfall, most of the area having 2300 mm. or more a year, but in this region topography and soil have more to do with subdivision of the flora than climate does.

Ducke and Black say: "It is not possible to establish phytogeographical subregions in the hylaea because we still ignore almost completely the flora of the uplands between the navigable rivers. And even in the easily accessible parts of the country, large extensions remain quite unexplored. Furthermore, in such an immense flora, no botanist can pay equal attention to all families of plants. . . ." They proceed, however, with a general description without drawing definite boundaries.

The hylaea as a whole can be typified floristically by endemics of wide distribution in the region and by taxons whose centers of specific development occur there. Groups essentially coextensive with the hylaea include *Bertholletia excelsa, Ravenala guianensis,* the genus *Hevea,* and the South American species of *Gnetum.* Groups having definite centers of development in the hylaea include the genera *Parkia, Dimorphandra, Hymenolobium, Coumarouna, Bixa,* and the scleriform lianas in *Bauhinia,* and the families Myristicaceae, Leguminosae (Amherstieae), Vochysiaceae (with a second center in central Brazil), and the Humiriaceae (arboreous Linaceae). Groups that are probably richer in species in the Amazon than elsewhere in the Americas include the genera *Sloanea, Buchenavia,* and *Diospyros,* and the families Moraceae, Rosaceae, Chrysobalanoideae, Lecythidaceae, Olacaceae, Dichapetalaceae, Icacinaceae, arboreous Tiliaceae, Lauraceae, Anonaceae, and Burseraceae. In contrast, some groups are well represented in other rain forests of tropical America but are comparatively scarce in the hylaea. They include the Polypodiaceae, Compositae, Cactaceae, and Gramineae. The hylaea is also characterized by an extreme frequency of myrmecophilous species and by a striking abundance of large woody lianas, especially those with flat or sclariform stems, although the number of species is small. The general richness of the flora is indicated by the fact that the best-studied family, Leguminosae, has 846 species known in the Amazon alone, with 206 species known in the neighborhood of Belém and 275 in Manaus.

In an essentially continuous formation of such vast extent, distance alone, without climatic or other important changes, leads to floristic differentiation. In terms of endemism, concentration of species in certain genera and families, etc., Ducke and Black contrast the eastern and western parts of the region, and the northern and southern parts, with such attention as is feasible to northwestern and southwestern, northeastern and southeastern, quadrants of the region. Peripheral segments of such a vast formation also gain differentiation as a result of exchange of floristic elements with contiguous nonrain forest floras. Details will be found in the paper by Ducke and Black.

Departing from the strictly geographical consideration of the flora of the hylaean rain forest, we find a strong topographic differentiation into the "mata da varzea" and the "mata da terra firme." The varzea is essentially floodplain.[4] It is subject to inundation by the white water rivers carrying a heavy silt burden during each year's high-flow period varying from a few weeks to several months (6 to 7 mo.). Also in the lowlands of the coastal belt and the estuary of the Amazon, it is under the daily influence of the Atlantic tide. Terra firme is nonflooded upland. In between there are strips and patches of land that are sometimes but not regularly flooded; these are called "restinga." Where the soil never dries out is the "igapó," or swamp forest, occupied by black waters from tributaries that are impeded by high water in the main rivers. Small shallow basins in varzea may stay wet from rain waters. These are also called igapó locally (as on Araparí).

Each of these types has its characteristic flora and vegetation, in general completely distinctive. Just a few characteristics of these types will be mentioned. In the swamps of the estuary region along the channels and upland drainage lines the palms *Mauritia flexuosa* and *Euterpe oleracea* are common, and along the shores there are thickets of *Machaerium lunatum, Dalbergia monetaria,* and the tall araceous *Montrichardia arborescens.* On the varzea occurs *Ceiba pentandra,* often of very large size and with spectacular plank buttresses (Figure 6). A large percentage of species is common to the whole varzea from Pará to eastern Peru, but there are regional differences. The varzea is richer in species westward in the Solimões than it is eastward, but is generally less rich than adjacent forests of terra firme. Besides the *Ceiba,* other varzea trees reaching a large size include *Olmediophaena maxima, Bombax munguba, Calycophyllum spruceanum, Couroupita subsessilis, Pithecolobium niopoides,* and several species of *Ficus.* The forest of terra firme is exceedingly rich in woody species and is characterized not so much by conspicuously large trees (although unbuttressed *Bertholletia excelsa* is known to reach 3 m. in diameter, *Caryocar villosum* is as large, and many other species grow to an impressive size) as by exceedingly tall, slender, unbranched trunks. Other species of terra firme include the mahogany, *Swietenia macrophylla, Cenostigma tocantinum, Bombax tocantinum, B. macrocalyx, Matisia bicolor, Dinizia excelsa, Eschweilera krukovii, E. odora, Micropholis guianensis, Sagotia racemosa, Trichilia smithi, Rinorea passoura, Protium polybotryum, Vouacapoua americana, Couepia hoffmanniana,* etc. (Some of the latter species are listed from the paper by Pires, Dobzhansky, and Black, 320; and extensive lists for all these types of forest are to be found in Le Cointe, 269.) True mata da terra firme is in no popular sense a jungle.

[4] The floodplain may be as wide as 80 to 160 km., and the annual rise of the river is often very great: average at Porto Velho, 13 m.; at Manaus, 10 m.; at the mouth of the Xingu, 2.5 m.

CONCLUDING STATEMENT ON THE RAIN-FOREST FORMATION

Problems in the analysis and description of vegetation are different for the different kinds of vegetation, and the investigator must adapt his techniques to his problem. At one end of the spectrum of vegetation are the world formations; at the other end are the concrete stands of microassociations. The point at which certain sampling techniques and quantitative methods must be relinquished or adapted, because they no longer yield fruitful results, must be determined by common sense. It is obvious that rain forest (in a generic sense) cannot be treated quantitatively. This, however, by no means suggests that local and even regional quantitative studies are not desirable and possible. They are. Although to know a local portion of a formation well does not permit generalization, it does provide a basis for a fuller comprehension of a larger and extremely complex whole.

Chapter 5

ANALYSIS OF VEGETATION

CONCEPTS and methods in the analysis of vegetation vary with the nature of the vegetation and the aims of the study. Although the *Manual* is concerned largely with methodology, the authors have no intention of proposing "standardized" techniques, nor, except within certain limits, do they believe this desirable. Methodology has to be adapted to the composition and structure of the vegetation with which a study deals. It has to accept the limitations of preexisting botanical information about the region, as well as that of climate, geology, soils, and such facilities for work as useful maps, accessibility of the territory, and the time, resources, and personnel available for the study. Finally, the aims of the study are preeminent in the determination of procedures.

The history of the study of the vegetation of most regions of the world has been a progression from reconnaissance, to primary survey, to intensive studies, and finally to experimentation and management. This is possibly the ideal sequence. It can be argued persuasively that extensive and general studies should precede intensive and local ones; that the large vegetational units should be known and understood before the smaller communities are dealt with; that qualitative work should precede quantitative analysis; that phytosociological studies should go before autecological investigations. Quite the reverse, however, has often been the case. Intelligent and effective work has been done on local stands when the community type has been known only in most general terms. Astute and productive work has been done in genecology, with only general information about the environment and an almost complete ignorance of the vegetation as such; yet one feels that such work would be more illuminating if it were related to the composition, structure, and interrelations of the plant communities involved. An investigator may work locally, whatever his desires and the ideal might be, for the very practical reason that he has neither the time nor the facilities for desirable extensive background surveys. All sciences tend to become more quantitative as they progress; but the drive for quantification can be a fetish, and a pseudo-exactness may not only have no meaning, but be misleading. So we repeat, the methodology in vegetation analysis must be determined by the objectives of the particular study, and the exigencies of the situation must prevail over the ideal. Comparability of data is a highly desirable end, and the habit of doing a thing a certain way can be efficient; but the student of vegetation in its almost infinite variability should beware of enslavement by his or anybody's methods.

RECONNAISSANCE

As used in geology, engineering, and military activities, the term "reconnaissance" means a preliminary examination of a territory. So it does also in the study of vegetation. In reconnaissance the country is traversed rapidly by the most convenient means, and the eye searches for the most general and obvious features. One sticks to the purpose, and asks himself such questions as the following: What are the major plant communities? What is the physiognomy of these types? What are the dominant and common species? What are the apparent correlations of the occurrence of the various types of vegetation with topography, geology, soils? What communities are natural or seminatural? What are the patterns of utilization in agriculture, forestry, the livestock industry? The aim of reconnaissance is to get a general idea of the landscape and its mantle of vegetation. Under modern conditions, ground study may be advantageously preceded by reconnaissance from the air; even regions that are remote and difficult to travel over on the ground can be seen from the air not only with speed but also cheaply, at least in comparison with the time and cost of extensive ground travel.

Where maps are available, the investigator should equip himself with topographic sheets of suitable scale as well as other aids to his understanding of the major patterns of vegetation. Effective reconnaissance is greatly facilitated by previous knowledge of the flora, especially the bulk of common plants. The reconnaissance itself provides an opportunity to learn more about the flora and to collect materials for the future identification and verification of the species most pertinent to general knowledge. When working in a strange region, it is extremely useful to obtain the help of local experts; for, even though untutored in a technical sense, they often have a keen knowledge of the plant species and even of the communities and the ecology of their home territory. In order to do effective work in a strange region, it may be necessary to overcome the strangeness by weeks, months, or even years of preliminary floristic study.

Although somewhat cursory, reconnaissance should not be haphazard. Although much can be said for traveling by the most convenient means, it should be borne in mind that for the objectives of reconnaissance the best routes cut across the salient features of the landscape and usually are not the paths of least resistance. For example, in the Amazon the highways are the rivers and their tributaries, and customary travel is by water. For this reason most observers have been impressed by the jungle screen at the water's edge; and while the mata de varzea (forest of the floodplain) is comparatively well known, the mata de terra firme of the upland remains largely terra incognita.

PRIMARY SURVEY

According to Tansley (384), the primary survey consists of recognizing and describing the major plant associations, making lists of their floristic composition, studying their relationships, and recording their distribution on maps. In the British Isles, for example, this work was started by Robert Smith (370) and William G. Smith (371). In their botanical survey of Scotland, and the making of a vegetation map was an end in itself. If topographic maps of suitable scale are available, the major features of the distribution of communities can be sketched directly upon them. Because a primary survey usually covers rather extensive territory, it is seldom possible for an investigator of the vegetation to prepare an original base map in the absence of a preexisting topographical survey; under such conditions it may be possible to produce planometric or even topographic sketches as substitutes. It should be kept in mind that such sketches are not maps in a strict sense.

The primary survey, whether or not it includes the preparation of a map, is of two basically different types. The general type purports to represent all the major vegetation of a region. The other has been called the monographic type. In this the interest centers on a formation, a complex of related associations, or some reasonably distinct association, and the effort is to study it in a general way throughout its area of occurrence. Other communities are not dealt with except as they bear some pertinent relation to the unit of concern.

Both reconnaissance and primary survey are extensive and general. They consider not only what occurs, they also ask why the observed patterns exist. At this level of investigation some questions can be answered with probable reliability. On the other hand, important problems are uncovered and their statement made precise so that they are amenable to later efficient intensive study.

Although each field worker has his own preferred equipment, for purposes of reconnaissance and primary survey the notebook is the essential item, together with suitable maps and photographic equipment.

INTENSIVE SURVEY

As with a primary survey, the intensive survey can deal with all the communities of an area, or it can treat a particular community in its extent or as represented in a local area. In general, the area of intensive survey is smaller than that of primary survey except when a considerable period of time is available for its completion.

Intensive survey deals with the whole flora, not just the dominant or abundant species; it treats all communities, not only the major ones, except when specializing as mentioned above. The studies tend to be detailed and concerned with particular problems, not merely general ones. With respect to composition and structure of communities, the intensive method often involves the gathering of quantitative and semi-quantitative data. Although maps may be employed and original ones made, various sorts of charts (such as transect and quadrat charts) and profiles are common and large in scale. Quantitative data are often assembled in tables, expressed in graphs, and extrapolated from samples to the "universe" involved. These data may be analytic (concerning a single stand) or synthetic (concerning several stands of a community type), and deal with size, number, distribution, etc., of the members of species populations.

Studies at all these levels of intensity and extent may be made for scientific reasons—to enable ecological understanding—or they may be carried out for economic motives, as in cruising woodland for the volume of forest products, or analyzing grassland to determine its livestock-carrying capacity. Techniques of surveying, charting, and sampling—especially at intensive levels—make up the bulk of this *Manual* and are to be sought at appropriate points throughout it.

SAMPLING SYSTEMS

SINGLE-PLOT METHODS. The single-plot method of studying vegetation consists of closely examining a single limited area in each stand of each type of community involved in the study, if carried out thoroughly. Such a plot must be at least as large as the minimal area of the community type. This concept is discussed elsewhere in the *Manual*, but for present purposes we repeat the definition. The minimal area of a community is the smallest area on which the community can develop its characteristic composition and structure. Minimal area is supposed to be a characteristic of associations, differing with the different types. Areas smaller than this size provide inadequate space or opportunity for the development of the association; however, stands of associations do occur on areas smaller than the minimal area. They are characteristically fragmentary and atypical. Once the minimal area has been ascertained for an association by the study of one stand, it is usually assumed that the same size is adequate for single-plot sampling of other stands. The customary approach to minimal area is through the species-area relationship, although when an indication of minimal area has been obtained by means of the species-area curve, the investigator should not follow the device slavishly but should examine the sample area to see whether, in his *judgment,* there does occur on it a portion of the association showing the composition and structure characteristic of the association.

The common procedure in determining minimal area (i.e., the minimum size of plot in the single-plot method) is to lay out a sample plot that is obviously smaller than the minimal area. On this plot the species are listed by name, unknowns being given a number and collected for future identification. The plot area is then doubled (or otherwise enlarged) and the newly encountered species are added to the list. The additions are always kept separate from the previously listed species. The process of increasing the sample area is continued as long as conditions warrant. Figure 9 shows an actual case, in an analysis of a savanna stand near Vigia, Pará, in which the smallest plot (1) was 0.5 × 0.5 m. Table 15 shows that 9 species were present on the first plot 0.25 sq. m. in area. It happened that in this case doubling the area (plot 2) added only a single new species. Although the additional territory examined was only 0.5 × 0.5 m., plot 2 actually is 0.5 × 1.0 m., for it includes the area of plot 1. One continues in the same manner; each additional tract examined is equal in area to all the previously examined area, making the plot as a whole now twice the area of the former plot. Although the series of progressively larger plots could be increased in area by arithmetic progression, the species-

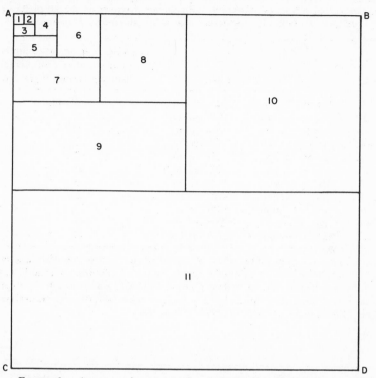

FIGURE 9.   A geometric system of nested plots for determining minimum area in the single-plot analysis of a community. The smaller units
of the series can be used to determine minimum quadrat size in the multiple-plot method of analyzing a community. This pattern is commonly
applied to grasslands and other nonforest vegetation.

area relationship makes logical the employment of geometric progression.

In the present illustration of the method the progression was continued through 10 successive enlargements of the quadrat to attain a
total area of 256 sq. m. for the largest quadrat. This, the eleventh
quadrat, had a total of 33 species. Cursory examination of the stand
outside the sample showed about 50 species on 10 ha.

Figure 10 is the species-area curve derived from the data and plotted on a 1 : 2 ratio between axes. This seems to be a "law of diminishing returns" curve, and inspection shows that the larger quadrats of
the series do not yield new information in proportion to the area examined. Judgment indicates that 64 sq. m. is certainly large enough
for the minimal-area plot; if a large series of stands were to be studied
by the single-plot method, 32 sq. m. would be adequate. A technique

TABLE 15. The nested-plot method for determining minimum area for single-plot analysis of a community. Figure 9 shows the arrangement of the subplots, and Figure 10 shows the species-area curve obtained from the sample.

	Plot Dimensions		Number of Species (accumulated) in an example from savanna (campo cerrado, Vigia, Pará)
Plot 1.	0.5 × 0.5 m.	0.25 sq. m.	9 species
Plot 2.	0.5 × 1.0 m.	0.5 sq. m.	10 "
Plot 3.	1.0 × 1.0 m.	1.0 sq. m.	15 "
Plot 4.	1.0 × 2.0 m.	2.0 sq. m.	16 "
Plot 5.	2.0 × 2.0 m.	4.0 sq. m.	18 "
Plot 6.	2.0 × 4.0 m.	8.0 sq. m.	19 "
Plot 7.	4.0 × 4.0 m.	16.0 sq. m.	20 "
Plot 8.	4.0 × 8.0 m.	32.0 sq. m.	22 "
Plot 9.	8.0 × 8.0 m.	64.0 sq. m.	26 "
Plot 10.	8.0 × 16.0 m.	128.0 sq. m.	29 "
Plot 11.	16.0 × 16.0 m.	256.0 sq. m.	33 "

For nested *circular plots* of the above geometric series of areas, the following lengths of radii can be used: (1) area of 0.25 sq. m., radius of 0.28 m., (2) area 0.5, radius 0.40; (3) area 1.0, radius 0.56; (4) area 2, radius 0.78; (5) area 4, radius 1.13; (6) area 8, radius 1.60; (7) area 16, radius 2.26; (8) area 32, radius 3.14; (9) area 64, radius 4.51; (10) area 128, radius 6.38; (11) area 256, radius 9.03.

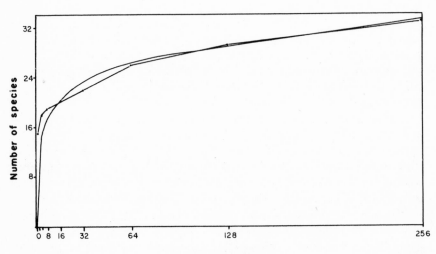

FIGURE 10. Species-area curve for the savanna (cerrado), Campo de Caembe, Vigia, Pará, obtained by the geometric system of nested plots. (Data from G. A. Black and S. A. Cain, 41.)

for determining plot size that is more accurate than inspection is described elsewhere in the *Manual*. Furthermore, if the notebook record is kept so as to distinguish clearly the species that are added with each additional enlargement in the series of nested plots, the data themselves will indicate the form of the species-area curve and the investigator will know in the field when the plot is large enough. The close examination of the vegetation that is required by the method also provides some basis for an impression as to the typical composition and structure, as does general observation of the whole stand, so there is no need to depend wholly and completely on the mechanical methodology that is involved.

The system proposed here is very convenient to use in the field when visibility is high. A point is selected somewhere well within the stand and in an apparently typical portion of it. It is more important to avoid a position where apparently atypical conditions will be encountered than it is to endeavor to judge an average or really typical portion. From the selected point a base line, AB, is laid out (Figure 9). The line AC is laid out at a right angle to the base line at the point of origin, A. A staff compass is convenient for sighting the lines and determining the right angle accurately, but it is not an absolute necessity. A right angle can be determined from the function that the square on the hypotenuse is equal to the sum of the squares on the other two sides. Simply swing a tape around point A so that a distance of proportion 3 is on line AB, 4 on line AC, and B and C are connected by 5. This will produce a right angle BAC. With stakes set at the corners A, B, C, D, and appropriate distances measured along lines AB and AC, corners of plots along the diagonal AD can be established with sufficient accuracy by inspection.

This system of nested plots has the theoretical disadvantage that the successive plots in the series are continually alternating in shape from square to a short rectangle of the proportion 1 : 2. There is no evidence that this seriously affects the results, although it is known that long rectangles of a given sample area are more effective than squares of the same area. It is a simple matter, however, to use the nested-plot technique in such a manner that successive plots will be of the same shape. The simplest method of doing this is to describe circular plots about the point of origin A. At the end of Table 15 we have given the appropriate lengths of radii for this purpose. A tape with its zero point at A and fixed so as to be moved freely about A can be used to describe the successively larger circular sample plots. A radius of 28 cm. determines an area of 0.25 sq. m.; a radius of 2.26 m. describes a circle of 16 sq. m. area, etc., through the series.

The circular-plot method is simple to use in low vegetation, such as grassland, where the tape can be freely rotated about point A. It would be very awkward in dense shrubby communities and woods. The square-plot method first described can be used on nearly any kind of vegetation. In tropical rain forest, however, we have found that rectangular strip plots are much more convenient (because of the denseness of the vegetation and the richness of species) and that additional species are less likely to be overlooked. The range from the smallest to the largest plot is determined pragmatically in relation to the physiognomy of the community and its homogeneity. In bryophytic communities on tree trunks, for example, the smallest plot might be as little as 1 sq. cm., and the largest only a few square decimeters. If only trees are being analyzed in rich forest vegetation, the smallest plot may be as large as 100 or 200 sq. m. and the largest plot as much as 1 ha. (10,000 sq. m.) or more. In an FAO study in forests of *Araucaria angustifolia* in the southern states of Brazil (Rogers, 349), tree plots of 0.1 ha. were used. These plots were either circular, with a radius of 18 m., or rectangular, 25 × 40 m.

Working with types of communities that occur in numerous small patches, Braun-Blanquet and his followers have sometimes used entire stands, rather than sample plots, for the determination of minimal area. The point on the resultant species-area curve where the curve flattens strongly is taken as minimal area for the community type, and stands above this size are included in association tables, whereas smaller stands are discarded as being fragmentary.

Once having determined minimal area (or minimum plot size for the single-plot method), the investigator proceeds to study several stands of the given association, in each case using plots that are constantly of this size. Sometimes differences in plot size are tolerated but theoretically they should not be. The resulting data are comparable and differences due to differences in stand area are obviated.

A different and easier system of determining minimal area (and minimum plot size for the single-plot method) is commonly employed in studying the tree layers of forest vegetation. Instead of nested plots about a point A being used, the subplots occur along a base line, as shown in Figure 11. Point A is selected in a typical portion of the community and line AB is laid out. It should run with the topography, not across it, and should remain constantly within the community type under study. In the present illustration intervals of 20 m. are marked along the base line and plots are laid to the right and left of the line. In this case each subplot is 10 × 20 m. Depending upon the richness of the type in species, the size of the trees, the relative heterogeneity of structure, and the presence of apparent dominance and codominance in a small number of species, the subplots can be 10 × 10 m. (smaller plots are generally useless for the analysis of trees), 10 × 20 m., or 20 × 20 m. In any case the data from the subplots are kept separate in the field notebook. Error on the side of too small subplots is better than the reverse, for the data can always be combined later. As in the case of nested plots, the sequence of subplots along line *AB* can be continued as long as necessary. The succession of sub-plots builds up a species-area curve; data taken on the plots (in addition to the species present), such as density, basal area, etc., can by inspection suggest when the series has been run far enough, even without the de-tailed calculations that may be made later.

In order to illustrate this method we shall use two examples from the *Araucaria* forest near Campo Mourão, Paraná. Tables 16 and 17 and Figure 12 show the data from a suc-cession of 10 subplots, each 10 × 20 m. It appears that 2000 sq. m. is entirely adequate for the single-plot method in such forest, and if many stands were to be examined an area of about half that size would probably be sat-isfactory. We shall also take this opportunity to suggest the variety of data on composition and structure that can be obtained quickly while laying out such a plot. Our trip through the territory of the Paraná pine (*Araucaria an-gustifolia*) was reconnaissance, but a period of not more than three hours was required in each woods to lay out the plots and obtain a series of useful data. The procedure itself re-sults in a closer inspection of communities than is customary in reconnaissance and gives

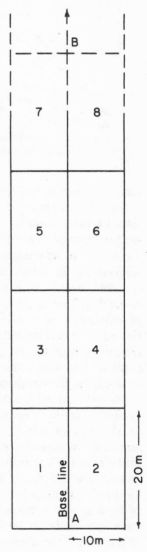

FIGURE 11. The accumulated rectangular forest-plot method of analysis. The 10 × 20 m. subunits lying to either side of the base line are of easily manageable size except in the densest forests. The accumulation of sub-plots 1, 2, 3, . . . can be continued as long as necessary as indicated by the resulting species-area relationships or other quantitative data that are being obtained.

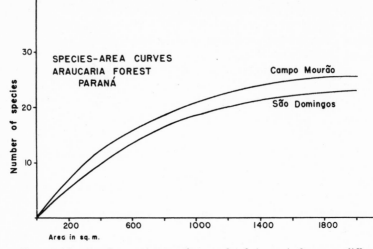

FIGURE 12.   Species-area curves for stands of *Araucaria* forest on different sites near Campo Mourão, Paraná.

valuable hints as to problems and methods for future study and application. It is therefore advisable, even in reconnaissance, to stop now and then for closer looks at the different associations of a region. Such data are not representative of the association, or even of a facies or locies of it. They have no statistical significance; they cannot be expanded as a fair measure of the whole stand. They are, however, samples, no matter how inadequate statistically, that represent their own small areas with accuracy. They are perhaps analogous to good detailed photographs of vegetation, in contrast to panoramic photographs of the landscape; the latter would correspond more closely to the common objectives of reconnaissance. In any case, let us go on with the procedure which, if replicated in many stands, will provide sound quantitative measures in applying the single-plot method.

Having run the baseline for five units of length (5 × 20 m.), we proceeded to identify each tree over 1 dm. in diameter at breast height (4.5 ft.) in each plot. Since we had with us neither calipers nor a diameter tape, we took circumference measurements of the trees. The name and size of each tree on subplot 1 were recorded. We then proceeded to subplots 2, 3, 4 . . . , keeping the data for each plot separate. Tables 16 and 17, already referred to, not only show the presence or absence of each species in each subplot, but also give the number of trees of each species. From these data we constructed the species-area curves (Figure 12), the frequency percentage and density determinations shown in Table 18, and the distribution of species in Raunkiaerian frequency classes shown in Table 19. The measurement of the circumference of trees permits the calculation of basal areas shown in Table 20. Basal area is the cross-section area of tree stems at the point of measurement. It is totaled for the entire sample in square meters (or

TABLE 16. *Araucaria-Alsophila* forest, Fazenda São Domingos, 65 km. south of Campo Mourão, Paraná. Each subsample is 10 × 20 m.; total 2000 sq. m.

Species	1	2	3	4	5	6	7	8	9	10	No.	F%
Pinheiro-Araucaria	2	1	1	2	3	5	1	3	2	2	22	100
(Cyathaea) Alsophila	7	11	17	6	4	8	4	7	5	8	77	100
Canela preta	2	1	..	..	1	2	3	1	1	1	12	80
Rabo de Bujo	1	..	..	..	..	..	..	..	..	..	1	10
Palmeira de Coco		2	1	3	..	1	..	..	1	2	10	60
Herveira-Ilex		1	..	..	..	2	1	..	..	..	4	30
Laranjerais de Mico		1	..	..	..	..	..	2	..	..	3	20
Sapouva		1	..	..	..	..	..	1	..	..	2	20
Peiroba amarela		1	..	..	..	..	..	..	..	..	1	10
Pau andrade		1	..	..	..	..	..	..	..	..	1	10
Guaçatunga branca			1	..	1	..	..	2	..	1	5	40
Caxí			1	..	..	1	2	..	..	..	4	30
Soita			1	..	..	1	..	..	..	..	2	20
Alecrim			1	..	..	..	..	..	..	..	1	10
Vaucumeira				1	..	..	..	..	1	..	2	20
Pororoca				1	..	..	..	..	..	..	1	10
Maria preta				1	..	..	..	..	..	..	1	10
Timboeira					2	..	..	..	..	..	2	10
Marmeleiro						1	1	..	..	..	2	20
Esparão						1	..	..	..	..	1	10
Monjoleiro							2	1	..	..	3	20
Tapieiro								1	1	2	4	30
Canjarana										1	1	10
Esporãoeiro										1	1	10
Species: Accumulated total	4	10	14	17	18	20	21	22	22	24		

square feet) for each species and this is then expressed as a percentage of the total basal area. The end of Table 20 shows what the basal area would be per acre and per hectare, on the basis of the results from the single sample. Such figures are probably about right for the immediate vicinity of the plots, although, as pointed out previously, there is no way of knowing how they apply generally.

While the trees on the subplots were being identified and measured, the person recording the data in the notebook also examined the forest for its stratification, recording the heights of layers and their gross

TABLE 17. *Araucaria-Ilex* forest, Campo Mourão, Paraná

Species	1	2	3	4	5	6	7	8	9	10	No.	F%
Pinheiro-Araucaria	1	2	1	2	..	1	1	..	1	..	9	70
Palmeira de Coco	5	1	..	1	..	2	1	..	..	1	11	60
Anjico	1	..	1	3	..	..	3	1	..	..	9	50
Pecegueiro bravo	2	..	..	..	..	..	..	2	..	1	5	30
Canela preta	2	..	..	..	1	..	..	..	..	..	3	20
Couratan	1	..	..	..	..	..	..	..	..	..	1	10
Pasto de Anta	1	..	..	..	..	..	..	..	..	..	1	10
Herveira		1	1	2	2	..	..	4	1	..	11	60
Caú una		1	1	1	..	1	2	..	..	..	6	50
Guaçatunga branca		1	1	..	1	..	..	..	..	..	3	30
Vassourão		1	..	..	..	1	..	..	..	..	2	20
Caroba		1	..	..	..	..	..	..	..	..	1	10
Araticum brava		1	..	..	..	..	..	..	..	..	1	10
Canela vermelha			1	..	..	..	..	..	..	..	1	10
Funeiro			1	..	..	..	..	..	..	..	1	10
Cedro				1	..	..	..	..	1	..	2	20
Tapiá				1	..	..	..	..	..	..	1	10
Canela imbuia					1	..	..	..	1	..	2	20
Canela amarela					1	..	..	..	..	1	2	20
Carne de Vaca					1	..	..	..	..	..	1	10
Canelinha						1	..	..	..	..	1	10
Guaçatunga amarela							1	..	..	..	1	10
Canela de Cibu							1	..	..	..	1	10
Capororoca							1	..	..	..	1	10
Acoita cavala									1	1	2	20
Amaralinga										1	1	10
Species: Accumulated total	7	13	15	17	20	21	24	24	25	26		

coverage. These data can be used to construct coverage-stratification diagrams. Let us see, then, what we have added to the reconnaissance method by the occasional use of single plots, when built up as described for the determination of minimal area.

The first plot was taken at the fazenda of Emilo B. Gomes, called São Domingos, about 65 km. south of Campo Mourão, Paraná. This fazenda is of about 4000 alqueires (about 25,000 acres) and is nearly all virgin Paraná pine. The highest stratum is composed solely of *Araucaria,* and although the trees are large (some measured up to 35 m. tall and about 1.5 m. in diameter) and so spaced that the branches of adjacent trees often just about touch (average spacing about 9.5 m.), the shading is light and the coverage was estimated at only 15 percent. The layers under the pine are formed by rain forest of an attenuated type.[1] Only occasional trees are tall, reaching the bottom

[1] This is temperate rain forest, according to Dansereau (154).

TABLE 18.   Samples of two types of primeval *Araucaria* forests, Paraná, based on 10 contiguous 10 × 20 m. plots in each stand

Species	Frequency Percentage		Number of Trees	
	São Domingos	Campo Mourão	São Domingos	Campo Mourão
Pinheiro (Araucaria)	100	70	22	9
Canela preta	80	20	12	3
Palmeira de coco	60	60	10	11
Herveira (Ilex)	30	60	4	11
Guaçatunga branca	40	30	5	3
Alsophila, some Cyathaea	100		77	
Caxí	30		4	
Tapieiro	30		4	
Laranjerais de mico	20'		3	
Sapuva	20		2	
Acoita cavalo	20		2	
Vaucumeira	20		2	
Marmeleiro	20		2	
Monjoleiro	20		3	
Rabo de bugio	10		1	
Peroba amarela	10		1	
Pau andrade	10		1	
Alecrim	10		1	
Pororoca	10		1	
Maria preta	10		1	
Timboeira	10		2	
Esporão	10		1	
Canjarana	10		1	
Esparaoeiro	10		1	
Anjico		50		9
Caúna		50		6
Pecegueiro bravo		30		5
Vassourão		20		2
Cedro		20		2
Canela amarela		20		2
Canela imbuia		20		2
Curatã		10		1
Pasto de anta		10		1
Caroba		10		1
Araticum bravo		10		1
Canela vermelha		10		1
Funeiro		10		1
Tapiá		10		1
Carne de vaca		10		1
Canelinha		10		1
Guaçatunga amarela		10		1
Canela de cebo		10		1

TABLE 18—*(Continued)*

Species	Frequency Percentage São Domingos	Frequency Percentage Campo Mourão	Number of Trees São Domingos	Number of Trees Campo Mourão
Capororoca		10		1
Amaralinga		10		1
Total density, or species:				
with tree ferns	24	26	163	80
without tree ferns	23	26	86	80

of the *Araucaria* crowns, but in the layer between 8 and 15 m. the coverage averages about 40 percent. The fourth layer is made up largely of the striking tree ferns, mostly *Alsophila* and some *Cyathaea,* covering about 15 percent. There is a heavy ground layer of pteridophytes and tree reproduction covering about 50 percent.

The second woods, close to Campo Mourão, was on a drier site. The tree ferns are completely absent and the corresponding layer is made up of a tangle of bamboo, with some thorned *Mimosa.* The araucarias are lower and smaller in diameter, and they make up a smaller dominance. Rain-forest trees are correspondingly more important, especially anjico, and occasionally are as tall as the pine. The rich carpet of evergreen ferns is absent from the ground layer, and shrubby Rubiaceae and Melastomaceae take their place along with tree reproduction. The araucarias are spaced about 15 m. apart and the branches of contiguous trees are usually separated by considerable space in which occasional broad-leaf evergreen trees may occur.

Figure 13 shows the single-plot method, described above, applied to a diagrammatic situation where each of two forest types is being sampled in a comparable manner—Type A on upland, Type B on flood-

TABLE 19.   Raunkiaerian frequency classes, *Araucaria* forests, Campo Mourão, Paraná

Frequency Classes	São Domingos Number	São Domingos Percentage	Campo Mourão Number	Campo Mourão Percentage
A. 10—20%	16	67	19	73
B. 30—40%	4	17	2	8
C. 50—60%	1	4	4	16
D. 70—80%	1	4	1	3
E. 90—100%	2	8	0	0
Total species	24		26	

plain. This same base is used for subsequent discussion of multiple-plot sampling.

Although the single-plot method, the minimal-area unit sample, is the basic field method of the European plant sociologists, and the relevés from such samples are combined into association tables for the characterization of associations, alliances, etc., it is clear that the method is highly subjective. There is no basis for locating the plot except the judgment of the investigator. It follows that the results have no statistical significance and that each sample is merely a description of the plant cover where it is located. Generalizations concerning the stand from which it is taken are not legitimate. The relevé may be compared with a photograph. Each can tell a lot about what is seen,

TABLE 20. Basal area of species of the *Araucaria* forests, Paraná

	São Domingos		Campo Mourão	
	Square Meters	%	Square Meters	%
Pinheiro—Araucaria	9.314	81.5	3.075	45.4
Canela preta	.319	2.8	.289	4.3
Palmeira de Coco	.240	2.1	.307	4.5
Herveira	.059	.5	.192	2.8
Guaçatunga branca	.053	.5	.061	1.0
Monjoleiro	.322	2.8		
Sapuva	.196	1.7		
Maria preta	.157	1.4		
Acoita cavalo	.131	1.1		
Anjico			1.454	21.5
Canela amarela			.279	4.1
Canela imbuia			.248	3.7
Cedro			.187	2.7
Cáuuna			.156	2.3
Gauçatunga amarela			.091	1.3
Pecegueiro bravo			.073	1.1
Vassourão			.073	1.1
15 other species, none equaling 1.0% b.a.	.637	5.2		
13 other species, none equaling 1.0% b.a.			.285	4.2
Total basal area:				
on plot	11.428 sq. m.		6.770 sq. m.	
per acre	22.848 sq. m.		13.540 sq. m.	
	245.8 sq. ft.		145.7 sq. ft.	
per hectare	57.120 sq. m.		33.850 sq. m.	
	614.5 sq. ft.		364.2 sq. ft.	

but nothing about what is not seen. This makes somewhat absurd the formalization of community types on such a basis and especially the selection of a "type" association table in a sense analogous to the plant systematist's selection of a type plant specimen. However, as we

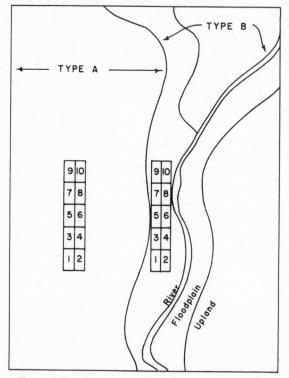

FIGURE 13. The accumulated rectangular single-plot method of sampling vegetation applied to vegetation types A and B. This method is especially adapted for work in dense forests when the subunits are kept to easily manageable size, such as 10 × 20 m.

have emphasized in several places in this *Manual,* methodology in the study of vegetation is no substitute for judgment that arises from experience and even from feeling that is not backed by objective data. So the single-plot method definitely has a place in ecological procedures, as has been amply demonstrated by the European plant sociologists, but one should not expect more from it than its shortcomings permit. A haphazard location of single plots has nothing to defend it. The investigator should frankly admit that he locates the plot where he wants it for the purpose of showing what he wants it to show, and this is usually what he *thinks* is typical or representative.

MULTIPLE-PLOT METHOD.   In the multiple-plot method the sample consists of a series of subplots that are scattered through a stand of a

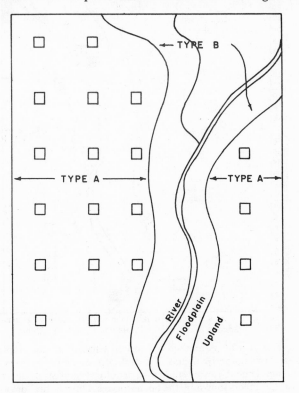

FIGURE 14.   The regularized multiple-plot method of sampling vegetation. Note that plots are evenly and widely spaced in Type A, and that plots that would fall in Type B are omitted. This is a commonly used system in the ecological study of forests in the United States.

community type. They are used to obtain analytic data, but comparable sets in different stands of a community type provide a basis for synthetic data, just as in the single-plot method.

A common method of subplot arrangement is called regularized. The quadrats are scattered regularly, often in a checkerboard pattern, more or less throughout the stand. This is illustrated in Figure 14. Twenty plots, spaced five units (five plot diameters) apart in both

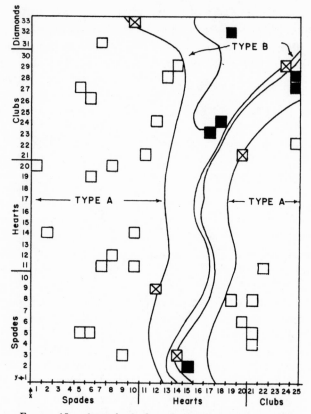

FIGURE 15. A method of random selection of subsample locations made by means of a deck of playing cards. Vegetation Type A can be studied in detail on the basis of the 25 random plots shown by the open squares. During this "drawing" only six locations were drawn for Type B, an inadequate number. Subplots crossed out are not used as they do not lie wholly within a single type of vegetation.

directions are used to sample forest Type A, on uplands. No effort is made to sample Type B.

Figure 15, using the same hypothetical territory as before, shows a system of random sampling. The open squares, of which there are 25, were located by chance. The system of random sampling which was used is as follows. The total area was divided into coordinate units, 25 on the x axis and 33 on the y axis. For purposes of these illustrations we assume the unit to be 10×10 m. The position of a subsample could be drawn from a table of random numbers, but since tables are not always at hand, we suggest a method based on common playing cards. The first 10 units from the point of origin on each axis are designated "spades," the next 10 units "hearts" the next group "clubs," and the last "diamonds." The "ace" counts as 1 and the corresponding numbered cards are also used. The face cards are discarded from the deck so that altogether 40 cards remain. The deck is thoroughly shuffled and cut, and the fifth card dealt is used to locate a square on the x axis. (Any other card in the deck would do as well as the fifth.) Shuffling, cutting, and dealing are repeated and a position on the y axis is found. The two drawings together, of course, locate the position of the subsample. Drawn cards are immediately returned to the deck so that each process involves the full 40-card deck. For example, the 7 of spades followed by the 1 of diamonds locates the subsample in the upper left-hand part of the area. The ace of clubs followed by the 4 of spades locates the sample plot in the lower right-hand part of the area. Because there are more cards than units on either axis, some drawings fall outside the area. The process was continued until 25 subsamples had been drawn that fell within Type A. During this process six plots fell within Type B (shown in black), and five plots fell on borders between the two types or partially in the stream. These, of course, are not usable.

Preparation for laying out the plots is made in advance of the actual work, it being necessary only to know the overall dimensions of the tract and the size of the sample unit to be used.

Many workers confuse haphazard arrangement of plots with random arrangement. In the haphazard method plots are laid out with no predetermined plan; just because the pattern is not regular does not make it random. In the haphazard method there is a strong likelihood of introducing bias by unconscious "selection" of positions for the sample units. For an arrangement of subsamples to be truly random, every unit must have an equal opportunity to be selected at each drawing. It is for this reason that after each drawing, in the card method, the card is returned to the deck and there is a new shuffle, cut, and deal. The selection of the fifth card dealt (or some other one) is merely an arbitrary device to overcome any defect that might arise from some unconscious, habitual "system" of shuffling and cutting.

Although the illustrations here involve comparatively large quadrats (10 × 10 m.), the techniques for regularized and random location of plots are directly applicable to the exigencies of the situation. Having gone to the trouble of locating tree plots by either method, many investigators use the same determinations for smaller plots for other purposes. For example, if 10 × 10 m. plots are used for trees of 1 dm.

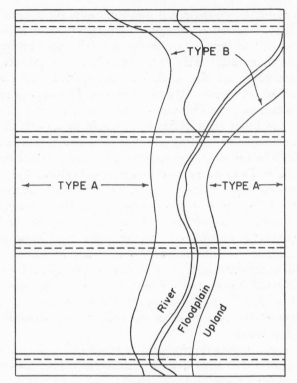

FIGURE 16. The 10 percent strip method commonly used by foresters in the United States in cruising timber. Note that the strips are laid so as to run across the topography, not with it. The center line of the strips is the path of the cruiser's movement. The strips are commonly 1 chain wide (66 ft., or about 20 m.).

diameter and over, subplots are placed at predetermined positions within them for the study of small trees, shrubs, and herbs. One common method is to locate 4 × 4 m. or 2 × 2 m. plots for small trees and shrubs always in the same corners of the larger plot. For the study of herbs and tree seedlings, four 1 × 1 m. plots may be located one in each corner, or in some other predetermined positions.

LINE AND STRIP METHODS. Figure 16 illustrates the common 10 percent strip method of sampling used by foresters. The strips are commonly 1 chain wide, and are placed parallel 10 chains apart on the strip centers. A chain is 66 ft., which is almost exactly 20 m. There are 4 rods to a chain, and 80 chains to a mile. The 2 × 2 m. subplots (6.6 ft. on a side) are almost exactly $\frac{1}{1000}$ of an acre. The timber cruiser—

that is, the person who is identifying, counting, measuring, or estimating the trees along strips—walks a compass line that is the center of the strip. He records everything (to predetermined size limits) to $\frac{1}{2}$ chain (10 m.) to each side of the line. For large heterogeneous areas, lines that are properly laid run across the topography, as shown in the figure. If they were to run with the topography there would be great danger of the strips' coinciding with long, narrow vegetation types (correlated with topography) and a corresponding overrepresentation of some types and underrepresentation of others. In some timber cruising the tallies are accumulated for entire tracts made up of two or more cover types. In many ways this is less satisfactory than keeping the tallies separate for each well-distinguished cover type. However, if only a single cover type is being analyzed and it bears a relationship to the topography, it is better to run the cruise strips with the topography rather than across it.

A 10 percent survey is often unnecessarily extensive. For this reason several modifications of the customary strip method have been introduced. A common modification is the line-plot method. Lines are run as described; but instead of examining the continuous strip, the cruiser examines alternate blocks, every third block, or some other predetermined system of blocks. If the blocks are tallied separately or by rational groups, the results are amenable to statistical treatment, and some evaluation of the reliability of the data is possible.

An extremely interesting modification of the forester's strip method is being employed by foresters of the Food and Agriculture Organization of the United Nations (FAO) in the vast rain forests of the Amazon, especially by Dr. D. Heinsdijk (237). On the basis of aerial photographs the boundaries of terra firme and varzea forest are placed on maps. As the region is accessible only by water and a fairly large party of workers is employed, appropriate riverside camp locations are selected. From these centers, which are widely scattered, long lines of definite bearing are cleared by a woods crew radiating from each camp center and so selected as to cut generally across the topography and encounter proportionate amounts of the various types of country. All the actual cruising is done by a single highly trained member of the party; the cruising unit is a strip along the line that is 10 m. wide and 1000 m. (1 km.) long, or 1 ha. Alternate kilometers along the lines are sampled. Although visibility within the forest is sometimes low, the cruiser works only 5 m. to each side of the line. Because the plot border is great in proportion to the plot area, determining whether a given tree is inside or outside of the plot is crucial. A 5-m. bamboo pole is carried for quick determination of this fact. Other details of this pioneering work are interesting but not pertinent to the present discussion.

SOME SPECIAL METHODS.   Dr. Castro has proposed a useful technique of sampling for preliminary studies. Vegetation often shows correlative changes with topographic changes. These may be changes from one association to another, or from one locies to another within an association, as from the top to the base of a hill. The changes may not be "type" changes, but more subtle and analogous to a continuum or cline. In such cases a line-plot strip is started at the top of the hill, for example, in which every other quadrat is examined. As the study continues along the line down the slope, no change is introduced in the method as long as successive quadrats are similar in character. But when a significant change occurs, a cross strip at right angles is used to explore the change to see whether a new type of vegetation has been encountered. If that seems to be the case, the cross strip, running with the topography, is continued until an adequate sample has been obtained. Afterwards there is a return to the original strip which is continued across the topography. The process is repeated as necessary. The resulting plot data can be organized in tables and graphs in either of the two directions to show the characteristics of the respective communities or the transitions between them.

Another special technique has been developed for situations where it is desirable to chart the exact position of trees or other conspicuous plants on strips or quadrats. The usual technique for locating positions is by right-angle coordinates. This not only is tedious, but can result in considerable error of position (unless great care is used) because it involves two angles and two distances. Cain and Evans (98) introduced a new method of surveying the positions of plants that is efficient and accurate under certain conditions. It can be used for trees and shrubs in rather open spacing, but was first used for large herbaceous plants in a grass community. From a staff compass position within a quadrat of fairly large size, bearing (direction relative to north) and distance were determined for each plant; the work is done progressively from north clockwise. The data are directly transferred at an appropriate scale from the notebook to a chart by means of a large three-arm protractor and scale. The closeness of the bearing reading and of measurement from the compass position to the plant in the field is determined by the charting scale to be used in the laboratory. There is no point, for example, in reading bearing to 30 sec. and measuring distance to 1 cm. if the charting scale does not permit such fine differentiation.

Although many devices have been invented for examining and

charting small quadrats, there is one that is especially efficient for 1 sq. m. quadrats. Four meter sticks are prepared with eye-screws at each end through which slender rods, such as surveyor's pins, can be inserted to fix the meter sticks in position on the ground with one edge up (causing minimum displacement of vegetation). When the plants are small and numerous, it is practical to advance a fifth meter stick, decimeter by decimeter, from one side of the quadrat to the other. Meter sticks are useful because they are accurately ruled and easily handled; they and the pins make only a small package.

SAMPLES AND SAMPLING

The communities that compose the vegetation of an area are usually so extensive and so complex that they have to be studied by samples; that is to say, they are never known completely. Even when the results of study make no pretense of quantification, observations are only partial, no community being seen or comprehended in its entirety. No community is ever inventoried; yet for descriptive purposes and as a base for experimental or managerial purposes, one of the first necessities is a characterization of the community or communities of interest. Basically, the essential composition and structure of a community must be known if it is to be compared with other communities or with conditions of the environment, whether they be present or historical, natural or experimental and managed. All of this means that a community, or a defined portion of it such as the tree layer or the field layer, is considered a statistical universe which for all practical purposes is infinite. Knowledge of it can therefore be gained from knowledge of portions of it, providing the sample portions are representative of the whole. The *sample* consists of one or more sample units that are examined closely and from which observational or more or less precise quantitative data are obtained. The *sample unit* is a portion of the whole universe (community) that "represents" the whole or is used in gaining a concept of the whole. In exceptional cases the sample unit may be unique; but it is more commonly duplicated, triplicated, or many times replicated, in which case all the comparable sample units together constitute the sample.

Following the present discussion of samples and sampling, various sections of the *Manual* will present certain topics in greater detail and will return, from specific points of view, to matters mentioned now only briefly. At this point we will examine briefly the various kinds of sample units, the kinds of records taken from them, and certain of their characteristics that must be considered, such as the size, shape, number, and distribution of the sample units.

KINDS OF SAMPLE UNITS.   Because communities occupy space, sample units usually also have spatial characteristics; that is, they are *plots* that occupy area or volume, hence have a boundary, and are considered to be representative of the community. A *subplot* is a portion of a plot. The sampling demands produced by certain features of a community, such as the layer of tall trees in a woods, are such as to require sample plots to have a size that is impractically and unnecessarily large for the examination of other features, such as the seedling or sprout reproduction of the trees of the high forest. In this case, one or more small areas laid out within the larger sample plot for the purpose of studying not the trees but their reproduction constitute subplots. In a forest the sample plots may have an area of an acre or a hectare each, subplots may be one milacre in size, etc.

It follows from the preceding discussion that it is convenient to keep certain terms distinct. A subplot is a subdivision or internal portion of a plot. A plot, if one of a series in the same statistical universe, is a subsample. The entire series of subsamples compose the sample.

The term *quadrat,* strictly speaking, is applied to square sample plots. Quadrats may be of any size; they may be subplots or they may be independent of larger sample areas. Considerable loose usage has resulted from the application of the term quadrat to sample areas of circular or rectangular shape. *Line plots* are usually square or circular plots that are spaced at intervals along a line of definite bearing, or a series of such lines in parallel arrangement, producing a regular spatial pattern of sampling. A *transect* is a long rectangular sample plot—a strip; it may also consist of a contiguous series of quadrats, i.e., the strip being divided into squares equal to its width. In American forestry, for example, cruising a stand of timber (in the sense of an inventory) for its volume of wood or quantity of wood products is commonly accomplished with strips that total 10 percent of the area. These strips are transects. Where total commercial yield is the sole interest, the cruise of the various strips may be tallied together; but in other cases tallies may be kept separate by forest types, cover types, site types, subwatersheds, etc., in which case there will be several samples rather than a single sample.

For special purposes the transect may be so narrow in relation to its width that it approaches a line. If actually or nearly a line, as formed by a stretched wire or cord, and the tally of organisms is based on the individuals that make contact with the line, it is called a *line transect,* or *line intercept.* With either the transect or the line intercept—both are normally laid out on the ground surface—there may also be an interest in the vertical relations of the vegetation being sampled, both above and below ground. In this case the sample unit is termed a *bisect* or *profile*. Although the data concerning plants may be recorded only by height above the ground, depth of root penetration, etc., the usual use of the bisect and representation of data from it involve a drawing or diagram visualizing the arrangements of the diverse elements found along the sample unit. This is a cross section of the community. Because of their great length relative to their width, transects, lines, and profiles not only are employed for analysis (as legitimate samples of a statistical universe), but are often used in heterogeneous vegetation. Often they are run across vegetational boundaries to show the changes from one community to another, or from one ecological situation to another.

Finally, in this series of sample units, there is the *point sample;* this is the logical reduction of the quadrat to its minimal size in the same sense that the line is the ultimate reduction of the transect in width. In its pure form, the point sample makes contact with a plant at the ground surface; in practice, however, the point is usually used to record data concerning its contacts with plants as it (the point of a pin) travels through space, vertically or at a specified angle from the horizontal. It is seen, then, that the point-contact method and the line-intercept method are similar, differing only in the direction in which they pass through the community and the technique of producing them.

Sample plots may be temporary or permanent. *Temporary sample plots* of whatever kind are used for a single examination; after it their boundaries are not marked on the ground in any way, for there is no intention of relocating them at any time in the future. Most sample plots are of this type. The so-called *permanent sample plots* are of use in observing and recording changes in the vegetation over a time. Since they must be reexamined, their boundaries must be marked on the ground or so surveyed and tied in to a permanent marker that they can be relocated with accuracy. Permanence is a relative matter, of course, and implies a span of time that usually exceeds a decade in natural and semi-natural vegetation, whereas under experimental conditions a few years may be the planned period of observation.

Quadrats and other sample units are often given further designations according to their uses or the data derived from them. A common type is the *list quadrat;* this is a sample unit on which each kind (species) of organism is merely listed by name. A species needs to be represented only by a single plant in the quadrat in order to be counted present in the quadrat. In most cases it is required that the plant be rooted within the area of the quadrat, but sometimes plants are counted present if any portion is within the space of the quadrat boundary projected vertically. A series of list quadrats provides for a floristic analysis of a community and its comparison with other communities in this regard. Presence or absence of representatives of a species in members of a set of list quadrats allows the assignment of a frequency index to the species, but does not directly permit inferences concerning other phytosociological characteristics, such as density, coverage, etc.

In *count quadrats* the number of individuals of the various species, or a selection of them, are recorded. In addition to data on number, count quadrats automatically provide as much data as list quadrats and may give other information. For example, on count quadrats used in analyzing the tree components of a community, it is common to give additional data regarding tree diameters, heights, volumes, etc.

A *cover quadrat* is one on which the actual or relative coverage of the plants of each species is recorded. Cover is usually recorded as the area or percentage of area of ground surface (quadrat surface) covered or shaded by an imaginary vertical projection of the mass of aerial parts onto the plane surface of the ground. This is often estimated in terms of a limited number of cover classes.

A *chart quadrat* is one that is mapped; the rooting locations of plants or masses of them and their coverage are shown to scale on a plat representing the quadrat. The chart quadrat may be made by a free sketch based on observation from above; it is more accurately constructed from photographs of low vegetation by means of a pantograph, or by survey methods employing rectangular coordinates.

When biomass is of interest, the clip quadrat is employed. A *clip quadrat* is one from which the vegetation is removed by clipping (if it is herbaceous). The product is then sorted on the basis of species or other categories (such as life-form groups) for which number and weight or volume are determined. Clipping may be at a predetermined height (such as grazing level), the quadrat may be denuded, or subterranean parts may even be excavated. Essentially the same technique has been used on extremely complicated tropical rain forest in which the component elements of the quadrat or transect could not be observed and measured without destroying the vegetation by felling the trees. A similar opportunity is sometimes offered by commercial lumbering operations. For example, some of the work done by Warming (408) at Lagoa Santa, Minas Gerais, on tropical rain forest was based on the study of forests that were being felled for other purposes, such as clearing for agriculture.

Experimental plots are circumscribed areas that receive particular types of treatment under artificial, semi-natural, or natural conditions. They usually call for *control plots* on which the treatment is not given or the special action (such as grazing) is not allowed. Thus both experimental and control plots must have some sort of isolation that separates them from the marginal conditions. This need has led to the use of *inclosures* and *exclosures,* sample plots that are provided in some manner with a peripheral barrier. This barrier is often a fence that is adequate to limit the action of some biotic factor such as a wild predator or a grazing wild or domestic animal. The factor may be a treatment or management practice carried on by man, such as a silvicultural treatment, the use of fire as a management tool, artificial planting, etc. All such experimental plots should have an adequate "surround" or *buffer zone* that will eliminate any marginal effects from the sample taken within the plot.

QUADRAT (SAMPLE PLOT) CHARACTERISTICS

Quadrats differ as to size, shape, number, and arrangement. These characteristics must be given due consideration, for they may influence the data that are derived from the sample.

The *size of quadrats* must be adapted to the characteristics of the community being sampled. In general, the greater the floristic richness and the more heterogeneous the life forms of the community, the larger the quadrat size. In very simple terms, a quadrat whose size is suitable for sampling ground vegetation (herbs and woody plant seedlings) is much too small for sampling the tree layer of a forest and much too large for sampling the ground cover of mosses, liverworts, lichens and algae; hence the size of the quadrat must be adapted to the layers of the community. The selection of a quadrat size is often made arbitrarily by the investigator on the basis of experience and judgment, but it may be arrived at by various objective methods, such as the use of the species-area curve. In any case, all the units of a sample must be of the same size, whether it be 1 sq. dm. for bryophytic communities or 4000 sq. m. for the dominant tree layer of a phytocoenosis.

Strictly speaking, the *shape of quadrats* is square, but sample plots can be any regular shape. They are commonly square, circular, short rectangular, or strips. In some cases one form is more efficient than another. In general, however, comparative studies have shown that relatively long plots are more efficient than isodiametric plots as sampling units, especially when some of the elements of the vegetation are highly aggregated in their occurrence patterns.

The *number of sample units* that constitute a sample will vary according to the characteristics of the community, the objectives of the investigation, the degree of precision of results that is sought, and the time that is available (i.e., the cost). In extensive work, when several stands of a certain type of community are being examined, European workers often employ a single sample plot per stand. In this case the single plot must be at least the *minimal area*. It is obvious that extremely good judgment must be employed in selecting the single plot (which in a statistical sense is representative only of itself) if it is to describe the stand as a whole. Theoretically the single plot should be "average" for the entire stand of which it is a part. In some rather rare instances of vegetation that occurs in a mosaic of very small patches of each community type, whole stands may be taken as "sample units." In this case the boundary of the plot is the boundary of the stand, and its shape will be irregular. In most cases, however, several relatively small units make up a sample. The exact number of such units may be arbitrary, limited by the time available, or determined by some objective statistical method related to the data derived from the sample units themselves.

Finally we must consider the *distribution of the sample units* within the sample area, i.e., their arrangement. Theoretically what is being sampled is the entire statistical universe (the stand of a community, for example), but in actual practice the area through which the sample units are scattered is usually somewhat less than that. From the statistical point of view, if the sample is to describe the whole within limits of accuracy that can be ascertained, the sample units should be distributed at random through the entire population. As we are dealing with spatial units, *random* means that each spatial unit of the entire stand of a size equal to the size of the sample unit should have an equal and independent chance of being examined (drawn). Although these requirements are very strict, they are seldom complied with in ecological sampling. There is a current trend, however, toward statistically valid methodology. Sometimes a haphazard arrangement of sample units is mistakenly thought to be random, although it may actually have a strong bias resulting from unconscious predilections of the investigator who locates the positions of the sample units. By far the most common arrangement in ecological work involves some kind of regularized pattern of plot locations. In some cases the sample units are evenly scattered throughout the area of the stand, only marginal influence being avoided, so as to provide maximum spacing between subsamples. The usual pattern, however, uses equal spacing along a line through the stand or along a series of evenly spaced parallel lines so that the sample units form a grid pattern. Regularized arrangements of quadrats are usually located more quickly in the field than are random positions. Pragmatic comparisons sometimes show that the theoretical advantages of randomization do not provide a more accurate description of a known population than a regularized arrangement does; but where practicable, a random sample is to be preferred.

PLOTLESS SAMPLING

Bitterlick (40) introduced a variable-radius sampling method that is applicable to trees to determine basal area (trunk cross-sectional area) on an acre basis. This method has been discussed in more readily available literature by Grosenbaugh (223, 224) and Shanks (365). A sighting gauge is constructed with an angle of 1° 44′; this is the proper angle to subtend tree trunks (at their breast-high diameter, d.b.h.) at distances equal to 33 times their diameter. This relationship was selected so that, when multiplied by 10, the count of trees that are subtended by the angle as the viewer sweeps a complete circle, gives a product exactly equal to the total basal area in square feet per acre. This is for an acre that is like the portion viewed, of course. It is a variable-radius plot because trees of smaller diameter that are closer to the viewer will be subtended by the angle and counted, whereas trees of larger diameter will more than subtend the angle if they are not far enough away. If the tree has 1.0 m. d.b.h., at 33 m. distance from the observer it will exactly subtend the angle; for a tree 0.5 m. d.b.h. the distance is 16.5 m., etc. The only measure of any value obtained by variable-radius sampling appears to be basal area. Frequency, studied by Rice and Penfound (341), is apparently too complex for this method.

Cottam and others, mostly at the University of Wisconsin, have been interested in plotless sampling and during the past few years have improved their methods and discovered much about both the usefulness and the limitations of the various methods that have been tried (Cottam, 133; Cottam and Curtis, 135, 136, 137; Cottam, Curtis, and Hale, 138; Clark and Evans, 119; Morisita, 297; Shanks, 365). Plotless samples are especially adapted for anlyzing the tree stratum of woods and are more rapid than the usual plot samples. All the methods depend for a starting point on random points located within the stand, or on some combination of random and regularized selection of starting points such as random points on parallel lines. All the methods assume that the individual trees are randomly distributed in nature. Whether or not they are, the methods yield results that are correct as relative measures among the species, if not as absolute measures. Four techniques have been used.

1. The simplest method involves measuring from the random points

to the closest individual to each point. 2. In one random-pairs method the closest individual to the random point is determined (but the distance is not measured as before) and distance between it and its nearest neighbor is measured. In both the closest-individual method (1) and the nearest-neighbor method (2) the mean distance obtained from a series of such measurements should be half the square root of the mean area occupied by each tree. Testing this in the field against a stand of known density (and consequently of mean area), Cottam, Curtis, and Hale (138) found this to be true for the closest-individual method; but Cottam and Curtis (137) found that for the nearest-neighbor method the correction factor is 1.67 instead of the theoretically expected 2.0. 3. The second random-pairs method involves as before locating the closest individual to the random point. An exclusion angle of 180° is formed at the random point by a line intersecting the point which is 90° from the line between the point and the closest tree. This exclusion angle having been determined, measurement is made to the closest individual outside the exclusion angle. Cottam and Curtis (136) found in this method that to obtain the square root of the mean area it was necessary to use a correction factor of 0.8. 4. The fourth method involves using quadrants about the random point. Perhaps the simplest method of determining the quadrants is from the cardinal directions, north, east, south, and west. Cottam and Curtis (137), using random points on lines transecting the woods, had one boundary of the quadrants already determined by the line, and the other boundaries were easily determined at right angles to the line. With this method the distances to four trees are measured about each random point, they being the closest one in each quadrant.

All four of these methods yield mean area and, as a consequence, density. Density is not determined without reference to the species involved, and it is customary to record not only the species of tree for each measurement but also its d.b.h. for determination of basal area. Relative density and relative basal area determinations for the various species are valid whether or not the distributions are random. The quadrant method gives the highest accuracy in determination of density and the closest-individual method the lowest; the random-pairs method is second best, when the same number of measurements is made by each method. There are some data showing that the random-pairs method is the most rapid.

Chapter 6

THE PROBLEM
OF NUMBER:
ABUNDANCE AND
DENSITY

THE number of individuals of a kind in a community is an important datum. When not counted but estimated, the data are referred to as *abundance* and are usually expressed by assigning the species to the appropriate one of a limited number of *abundance classes*. The term *density* is properly limited to the reference of an exactly known number of individuals of a kind to a definite unit of area. We should note that the phytosociological use of the term abundance is an arbitrary limitation of its connotation to estimated number, just as elsewhere such terms as frequence and dominance are given specific meanings.

The abundance of plants has been given rhetorical description by taxonomists and geographers for a long time, and it seems always to have been a more or less objective concept that man has used for natural things to express the general idea of relative plentifulness or scarcity. As persons interested in vegetation have concerned themselves more and more with practical problems of pasture management and forestry, and with increasing the precision of their concepts, it was a natural development for descriptive abundance terms to be limited to an arbitrary small number of abundance classes, thereby forcing an apparent increase in comparability of data concerning different species and communities. Many investigators have used five abundance classes, as follows:

Abundance Class 1:	Rare	Very sparse	Very scarce
Abundance Class 2:	Occasional	Sparse	Scarce
Abundance Class 3:	Frequent	Not numerous	Infrequent
Abundance Class 4:	Abundant	Numerous	Frequent
Abundance Class 5:	Very abundant	Very numerous	Abundant

The first column of adjectives is from Tansley and Chipp (386), the second from Braun-Blanquet (58), and the third from Hanson and Love (229). Among these Braun-Blanquet's terminology is perhaps preferable because it avoids the word "frequent" which he gives another meaning distinct from number. At best, such classes are vague and can have little definite meaning that can be communicated, although a single investigator (or a group working closely together) can establish class values and assign species to them with considerable consistency.

Oosting (303) has published a table from Böcher (46) that shows how the assignment of abundance classes to species in an extensive survey can show the progressively changing importance of the species. The data in Table 21 refer to 14 localities on the east coast of Greenland, ranging from 70° N. lat. (Station A) down to 65° (Station N). The table also shows presence and limits of range. Böcher uses six classes, described as follows: (*) merely present, (1) rare, (2) uncommon, (3) here and there, (4) common, but with more scattered occurrence than the following class, (5) very common, being an important constituent of several closed communities. We should note in this case that the concept is not purely one of number

Some investigators have felt that it is possible to sort species into more than five classes with a sufficient relation to reality, and that if the number of species in a community is large, ten classes should be used. Vestal (402) recommends ten classes when the number of species is more than forty.

The estimation of abundance is extremely subject to personal bias, as was long ago pointed out by Pound and Clements (329), who said that to secure even approximately accurate results, it is necessary to resort to some method of checking abundance estimates by sampling a community and counting the number of individuals in the sample. Some species of a community, because of their color, form, economic importance, aesthetic appeal, etc., are appreciated more than others and tend to be overestimated. Contrariwise, obscure, ordinary, and "difficult" species tend to be underestimated. It is for these reasons that

TABLE 21.   Presence and abundance of certain species on the east coast of Greenland in 14 localities from 70° N. lat. (Station A) to 65° (Station N). (Böcher, 46). Explanation of abundance classes in the text

Species	|	Stations (Localities)												
	A	B	C	D	E	F	G	H	I	J	K	L	M	N
Salix herbacea	5	5	5	5	5	5	5	5	5	5	5	5	5	5
Polygonum viviparum	5	5	5	5	5	5	5	5	5	5	5	5	5	5
Sedum roseum	4	*	4	2	4	*	1	5	5	4	3	4	5	5
Silene acaulis	5	4	4	4	4	*	4	5	4	4	5	4	5	5
Oxyria digyna	5	5	5	4	4	4	4	5	5	5	5	5	5	5
(More important northward)														
Cassiope tetragona	5	5	5	5	4	..	..	..	1	1	4	..	..	1
Draba alpina	4	4	4	4	3	..	3	..	..	..	..	..	..	..
Dryas octopetala	5	*	2	..	2	..	..	..	..	..	..	..	..	..
Draba lactea	4	*	*	*	*	..	..	..	..	..	..	..	..	..
Ranunculus sulphureus	3	..	2	..	..	..	..	..	..	..	..	..	..	..
Potentilla pulchella	3	*	..	..	..	..	..	..	..	..	..	..	..	..
(More important southward)														
Salix arctophila	*	*	*	*	*	*	4	4	5	5	5	5	5	5
Empetrum nigrum	3	2	2	1	2	*	5	5	5	5	5	5	5	5
Draba rupestris	..	..	3	..	..	..	3	3	4	4	4	4	4	4
Sagina intermedia	..	*	..	..	..	*	3	3	4	..	4	*	3	3
Alchemila filicaulis	..	..	..	1	..	..	..	..	3	5	4	..	5	5
Polystichum lonchites	..	..	..	..	..	..	..	..	1	..	..	..	2	3
Potentilla tridentata	..	..	..	..	..	..	..	..	..	1	..	3	..	3

most investigators resort to density data when their problems permit.

Because of the time required for counting, several investigators have combined abundance and density determinations, using density data on sample areas as "controls" or constant guides to their abundance estimates. Hanson, for example, in a study of mixed prairie (228), assigned the following densities to his abundance classes (the densities being the number of plant units per square meter quadrat sample unit):

Abundance Class 1:   Scarce—1 to 4 stalks or plants per sq. m. quadrat
Abundance Class 2:   Infrequent—5 to 14 plant units
Abundance Class 3:   Frequent—15 to 29 plant units
Abundance Class 4:   Abundant—30 to 99 plant units
Abundance Class 5:   Very abundant—100 or more plant units per sq. m. quadrat

In a study of South African veld types, Acocks (1) used abundance classes for extensive and apparently successful survey of vegetation. This work is distinguished for its constant effort to control abundance class estimates by reference to average spacing measured on relatively small sample areas. The survey employs 20 abundance classes, as shown in Table 22. The procedure is as follows:

1. A representative sample of a veld type (perhaps an association, at least a distinguishable cover type) is selected and a complete list of species is assembled by inspection. For complex vegetation this step takes an experienced worker up to three hours. About 20 lists (from

TABLE 22. Abundance classes related to average spacing of plants as employed on South African veld types by Acocks (1). (See Brown, 65.)

Symbol	Description	Average Spacing	Number per Morgen (2.1165 Acres) (About 8500 sq. m.)
vvab	Extremely abundant	1 inch	12,960,000
vab	Very abundant	3 inches	1,440,000
ab⁺		4.5 ″	640,000
ab	Abundant	6 ″	360,000
ab⁻		9 ″	160,000
c⁺		1 foot	90,000
c	Common	1.25 feet	57,600
c⁻		1.6 ″	32,400
f⁺		2 ″	22,500
f	Frequent	3 ″	10,000
f⁻		6 ″	2,500
ff⁺		12 ″	625
ff	Fairly frequent	15 ″	400
ff		20 ″	225
o⁺		30 ″	100
o	Occasional	50 ″	36
o⁻		75 ″	16
r⁺		125 ″	6
r	Rare	200 ″	2
vr		300 (and over)	1

20 different examples) are prepared for each veld type. A larger number of stands could be used in order to refine the results; but as Acocks was dealing with 70 different veld types, time could not as a rule be allowed for more examples.

2. Abundance class symbols are next added to the list of species from a station, and all the lists from a veld type are assembled into a single alphabetical table.

3. Numerical values determined from samples are substituted for the abundance symbols, and the average number per unit of area is calculated.

4. Because most species have a patchy occurrence, *relative abundance* of a species is computed by multiplying the number of plants per unit area by the number of lists in which it occurs and dividing by the total number of lists. In order to compare relative abundance figures, a constant unit of area must be used in their calculation.

Density data are often used not only to describe a certain quantitative aspect of a community at a given time but also to suggest the nature of change that may be occurring in the community. This is illustrated in Table 23, in which the density data are given in size classes for the leading tree species in an Indiana woods, sampled by 25 quadrats, each 10 × 10 m. For example, although *Quercus alba* is the dominant species, it seems not to be reproducing well, as shown by the fact that there are 325 seedlings less than 1 ft. high but no saplings up to 12 ft. high. On the other hand, *Acer saccharum, Fraxinus americana, Fagus grandifolia,* and *Acer rubrum* are poorly represented in the superior

TABLE 23.   Density of selected tree species by size classes, Donaldson's Woods, Indiana, suggesting dynamic trends in the community (Cain, 82)

Species	Density on 25 Quadrats, 10 × 10 m. Each				
	Up to 1 ft. High	1.2–12 ft. High	1–3 in. d.b.h.	4–9 in. d.b.h.	10 in. and over
Quercus alba	325	. . .	2	5	19
Quercus borealis var. maxima	31	. . .	1	. . .	3
Liriodendron tulipifera	69	.__.	. . .	. . .	3
Fagus grandifolia	44	12	20	6	2
Nyssa sylvatica	25	50	4	. . .	3
Acer rubrum	800	31	9	7	. . .
Carya cordiformis	44	25	. . .	. . .	. . .
Carya glabra	400	150	8	1	3
Fraxinus americana	1150	319	35	. . .	1
Acer saccharum	175	100	37	4	2

arborescent stratum, but well represented among seedlings, saplings, and poles.

The determination of density is tedious when plants are small and numerous, yet not otherwise difficult; but for plants of certain life forms this proves not to be the case. For example, *Juniperus monosperma*, the small tree of the juniper-piñon woodland of the Rocky Mountains, often branches at or below the ground surface. Some small trees and large shrubs in old fields in the eastern United States, such as *Populus tremuloides, Sassafras variifolium, Rhus glabra*, etc., often form extensive clones by root sprouts. In the cerrados (savannas) of central Brazil many species have xylopodia. Some xylopodia are relatively massive subterranean organs from which several to many shoots may arise, as in the case of *Andira laurifolia, Byrsonima verbascifolia*, and *Calliandra* sp., a single plant spreading over considerable area (Warming, 408). In such cases as these, although the whole mass may be connected below ground and be a single plant in one sense, it seems feasible merely to count separate shoots. On the other hand, many low shrubs of chamaephytic type are spread by runners (stolons) that creep over the ground. *Evonymous* and *Pachystima* species, for example, may make a dense plant mat of a single plant, or an intertwined mass of scarcely separable plants, the rooted nodes of which would survive as individual plants should they become separated. Among geophytes (with bulbs, rhizomes, rootstocks) there are cases in which the single subterranean organ produces more than one shoot or flowering scape, as in *Allium, Trillium, Polygonatum, Aster*, etc. Finally, grasses present a most difficult problem in counting. When shoots from low buds do not break horizontally through the sheaths, grass plants tend to form distinct clumps, the bunch-grass type common in Andropogoneae. Bunch grasses can be counted by the distinct and obvious bunches. The other life form, however, spreads laterally, the branches rooting at the nodes, and often resulting in dense sods, as in *Poa pratensis*. Here it is difficult to decide where an individual plant begins and where it ends, and what one should count. Pasture investigators usually devise some more or less arbitrary system of units for counting, but they still have difficulties, even when sample units of the sod are collected and washed and dissected out in the laboratory (Brown, 65).

There are cases of natural grassland with a mixture of bunch-type and sod-type grasses, as in the prairies of Vacaria, Rio Grande do Sul, Brazil. Here it would be grossly misleading to compare density figures for bunch grasses and sod grasses because of the great differences in coverage between the units of the two types. Any counting units that might be devised would scarcely be comparable.

Although density is an important characteristic of most species of interest in the analysis of communities, and is not subject to the influence of quadrat size as frequency is, there are many instances in which density data are not worth the time it takes to obtain them. Furthermore, density data often have an apparent though spurious accuracy. Counts that are made in the same way are comparable for a given species in different stands of a community, or for the same stand at different times. This is of importance in grazing studies, in seed testing, etc. But counts of different species when related to each other may not have the real significance that the numbers express. For example, differences in dynamism of two species may be inferred by numbers when the phenomenon is related not to interspecies number differences but to intraspecies number differences. In a several-layered forest seedling counts have comparability for species that, when mature, share in the superior arborescent stratum, as do seedling counts for species sharing some lower layer at maturity; but between the two groups there are not the same comparability and significance as to, for example, successional trends. Perhaps our real advice is that a student of vegetation should not bother to obtain density data as an arbitrary or standard procedure but should do so only when a clear need for such information has appeared.

Sometimes density data are given more meaning or are more easily interpreted when they are expressed as a relationship among the several species. The *relative density* of a species is the percentage the number of its individuals is of the total number of individuals of all species in the sample.

The reciprocal of density has been termed *mean area* by Kylin (266). Cottam and Curtis (137) have used the mean distance between trees for an estimation of density, hoping to avoid the more tedious laying-out of sample plots for the direct determination of density. Although sound in theory, the determination of mean distance proves to be complicated because of the different patterns of occurrence of individuals of different species which range on both sides of random distributions to over- and under-dispersed.

It should also be kept in mind that a species may have a high density at a certain time only, and consequently its significance in the community as a whole may be overemphasized if density is determined only for one point in time. It follows that density should be related to seasons and aspects, to vitality, etc., if it is to be understood and to form a useful datum. For example, a relatively high density of tree seedlings may be observed one year, as in the case of *Fagus grandifolia* in northern Michigan, and in the same woods the following year the density may be very low. In rain forest near Rio de Janeiro a high density of seedlings of *Piptadenia communis* might be observed one month and scarcely any be seen at another season of the same year. A well-known example is the desert annuals (therophytes) which occur in numbers only after suitable rainfall. The same phenomenon, of course, is important among animals also. First instar mosquito larvae may be very numerous at a certain time. Under one set of conditions a large majority would reach maturity and under other conditions a very small number might reach maturity. All such considerations affect the meaning of density data if, as often is the case, density determination in a community is made only once.

Sometimes data on numbers are worked into a scale involving other quantitative aspects of community structure. A good example is the abundance-vigor-coverage scale of Domin (166), as modified by Dahl (Evans and Dahl, 191).

+	Occurring as a single individual with reduced vigor; no measurable cover
1	Occurring as one or two individuals with normal vigor; no measurable cover
2	Occurring as several individuals; no measurable cover
3	Occurring as numerous individuals but with cover less than 4% of total area
4	Cover up to 1/10 (4 to 10%) of total area
5	Cover about 1/5 (11 to 25%) of total area
6	Cover 1/4 to 1/3 (26 to 33%) of total area
7	Cover 1/3 to 1/2 (34 to 50%) of total area
8	Cover 1/2 to 3/4 (51 to 75%) of total area
9	Cover 3/4 to 9/10 (76 to 90%) of total area
10	Cover 9/10 to complete (91 to 100%)

The various grades are estimated, not measured. The first four classes concern abundance and vigor when cover is negligible. The seven higher classes are concerned strictly with coverage. Note that these classes are of unequal value; from Class 3 to Class 10, respectively, the class ranges are 7, 15, 8, 17, 25, 15, and 10%. The rationale of such a system is not readily apparent. The problem will be returned to in our discussion of coverage (dominance) elsewhere in the *Manual*.

It must be emphasized that the use of frequency symbols or estimates of number is widespread and commonly thought to be elementary and easy, whereas the technique actually is difficult and treacherous. Whether or not the symbols are words such as "rare," "occasional," or "common," or class numbers, difficulties arise for a number of reasons. Differences among investigators, or in the evaluations of one investigator at different times or in different kinds of vegetation, arise both from personal factors and from the characteristics of plants. Hope-Simpson (240) and Smith (369) both studied the importance of the personal factor and found that assigned values vary widely among workers and for the same investigator at different times. Results cannot be compared with confidence unless strenuous measures have been taken to train oneself or a cooperating group.

In the main it appears that investigators are endeavoring to express relative numbers of the different species, unless the scale of symbols quite frankly is described as multiple-based; yet several characteristics of plants seem to influence the personal factor. In addition to density, coverage, or the total area or volume occupied, they include differences in life form of the component species of the vegetation being studied, differences in ontogenetic stage of the species involved, and differences in pattern of occurrence. Most estimators tend to overestimate species in flower or conspicuous fruit, broad-leaf over small- or grass-leaf plants, and gregarious in relation to highly dispersed species.

The method of describing communities by attaching "frequency symbols" to the species of complete lists has long been used by ecologists and undoubtedly will continue to be used because of its speed. This leads especially to its use when extensive surveys are attempted in a comparatively short time. It is not our intention to discourage its proper use, but rather to encourage realization of the many factors contributing to the assignment of values to the species and, consequently, the consistent employment of efforts toward consistency on the part of an individual worker or a group of co-workers. Under the most favorable circumstances, the derived data have only relative validity; furthermore, they seldom concern number alone.

Chapter 7

THE PROBLEM OF PATTERN: FREQUENCY

FREQUENCY is concerned with the uniformity or regularity with which plants of a species are distributed throughout a community; i.e., it has to do with homogeneity and is expressed as the proportion of the units of a sample that contains a given species. A species has merely to be represented in the sample unit in order to enter into the computation of frequency percentage. Many plants in a quadrat carry no more weight than a single one. The number of frequency classes is actually as great as the number of units in the sample. Because less than 10 units are seldom employed, the number often being at least 25 and sometimes as many as 100, it is common practice to group the frequency percentages of the various species into a limited number of equal classes, usually five, as follows:

Frequency Class 1: Up to 20% of the sample units have the species represented
Frequency Class 2: Species of 21 to 40% frequency
Frequency Class 3: Species of 41 to 60% frequency
Frequency Class 4: Species of 61 to 80% frequency
Frequency Class 5: Species of 81 to 100% frequency

Raunkiaer (332, 335, 336, 337) was the first to analyze communities by treating statistically the occurrence and absence of species in a series of small sample units, the results of which he termed "frequency." It should be noted that the term as applied to a species is used in the mathematical sense of the ratio of the number of actual occurrences of an event to the number of possible occurrences (in the same time); but when all the species of a community are grouped into frequency classes, as above, the term is used in the statistical sense of the ratio of the number of species taken as individuals falling within a single class to the total number of classified or classifiable kinds of plants (species). From the above it is clear that frequency in the Raunkiaerian sense, which has become widely employed all over the world, is not a simple concept of number. As Brown (65) has pointed out, frequency and density are linked, but the relationship is not between density and occurrence of a species in quadrats, but between density and absence. Species of high frequency in a community are not necessarily also of relatively high density or coverage, although they may be.

Greig-Smith (221) makes clear the roles of density and pattern of occurrence in the resultant frequency data when sample plots are employed within a stand. In a square 5 m. on a side, 25 plants may be equally spaced, one in the center of each square meter. If each square meter is taken as a subsample, the frequency is $\frac{25}{25}$ or 100 percent. If, however, the 25 individuals of the species happen to be clumped so that they fall within a single square meter, only $\frac{1}{25}$ of the subsamples will contain it and the frequency will be 4 percent. If instead of these extreme cases the individuals were scattered but still 25 in number, they might be encountered in seven of the square-meter subsamples and the species would have a frequency of 35 percent. In each of these cases the density is the same, the area sampled is the same, and the size and number of the subsamples are the same, but the frequency varies from 4 to 100 percent.

In determining frequency the first question to arise is what constitutes occurrence of a species within the sample unit. Raunkiaer included as occurring in a quadrat any plant with a perennating bud within the area, whether or not the plant was rooted within the area. Most American workers require the plant to be rooted within the sample unit. A rooted tiller of a sod-forming grass, or a rooted stolon of a chamaephytic herb or shrub, for example, is counted even though the central and original locus of the plant is outside the area.

There seems to be a conflict of different concepts here. In one case we are interested in counting individuals or in the representation of different kinds of species. The unit is the independent rooted plant, whether it originated from seed or vegetatively. We need to study the entire clone to see which is isolated and which is linked with the mother plant. The second case concerns the ecological role of the individual or of each kind of species. Here we need to know the spatial relations of each, from roots to branching and foliage. In the first case when the unit area becomes smaller and smaller, frequency tends to approach density. In the other case frequency tends to be greater as the size of the plant increases as a consequence of the increasing number of unities of area in which some part of the individual is present. The choice of buds alone as a criterion of occurrence in a sample unit is biased to the ecological role. In frequency determinations the choice of rooted "buds" seems better whether what is counted is an individual or a potentially independent unit. If interest is in the ecological role of the species, it would seem that transects and line intercepts are more appropriate than quadrats.

Because of the obvious species-area relationship, all investigators have realized that the size of the sample unit influences the probability of a given species' being present in the unit; therefore the frequency of a species is not a function solely of its density and pattern of occurrence in a community, but of these and the size of the sample unit taken together. This being true, the only frequencies that are directly comparable are those that have been determined by using equal-sized sample units. (See below.) It is equally obvious that the size of the sample unit not only affects frequencies, and in turn frequency size classes, but for practical reasons must be adjusted to the vegetation being studied. A sampling unit of a size appropriate for trees would be unnecessarily large for shrubs and herbs, and of completely unmanageable magniture for a ground layer composed of bryophytes, lichens, and algae. Although the logic of this situation is apparent, some methods of vegetation analysis nevertheless depend upon a single large sample area for determining the characteristics of all the members of all the synusiae of a phytocoenosis. In this case, however, the recorded data are usually limited to sociability and coverage. Although different investigators have used sample plots of different sizes for roughly the same kind of vegetation or similar synusiae, most of them have been consistent within their own surveys. Feeling a need for some reduction in the variety of sizes of quadrats being employed, Cain (81) suggested the following:

1. For the soil layer, small cryptogamic synusiae, etc.: 0.01 or 0.1 sq. m., depending on the complexity of the synusia.
2. For herbaceous layers: 1.0 or 2.0 sq. m.
3. For rank herbs and low shrubs: 4.0 sq. m.
4. For tall shrubs and low trees: 16.0 sq. m.
5. For the superior arborescent synusia of tall trees: 100.0 sq. m.

This recommendation was for the multiple-plot method, of course. These metric areas are related to the acre system of measurement. The

4.0 sq. m. plot is approximately a milacre (6.6 × 6.6 ft.). The 100 sq. m. plot is about $\frac{1}{40}$ acre (25 milacres) and 0.5 chain (33 ft.) square.

In connection with the above suggestion it is obvious that ten times as many 0.01 quadrats as 0.1 quadrats, or twice as many 1.0 quadrats as 2.0 quadrats, will produce total samples of the same area. It does not follow, however, that the results will thereby by comparable. The larger number of smaller quadrats, when both types are scattered through a community, would tend to yield a larger number of species; yet this does not mean that individual or average frequencies would be greater.

As great as are the advantages in using a limited number of stand-ard-sized quadrats, there are other advantages in the objective deter-mination of the most appropriate size for sample units for studying a particular community based on the characteristics of the community (richness, heterogeneity, structure) and the objectives of the study (quantitative or qualitative data, intensive or extensive study)

There have been several objective determinations of the influence of quadrat size on frequency data when the number of quadrats is con-stant (Hanson and Love, 229). Cain, Nelson, and McLean (102), studying a natural grassland on Long Island, New York, found that sets of 0.25 sq. m. quadrats yielded 26 species with an average fre-quency of 37.7 percent, and sets of 1.0 sq. m. quadrats yielded 29 species with an average frequency of 42.7 percent. In studying alpine fell-field vegetation in Wyoming, Cain (92) found that sets of 0.1, 0.25, 0.5, and 1.0 sq. m. quadrats yielded lists of 15, 16, 16, and 18 species, and average frequencies of 42.0, 45.6, 48.7, and 52.2 percent, respec-tively (Table 24). Evans and Cain (190), studying an old-field grass-land in Michigan, found that sets of quadrats of the following sizes— 0.01, 0.05, 0.1, 0.25, 0.5, 0.75, and 1.0—yielded lists of 11, 18, 22, 24, 27, 27, and 28 species, respectively. These examples show that there is not a direct relationship between sample-plot area and number of species sampled, individual frequencies, and average frequency when the number of plots is constant.

The common procedure when testing quadrat size for the purpose of selecting the most efficient size is to lay out the quadrats in "nested sets," each set containing one quadrat of each size, and to plot the re-sultant data in the form of a species-area curve. (Specific uses of the species-area relationship are discussed more fully in another section of the *Manual.*) Species-area curves, following in general the "law of diminishing returns" curve, indicate the relative efficiency of sampling with quadrats of different sizes, and permit the selection of a size that yields sufficiently "accurate" data with the expenditure of as little work as possible.

TABLE 24.　Frequency percentages of species according to quadrat size, alpine fell-field vegetation, Class Lake region, Snowy Range, Wyoming (Cain, 92)

Species	10 quadrats each of:			
	0.1 sq. m.	0.25 sq. m.	0.5 sq. m.	1.0 sq. m.
Arenaria sajanensis	100	100	100	100
Selaginella densa	100	100	100	100
Trifolium dasyphyllum	80	100	100	100
Eritrichium argenteum	80	80	90	90
Sieversia turbinata	50	50	60	80
Polemonium`confertum	40	40	40	50
Phlox caespitosa	30	50	50	60
Sedum stenopetalum	30	50	50	60
Paronychia pulvinata	30	30	50	50
Silene acaulis	20	30	30	70
Potentilla nelsoniana	20	20	30	30
Potentilla quinquefolia	20	20	20	30
Potentilla sp.	10	20	30	30
Polygonum bistortoides	10	20	20	20
Artemisia scopulorum	10	10	20	20
Sieversia ciliata	. . .	10	20	30
Arenaria macrantha	. . .	. . .	. . .	10
Erigeron compositus	. . .	. . .	. . .	10
Total species sampled	15	16	16	18
Average frequency	42.0	45.6	48.7	52.2

Investigators who attempt an objective selection of sample-unit size also usually study the effects of quadrat number on resultant data. Here again the species-area relationship is employed in many studies, such as those cited above.

The effects of quadrat size and number on the basal-area data for trees of the *Piceetum rubentis* (red spruce forest type) and the *Abietum fraseri* (Fraser's fir forest type) of the Great Smoky Mountains, Tennessee, have been studied by Cain (85). In a well-developed virgin stand of *Piceetum* at 5100-ft. altitude and a typical pole stand of *Abietum* at 6300-ft. altitude, 10 sets of quadrats were taken of the following sizes: 25, 50, 75, 100, and 200 sq. m. each. In the *Piceetum,* in which the trees are very tall (30 to 40 m.), additional quadrats of 400 sq. m. were laid out. From these data it was found that the minimum quadrat size was 200 sq. m. for the *Piceetum* and 50 sq. m. for the *Abietum.* The next step was to take additional quadrats of these sizes and compare the results in terms of basal area of the trees sampled. Each time 10 plots were added the average basal area per plot was recomputed until 50 plots had been surveyed. The results for the *Abietum* are shown in Table 25. In this table S.D. is the standard deviation of the mean,

M.E. is the probable error of the mean, E% is the error percentage, and L% is the "limit of accuracy" selected as three times the probable error of the mean and expressed as a percentage of the mean. With this limit of accuracy the odds are about 20 to 1 that the true mean falls within those limits. The table shows that 20 plots are not a true sample of the 50 plots because the standard deviation is too low, but that the standard deviation is essentially constant for 30, 40, and 50 plots. These data can be interpreted to mean that 30 quadrats 50 sq. m. in size constitute a satisfactory sample of the trees of the asso- ciation, as determined by basal area, but that an increase from 30 to 50 plots reduces the limit of accuracy from 14.2 to 9.3 percent for the dominant species and from 13.7 to 8.8 percent for all species together.

In connection with studies of the cove hardwood forests of the Great Smoky Mountains, Cain (95) sampled the field layer (herbaceous synusia) in both the spring and summer aspects. Relatively low plants with a strong representation of geophytes characterize the vernal as- pect, and considerably ranker hemi-cryptophytes predominate in the aestival aspect of the same layer. For this reason, Cain adjusted the quadrat size to the stature of the vegetation. The vernal aspect was sampled at 10 stations by means of 10 quadrats each 1 sq. m., for a total of 100 quadrats. The aestival aspect was studied at 9 stations, each with 10 quadrats of 6 sq. m. area. The combined frequencies— that is, the frequency indexes for all species at all stations—yielded 1309 frequency points for the study of the vernal aspect of the herb layer under cove hardwoods, for an average of 13.09 species per 1 sq.

TABLE 25. Influence of increasing numbers of minimum-area quadrats (50 sq. m.) on the probable accuracy of sampling in virgin *Abietum fraseri* at 6300-ft. elevation on Mt. LeConte, Great Smoky Mountains, Tennessee (Cain, 85)

Number of Plots	Abies fraseri					All species				
	Aver. B.A.	S.D.	M_E	E%	L%	Aver. B.A.	S.D.	M_E	E%	L%
10	3.74	.91	.19	5.2	15.2	4.32	.96	.20	4.7	13.9
20	3.34	.90	.14	4.1	12.6	3.75	1.01	.15	4.1	12.0
30	2.96	1.14	.14	4.8	14.2	3.34	1.21	.15	4.4	13.7
40	3.23	1.15	.12	3.8	11.1	3.56	1.17	.12	3.5	10.1
50	3.23	1.09	.10	3.2	9.3	3.76	1.17	.11	3.0	8.8

B.A. is basal area, the cross-section area in sq. ft. of trees measured at 4.5 ft. above the ground. S.D. is the standard deviation. M_E is the probable error of the mean. E% is the percentage the probable error of the mean is of the mean. L% is the limit of ac- curacy, selected as three times the M_E which gives odds of 20 to 1 that the true mean lies within the limits of accuracy thus defined.

m. quadrat. The combined frequencies for the aestival aspect yielded 1258 points, for an average of 13.88 species per 6 sq. m. quadrat. In other words the adjustment of quadrat size, for the sets of samples of the two aspects, to the stature of the vegetation resulted in closely comparable total frequency points for the two surveys, and closely comparable average number of species per quadrat. Both aspects of this synusia are rich in species and without true dominance by one or a few species. There were 72 species sampled in the vernal aspect and 75 species in the aestival aspect.

Another question in sampling for frequency data, besides quadrat size and number, concerns quadrat arrangement. Most investigators have employed some regularized system of quadrat positions, spaced either along a line running through the stand or in a rectangular pattern (Clements, 124, and many subsequent investigators), or, following Raunkiaer (337), they have used a haphazard arrangement often incorrectly referred to as random. A few researches, especially of more recent date, have used truly random locations. On the basis of work by Evans and Cain (190) we can illustrate frequency data obtained from regularized and random sets of quadrats of the same size and number laid in the same community or stand (Table 26). With the objectively determined quadrat size of 0.25 sq. m. and 20 plots,

TABLE 26.   Comparisons of frequency percentages of species from different sets of quadrats (0.25 sq. m.) in the grass-dominated old-field community on the Edwin S. George Reserve, Michigan (Evans and Cain, 190)

Species	Regularized Set 20 plots	Random Set #1 20 plots	Random Set #2 20 plots	Random Set #3 20 plots
Poa compressa	95	100	100	100
Aristida purpurascens	90	90	80	75
Rumex acetosella	100	95	100	90
Hedeoma pulegioides	55	80	75	65
Solidago nemoralis	75	70	65	70
Gnaphalium obtusifolium	50	40	30	50
Erigeron canadensis	25	35	35	50
Solidago rigida	20	30	30	15
Lespedeza capitata	10	5	10	5
Antennaria neglecta	25	25	20	15
Ambrosia artemisiifolia	5	10	15	20
Oxalin stricta	20	25	30	20
Potentilla arguta	. . .	. . .	. . .	5
Hieracium longipilum	20	15	25	20

TABLE 26—*(Continued)*

Species	Regularized Set 20 plots	Random Set #1 20 plots	Random Set #2 20 plots	Random Set #3 20 plots
Panicum oligosanthes v. scribnerianum	. . .	15	30	20
Poa pratensis	5	30	20	20
Tragopogon pratensis	. . .	5	. . .	15
Asclepias syriaca	5	. . .	15	5
Oenothera rhombipetala	. . .	. . .	5	5
Liatris aspera	10	10	15	10
Panicum meridionale	5	10	20	5
Lespedeza virginica	10	. . .	5	10
Lechea villosa	. . .	. . .	. . .	5
Carex pensylvanica	. . .	10	. . .	5
Potentilla argentea	. . .	. . .	. . .	5
Panicum sp.	35	30	30	10
Cyperus filiculmis	. . .	. . .	. . .	10
Antennaria fallax	10	10	5	5
Krigia virginica	5	5	. . .	10
Solanum sp.	. . .	. . .	5	. . .
Carex sp.	. . .	5	5	. . .
Anemone cylindrica	. . .	5	. . .	. . .
Desmodium illinoense	. . .	5	. . .	. . .
Prunus serotina (seedling)	. . .	5	. . .	. . .
Fragaria virginica	5	. . .	. . .	. . .
Blephilia hirsuta	5	. . .	. . .	. . .
Lactuca sp.	5	. . .	. . .	. . .
Number of species (total 37)	24	26	24	29
Average frequency percentage	28.7	29.4	32.1	25.5

The three random sets of quadrats averaged 26.3 species and 29 percent frequency.

in this grass-dominated old-field vegetation there is little to choose from between the two sets of results. The regularized set yielded 24 species, and the three random sets gave an average of 26.3 species; the results for average frequency were remarkably close: 28.7 for the regularized set and an average of 29.0 percent for the three random sets.

Bourdeau (52) has published a study of systematic, random unrestricted, and random stratified sampling that, like the work of Evans and Cain, is based on a known population. Bourdeau deals with density and basal area, rather than frequency, of all trees and of selected species on a plot divided into 144 quadrats, each 10 × 10 m. Precision and relative efficiencies of sampling were derived from variance and percentage standard errors. Bourdeau says that ecologists have a reluctance to substitute random sampling for systematic sampling because they feel that the latter is more precise and easier to apply in the field. He found that the overall average loss in efficiency for stratified random sampling was only 6.6 percent and that it is possible to design such a sample, as is sometimes done in timber cruising, that is not difficult to manage in the field. This being true, he recommends stratified random sampling because it is more precise than unrestricted random sampling, and the randomness permits measures of accuracy impossible with systematic samples. Quantitative data on the composition and structure of communities have much more value when their accuracy is known than when the methodology does not permit estimation of accuracy. He also reached the conclusion from this interesting study that low errors of estimate are possible for important members of a community but that common sampling methods provide only highly inaccurate estimates of secondary and scattered components. In this sense, importance would be measured by relatively high density, dominance (basal area), and, presumably, frequency. This judgment applies to common sampling methods covering 5 to 20 percent of the total area of forests, in comparison with stratified random sampling that is more efficient.

Another consideration in the problem of sampling for frequency data concerns sample plot shape. In a strict sense, the quadrat is a square sample unit. The term is applied loosely also to sample units that are circular or short rectangular, even as long as 0.1 × 1.0 m. In general, it is better to restrict the term quadrat to square units and use such expressions as sample plot or unit for nonsquare areas. In any case, in a given study, it is important to be consistent as to shape just as it is to size, unless there are strong reasons for variation, although it has not been demonstrated that minor differences in shape affect data significantly.

Frequency data are sometimes computed from segments of transects (very long rectangles) and even from segments of lines. These segments are then lineally contiguous subsamples. When the plants of a species are not randomly dispersed in a community, as is often and perhaps usually the case, there is evidence that long sample units (such as transects and line intercepts) produce results that are more nearly comparable for the different species of the community than do approximately isodiametric plots. Buell and Cantlon (70) have shown that the use of line-intercept samples introduces a bias in frequency data because of the overrepresentation of large-crowned species. Woodin and Lindsey (424), in connection with the line-strip method, say that the advantage of great length is that the results can be treated statistically as if the stand were assembled randomly even though this may not actually be so.

A number of investigators have been critical of certain common sampling practices of plant ecologists, such as the use of nested plots in species-area determinations and the nonrandom placing of sample units. Clapham (118), Ashby (19, 20), Pechanec and Stewart (312), and others have urged methods that yield to statistical treatment. Studies of size and shape of sample units, and also arrangements, have been made by several workers in agronomy and forestry—among them Kalamkar (251), Justesen (250), Hasel (231), etc.—as well as of natural vegetation. Clapham used statistical variance in a study of the most effective size and shape for plots, and a modification of this has been made recently by Bormann (51). The latter author reached the following conclusions: (1) Some form of rectangular plot should be used instead of the common isodiametric plot. (2) If the stand to be investigated shows any graduation in composition or structure, such as might occur on a slope because of soil-moisture gradients, the long axis of the rectangular plot should run with the gradient. (3) The units of the sample should be distributed at random. (4) The number of plots commonly used is too small; the actual number should be determined on the basis of the characteristics of the vegetation and the sampling precision required.

Bormann's application of variance in a study of sample-plot size and shape was made in a climax oak-hickory *(Quercus-Carya)* forest in North Carolina on trees greater than 1 in. d.b.h. He used derived data on basal area which he considers a quantitative expression of dominance. *Variance* is a measure of dispersion among observations that would be zero if all observations were identical, would have relatively small values if the observations were similar, and would have high values if the observations were discordant or greatly variable. For any set of data, as for plots of a given size and shape, the sum of the individual squared deviations from the mean value divided by the number of observations from which the deviations were obtained gives the variance (Schumacher and Chapman, 363). Bormann represents this as follows:

$$\frac{1}{n}S^n\,[(y - \bar{y})^2] \;=\; V(y)$$

where y represents the individual observed value on each plot; $\bar{y}$ represents the average value per plot; $S^n [(y - \bar{y})^2]$ represents the summation of all the individual deviations from the average squared; n represents the number of observations; and $V(y)$ represents the variance of each observation.

As an illustration of the method, Bormann uses a plot of 4 × 4 units with an average of three items per plot, but varying in the different units from zero to seven items. The total is treated as 16 plots of 1 sq. unit each; four plots of 2 × 2 unit dimension; eight plots of 1 × 2 unit dimension; four plots of 1 × 4 units; and two plots of 2 × 4 units. In each case of rectangular plots there are two sets, one with long axes at right angles to the other set. In order to compare the variances, the variance must be reduced to the 1-unit level by dividing the variance of the larger plots by the number of contained units. The results are as follows:

Unit dimension in one direction

		1	2	4
Unit dimension in the other direction	1	4.625	4.000	0.875
	2	4.125	1.865	0.125
	4	0.500	0.500	

The 16 single-unit plots have the greatest variance in this example, and the 2 × 4 and 1 × 4 unit rectangles have the smallest variances and would produce the most consistent sampling.

The above simple illustration of the method is concerned with too small a population. Hence Bormann applied the method to the forest on the basis of a plot 140 × 140 m., sampled by 4900 units that are 2 × 2 m., and various larger square and rectangular plots containing definite numbers of these units. The basal area data were treated in two groups: distribution 1 contained 82.5 percent of the total and represents the trees widely and evenly distributed over the area, and distribution 2 contained the sporadically distributed trees. His results showed that the variance per unit area decreases as the sample plots are increased in length, providing the long axis of the plot is laid across the contours, especially in distribution 2. It should be noted, however, that in long narrow plots there is a greater hazard of "edge errors" than in isodiametric plots, the edge increasing rapidly in proportion to area in progressively longer plots. Bormann goes on to point out that in using long plots (essentially transects) labor can be saved without loss of efficiency in sampling by the skip-unit method. For example, instead of a plot of 4 × 140 m., a line plot of 4 × 4 units alternating with 4 × 4 skips yields about the same accuracy, and the labor is cut nearly in half.

Although there is a relationship between frequency and density, that it is not directly proportional has been pointed out by several investigators, among them Kylin (266), Blackman (43), Ashby (19), Fisher (197), Cole (131), and Dice (162). The relationship is regular and can be deduced when species are distributed at random, but there are many species in nature that are not so distributed. In fact, Cole thought that random dispersal is rare in nature. In a case where the exact positions of plants of three species were known over a considerable area, Thomson (387) measured the departure from randomness. For a census of plants of *Daucus, Achillea,* and *Vernonia,* Dice (162) determined the Raunkiaerian frequency and the actual density of plants per unit sample. He also calculated the mean density per sample unit from the frequency index and found that the erroneous estimate of population by this method ranged from about two-thirds to less than one-tenth of the actual densities. This was a consequence of the clumping of the species in their distributions; i.e., they were hyperdispersed or more aggregated than would be the case in normal distributions.

RAUNKIAER'S LAW OF FREQUENCY

Raunkiaer (337 and earlier) grouped the frequencies of species in five equal classes which he referred to as Classes A-E, ranging from the smallest to the largest class. On the basis of 8087 frequencies obtained from various surveys, he established his "law of frequency" as:

$$A > B > C \gtreqless D < E$$

The size of the classes was as follows:

Frequency Class A:	(0 to 20%)	53% of all frequencies
Frequency Class B:	(21 to 40%)	14% of all frequencies
Frequency Class C:	(41 to 60%)	9% of all frequencies
Frequency Class D:	(61 to 80%)	8% of all frequencies
Frequency Class E:	(81 to 100%)	16% of all frequencies

Kenoyer (254), on the basis of 1425 frequency percentages available to him, reported the following class relationships for American vegetation: Class A, 69%; Class B, 12%; Class C, 6%; Class D, 4%; Class E, 9%. This was a general confirmation of the J-shaped frequency-class curve, with a high peak in Class A (formed by a large number of species of low frequencies) and a secondary peak in Class E (formed by species of high frequencies). The difference between the European results of Raunkiaer's studies and those of American studies —the larger size of Class A and the smaller size of Class E in American data—were attributed by Kenoyer to the greater richness in spe-

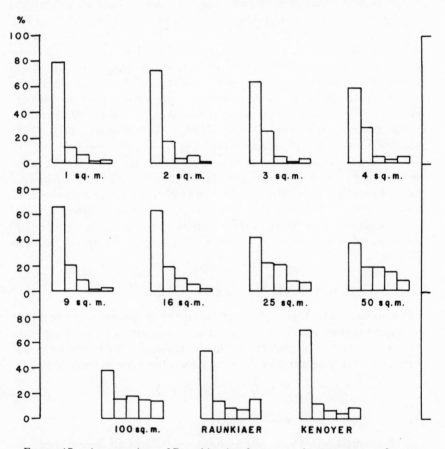

FIGURE 17.   A comparison of Raunkiaerian frequency-class percentages from surveys of the same vegetation based on sets of 25 quadrats each of nine sizes (Cain, 83), compared with Raunkiaer's and Kenoyer's "normals." Note the reduction of Class A and the increases in Class B and Class E as the subsample size is increased. In the experimental case no sample produces a frequency-class distribution close to Raunkiaer's "normal."

cies of the American flora in comparison with that of northern Europe. Another cause of the difference is to be found in the American practice of counting only plants rooted in the sample area as "present," whereas Raunkiaer counted any plant with a perennating bud in the space above the quadrat whether or not it was rooted in the sample plot.

It has always been apparent that the size of the sample plot affects frequency, whatever the biological situation may be, and consequently must affect the size of frequency classes. Data illustrating this point are available from many studies, but one study by Cain (83) on a stand of virgin hardwood forest in southern Indiana is more complete than most. Nine different quadrat sizes were used in samples of 25 quadrats for each size. Three of the smaller sizes were duplicated. From Table 27 and Figure 17 we can see that an increase in quadrat size decreases Class A and increases Class E. This occurs for the simple reason that the larger the sample unit, the more species it is likely to contain. This being the case, we must consider what, if any, legiti-

TABLE 27. A comparison of frequency-class percentages from samples of 25 quadrats each of nine different sizes, from a virgin hardwood forest in Indiana (Cain, 83)

Size of Sample Unit in Square Meters, and Survey Date		A 0-20%	B 21-40%	C 41-60%	D 61-80%	E 81-100%	No. of Species
1 sq. m.	(June)	78.6	10.7	9.1	1.6	0.0	56
	(August)	79.0	13.0	4.0	0.0	4.0	58
	Average	78.8	11.8	6.5	0.8	2.0	57
2 sq. m.	(June)	70.8	17.0	3.2	9.0	0.0	65
	(August)	74.0	17.0	3.0	3.0	3.0	69
	Average	72.8	17.0	3.1	6.0	1.5	67
3 sq. m.	(August)	64.0	25.0	5.0	2.0	4.0	72
4 sq. m.	(June)	57.3	30.6	2.6	5.3	4.2	75
	(August)	60.0	25.0	9.0	0.0	6.0	75
	Average	58.6	27.8	5.8	2.6	5.1	75
9 sq. m.	(July)	66.2	20.2	9.4	1.5	2.7	74
16 sq. m.	(July)	63.3	18.8	10.0	5.5	2.2	90
25 sq. m.	(June)	42.8	22.0	21.0	7.7	6.5	91
50 sq. m.	(June)	38.0	19.0	19.0	15.0	9.0	100
100 sq. m.	(June)	38.1	15.4	18.1	14.5	13.6	110[a]

[a] The largest sample (25 quadrats 10 × 10 m.) included 2.5 percent of the area of the woods, which contained a total of 132 species of flowering plants.

mate use can be made of frequency-class data. Opinion on this question is by no means uniform.

Gleason (213) wrote, "We may say that Raunkiaer's law is merely an expression of the fact that in any association there are more species with few individuals than with many, that the law is more apparent when quadrats are chosen of the most serviceable size to show frequency, and that it is obscured or lost if the quadrats are either too large or too small." Frequency is, of course, not dependent only upon numbers of individuals of a kind (and the unit by which they are sampled); it is also a function of dispersion. Numbers can be large and hyper-dispersed or clumped and the frequency will be low relative to another species with smaller abundance and hypo-dispersion or more regular than random arrangement. Oosting (303) says that "when Classes B, C, and D are relatively high, the stand is not homogeneous," but we notice in Table 27 and Figure 17 that the central classes can become about equal in size with the use of relatively larger quadrats, and the homogeneity of the stand, which is a biological property, has not been changed. Oosting's subsequent statement, "In general, the higher Class F may be, the greater the homogeneity," is probably biologically true unless inordinately large sample units are used. This conclusion had been reached earlier by Braun-Blanquet (58). Lüdi (277) and others have recommended the adjustment of quadrat size so that the results give a distribution of species frequencies through the classes that approaches the "normal" relationship described by Raunkiaer. In other words, when the sample is "rightly taken" so that the most "important species" are represented in Class E, the remainder of the species will be grouped appropriately. The correlation between frequency and density would be high if all species were randomly distributed, but the evidence is increasing that most species are not distributed at random but are more or less aggregated (Romell, 351; Cain and Evans, 98; etc.). McGinnies (287), working with random populations, concluded that larger quadrats give a better frequency differentiation of the less abundant species, whereas smaller quadrats give a better differentiation of the more abundant species. One would think that a quadrat size pragmatically adjusted on the basis of the species-area relationships in a given community would yield the J-shaped frequency-class pattern. Sometimes it does; sometimes it doesn't.

We are forced to the conclusion that a close fit of data to Raunkiaer's law of frequency is no real measure of adequacy of sampling, nor is it of itself an adequate measure of the homogeneity of a community.

RAUNKIAER'S LAW OF FREQUENCY AND THE GAUSSIAN CURVE

In connection with a study of the commonness and rarity of species, Preston (330) has made a most astute analysis of the law of frequency. He shows that random samples of certain taxons, such as moths caught by a light trap, and quadrat analyses of ecological assemblages "indicate that the universes from which they are drawn have, at least approximately, the form of an ordinary Gaussian [probability] curve drawn upon a logarithmic base (a 'lognormal' curve). The sample has the same general form as the universe, but is decapitated."

It is a common observation that in many ecological situations a few species are extraordinarily abundant (at a particular time and place) and that many other species seem rare in comparison. Since commonness is a relative matter and the range of numbers is great, there are practical and cogent reasons for plotting number of individuals per species (commonness) on a logarithmic base. A natural series of groups would run (approximate number of specimens observed of a species): Group A, 1; Group B, 2; Group C, 4; Group D, 8; Group E, 16; Group F, 32; Group G, 64; Group H, 128 . . . As Preston says, these groups of species are a sequence of *octaves* of frequency, an octave being an interval of 2 to 1. He denotes the interval 1 to 2 as Group A, the interval 8 to 16 as Group D, etc. Species represented by 9 to 15 specimens clearly fall in Group D and have roughly the same degree of commonness; species with 65 to 127 specimens fall into Group G and, despite the larger range of numbers, have the same commonness in comparison with each other octave. Species with numbers falling on an octave boundary are credited half to the octave on each side: for example, species with 16 specimens would be assigned half to Group D and half to Group E. Octave A is composed of half the species represented by singletons (1 specimen) and half those by doubletons (2 specimens); half the singletons have to be assigned to octaves below A.

Raunkiaer characteristically used 25 quadrats of equal size, and the only question was whether a species was present or absent in a quadrat. The species sampled were then assigned to frequency classes. Those occurring in from 1 to 5 quadrats out of a series of 25 quadrats compose Class A; those in 6 to 10 quadrats Class B, etc. Incidentally, Preston points out that the boundaries of the Raunkiaerian classes as usually given are incorrect for the following reason: a species cannot occur in $5\frac{1}{2}$ quadrats. If it occurs in 5 quadrats its percentage is 20, if in 6 quadrats it is 24 percent; therefore the boundary between Classes

A and B is 22 percent. For data derived from 25 quadrats, the classes should read:

Frequency Class A	2—22%
Frequency Class B	22—42%
Frequency Class C	42—62%
Frequency Class D	62—82%
Frequency Class E	82—100%

In order to find the boundaries of the classes more accurately, Preston calculates the probability (in percentage) that a species is not unrepresented and compares the results with perfect representation according to Poisson distribution, the octaves of the series mentioned, and the Raunkiaerian frequency classes. These data are given in Table 28 and Figure 18. The octaves to the left of Group A of the logarithmic series mentioned above are designated by Greek letters. The veil line is at the

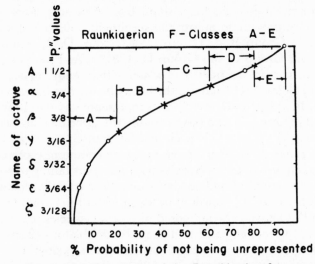

FIGURE 18. Boundaries of the Raunkiaerian frequency classes according to Preston (330), on the basis of probability in percentage that a species is not unrepresented.

left of Octave A at a representation of one specimen of a species. The veil line is present because the universe contains species so rare that the sample should theoretically contain only a fraction of a specimen, but a species cannot be represented by less than a whole specimen. Most such species are unrepresented in a sample, but some of them get sampled and are thus overrepresented. Other species that should be represented

TABLE 28. Relation of the frequency classes of Raunkiaer to the octaves of Preston in the commonness and rarity of species (Preston, 330)

Arbitrary name of octave	ζ	ϵ	δ	γ	β	α	A	B	C	etc.
Perfect representation p	$\frac{3}{125}$	$\frac{3}{64}$	$\frac{3}{32}$	$\frac{3}{16}$	$\frac{3}{8}$	$\frac{3}{4}$	$1\frac{1}{2}$	3	6	etc.
Probability that the species is not unrepresented (%)	2.4	4.6	8.9	17.0	31.3	52.7	77.7	95.0	99.8	etc.
Raunkiaer's frequency class	A	A	A	A	B	C	D	E	E	etc.

Veil line

by 1, 2, 3 . . . specimens may not occur in the sample and are under-represented. Species to the left of the veil line belong to different octaves just as those to the right do. On the above basis Preston defines the Raunkiaerian frequency classes (for a sample of 25 quadrats) as:

Less than Class A (missing species): All octaves to the left of ζ
Frequency Class A: $\zeta \, \epsilon \, \delta$ and about 90% of γ
Frequency Class B: β and about 10% of γ
Frequency Class C: about 85% of α
Frequency Class D: about 15% of α and 70% of Octave A
Frequency Class E: about 30% of A and all octaves to the right of A

What is directly measured by the Raunkiaerian technique is not commonness, but ubiquity; and although there is a reasonable assumption that a ubiquitous species is more common than a more local one, there is no necessary connection, as Preston and others have pointed out. Yet on the average there will be a definite relationship between ubiquity and commonness. If a species occurs in 10 out of 25 sample units, it has a frequency of 40 percent and there is a probability of 0.40 that it will be represented in any quadrat chosen at random. There may be some species in the community to which the Poisson distribution laws do not apply, but as Preston says, "Experience shows that normally such species, in a Raunkiaer test, are few or absent, and that therefore we can apply the Poisson distribution series with a sufficiently high degree of accuracy to all species."

Preston shows that the distribution of species in the Gaussian universe, arbitrarily assuming the modal octave to contain 100 species, has the following values:

The modal octave	n equals 100 species
Plus or minus 1 octave	n equals 96.1 species
Plus or minus 2 octaves	n equals 85.2 species
Plus or minus 3 octaves	n equals 69.8 species
Plus or minus 4 octaves	n equals 52.7 species
Plus or minus 5 octaves	n equals 36.8 species
Plus or minus 6 octaves	n equals 23.7 species
Plus or minus 7 octaves	n equals 14.1 species
Plus or minus 8 octaves	n equals 7.7 species
Plus or minus 9 octaves	n equals 3.9 species
Plus or minus 10 octaves	n equals 1.8 species
Plus or minus 11 octaves	n equals 0.8 species
Plus or minus 12 octaves	n equals 0.3 species

These are the ordinates of a Gaussian curve based on the assumption that the modal octave contains 100 species (total number 674.2 species) with an *a* value of 0.20 that has been shown to be typical for moths and birds. With the veil line between octaves +3 and +4, the Raunkiaerian frequency classes are found to contain the following numbers of species:

Class A	368.0 species	[85.2 + 96.1 + 100.0 + (0.9)(96.1)]
Class B	94.8 species	[(0.1)(96.1) + 85.2]
Class C	59.3 species	[(0.85)(69.8)]
Class D	47.3 species	[(0.15)(69.8)] + [(0.70)(52.7)]
Class E	104.9 species	[(0.30)(52.7) + 89.1 and all to the right]
Total	674.2 species	

As Raunkierian results are expressed in terms of the sample itself, in the above illustration the distribution of the species among the frequency classes can be expressed as class percentages of the total. When this is done and the results are compared with empirical results, there is such a remarkable similarity (Table 29) that it seems correct to say that the universe is Gaussian and that Preston placed the veil line properly.

TABLE 29. A comparison of experimental determination of the Raunkiaerian frequency-class sizes and Preston's theoretical values (330) based on the assumption of the logarithmically Gaussian form of the sampled universe

Raunkiaer's Frequency Classes	Raunkiaer's Experimental Values	Preston's Theoretical Values
A	53.0%	54.6%
B	14.0%	14.1%
C	9.0%	8.8%
D	8.0%	7.0%
E	16.0%	15.6%

If the veil line is placed somewhere else (in Preston's theoretical work), it would be equivalent to choosing larger or smaller quadrats. The frequencies of species and the frequency classes would change, as nearly all ecologists have recognized, but they would change in a manner appropriate to that which is inevitable if the universe is Gaussian (i.e., a probability distribution).

Preston's work removes the perplexities felt by Gleason (213), Romell (351), and others who have commented on Raunkiaer's law of frequency. Preston says that Gleason's statement: "Raunkiaer's Law is merely the expression of the fact that in any association there are more species with few individuals than with many; that the law is most apparent when quadrats are chosen of the most serviceable size to show frequency, and that it is obscured or lost if the quadrats are either too large or too small," should read: "In any *association* there are just as many very rare species as there are very common ones, but species of moderate abundance are vastly more numerous than either. In a *small sample,* however, there will be more species with few individuals than with many, because those with many are the excessively common ones, and these species are few."

Preston next shows that despite the conclusion of Romell (351) and others that statistics obtained from quadrats of one size cannot be compared with those obtained from another size of sample unit, it is possible, and he presents a chart (Figure 19) permitting this transition.

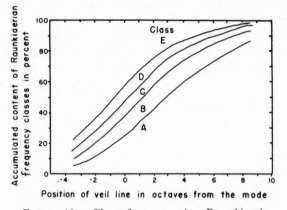

FIGURE 19.   Chart for comparing Raunkiaerian frequency-class data obtained by surveys using different sizes of quadrats, according to Preston (330). See text for explanation of the use of the chart.

In Figure 19 the vertical intercept between any two lines (including the base and top of the diagram) represents the percentage of species falling into the group with these boundaries. To use this chart, Preston says, "Take any experimental Raunkiaer grouping, and, on the edge of a piece of paper of this same height, mark off the accumulated percentages, in sequence, A, B, C, D, and E. Move this strip of paper, with its ends in register with the base and ceiling lines, from left to right till the best fit is obtained with the sigmoid lines. We have then located our sample with respect to its 'universe': i.e., we have located our veil line." The experimental conclusions as to the law of frequency

$$A > B > C \gtreqless D < E$$

are immediately deducible from Preston's chart. Classes A and E always together exceed Classes B, C, and D combined; Classes C and D are usually comparable; Class B is usually larger than C or D; Class A is usually *much* greater than B; Class E is greater than D. The reason that many experimental results show Class E only slightly larger than D is that the samples are usually very small.

The conclusion is that many biological universes, not only taxonomic ones but also assemblages in communities, have the logarithmic Gaussian form with a coefficient a not far from 0.20.

RELATIONSHIP BETWEEN SPECIES AND AREA

At several points in the *Manual,* in discussing various quantitative analytic and synthetic characteristics of communities, we have mentioned the species-area relationship, i.e., that the number of species increases with increases in area. The nature of this relationship, however, must be examined more closely, for (1) a particular species-area relationship *is* a characteristic of a community, and (2) the relationship can be used in various ways to assist in developing a plan for sampling a community when its stands are too large to be considered as a whole.

Early studies of the species-area relationship were all European. Jaccard (247, 248) gave it the first scientific treatment; others who have produced interesting demonstrations, explanations, and criticisms include Palmgren (307), Brenner (61), DuRietz (172), Ilvessalo (246), Romell (350, 351), Kylin (266), etc. *Species-area curves* are produced when area is plotted on the x axis, and species number, percentage of total species, etc., are plotted on the y axis (Figure 20). Such curves all have a similar form—rising rapidly at first, the curve more or less gradually seeming to approach asymptote with the x axis. Romell was the first to show (on the basis of Palmgren's empirical data that species-area curves correspond closely with theoretical curves based on the laws of chance. Romell's curves were made by plotting the number of species on any given area as a percentage of the total species on the largest area sampled or the total area of the stand. In this manner of plotting the species-area curve, the form of the curve results from the area and the spacing of the species. When the manner of plotting involves actual number of species against area, the form of the curve not only results from area and spacing, but is also

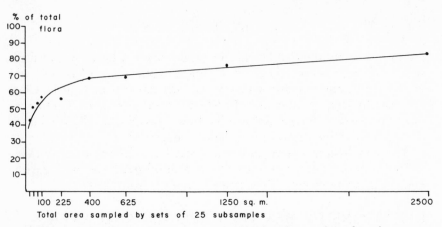

FIGURE 20.   Species-area curve formed by plotting the number of species on any given area as a percentage of the total species on the largest area sampled (Cain, 83).

conditioned by the floristic richness of the community. As Braun-Blanquet (58) points out, curves formed in the latter way have more phytosociological significance. This is shown by Figure 21 from Braun-Blanquet, in which the higher curve for *Festucetum* is due to the greater richness in species of that community than the *Curvuletum*.

The early work with species-area curves was based on data obtained in two ways: (1) for communities occurring as relatively small patches, whole stands were used; (2) for communities typically of larger stand

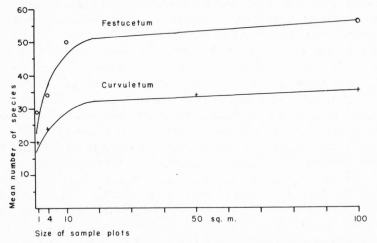

FIGURE 21.   Species-area curves for two communities. The richness in species of a community influences the form of the curve. (Redrawn from Braun-Blanquet, 58.)

area, various-sized single plots within a stand were used to provide the species lists. In the first method a stand is examined for its species composition (due care being taken to eliminate border effect or ecotone) and its area is measured or, when very irregular, estimated. The numbers of species on the lists derived from stands of different areas are then plotted against area to produce the species-area curve. In the second method a species list is made for a relatively small plot. The plot is then enlarged (commonly doubled in size) and the additional species noted. This process is continued until larger areas add either no new species or only an insignificant number of new species. This system produces nested plots; i.e., each succeeding larger plot contains all the previous smaller ones.

An important concept to come out of studies of the species-area relationship is that of minimal area. The association is a plant community of definite floristic composition (Flahault and Schröter, 198), with the characters common to the individuals of the association. These characters are the sociologically important ones of analytic nature (such as abundance, coverage, frequency), of synthetic nature (presence, constancy), and of differential importance among community types (fidelity). Which particular characters are given most emphasis in the recognition and classification of communities depends upon the philosophy or system of the investigator—for some, constant-dominants are the most important species; for others, the species of high fidelity. In any case, each kind of community has its own "characteristic combination of species," that is, a characteristic composition and structure. *Minimal area* is the smallest area that provides sufficient space or combination of habitat conditions for a particular stand of a community type to develop its essential combination of species or its characteristic composition and structure. This concept is important, for it permits the recognition of what Braun-Blanquet called "fragmentary associations," or stands which exist in nature in abundance because of lack of space, unfavorable habitat, biotic disturbance, interference by man, etc. Minimal area of a community type is suggested by the form of the species-area curve as the area corresponding to the point on the curve where it flattens strongly, or approaches asymptote. If it were a simple mechanical matter, if the number of species were the only criterion, that would be the end of the matter; but the investigator must still bear in mind whether the area of that size is truly the minimal area and he must see not only whether the area supports the required floristic composition but also whether it has the required structure.

The European use of the species-area relationship has been twofold:

(1) to assist in the determination of fragmentary stands that are not to be included in sociological tables, and (2) to determine the size of sample plot to employ when each stand of a community type is sampled by a single plot. Two additional uses of the species-area curve in community statistics are, so far as we know, a contribution of American plant sociologists—Hanson and Love (229), Cain (81 and later), Pen found and Watkins (314), etc. These uses are (1) to assist in selecting an appropriate quadrat size when numerous quadrats taken in a single stand are to constitute a sample; and (2) to assist in determining the smallest number of such quadrats that will yield satisfactory data. If we reserve the term minimal area for the original concept, as related to communities, we can apply the terms minimum quadrat area and minimum quadrat number for matters relating to sampling technique.

Minimal area (single-plot method) in secondary grassland in southern Michigan is illustrated by data from Evans and Cain (190) in Table 30 and Figure 22. These data are unusual in that they carry the objective determination of the relationship from a small plot of 0.25 sq. dm. to a large one of 204,800 sq. dm. In the figure, Curve A is a plotting of the species-area relationship up to 32 sq. dm.; Curve B, up to 32 sq. m.; and Curve C up to the total flora sampled by the largest quadrat, 2048 sq. m. In each case the ratio of x to y axis length is 2 to 1. If examination of progressively larger quadrats had been stopped at the 32 sq. dm. size, visual inspection of the species-area curve would have suggested about 16 sq. dm. as the minimal area for this community (Curve A). With continuation of sampling to 100 times the former area, visual inspection of Curve B suggests a minimal area of about 16 sq. m. Finally, using the total area in Curve C, which is 6400 times the total area in Curve A, visual inspection suggests yet another minimal area, perhaps somewhere around 128 sq. m. Obviously more is going on here than "meets the eye." *The curve is parabolic and never becomes asymptote with the x axis.*

Cain (88) noticed that different investigators used x-y ratios ranging from 1 : 1 to about 5 : 1 in plotting species-area data, and that the ratio affected the visual interpretation of the relationship, especially the selection of minimal area, minimum quadrat size, etc. Field experience has shown that the species sampled by areas forming the steep initial rise of the curve are the most important ones in the community when importance is determined separately in terms of frequency, density, coverage, constancy, etc. The species of the gradually rising part of the curve are usually of lesser importance, and those of the more or less asymptote limb of the curve are usually of little significance. It

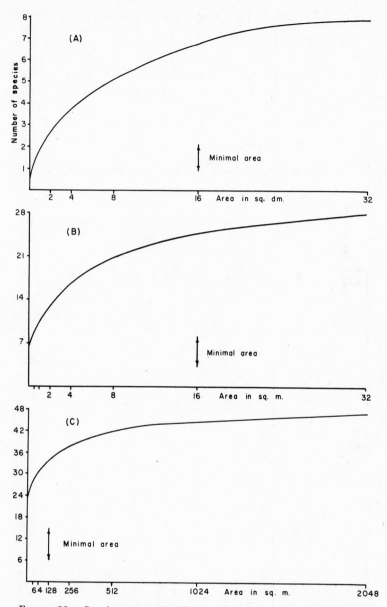

FIGURE 22.   Species-area curves from a geometric series of nested quadrats in secondary grassland in southern Michigan, the subplots ranging from
0.25 sq. dm. to 2048 sq. m. Curves A–C are plottings of data for three segments of the total analysis, in each case with a 2 : 1 ratio of plotting axes.
These curves suggest different minimal areas for the community depending
on the extensiveness of the survey. (Data from Evans and Cain, 190.)

TABLE 30. Occurrence of plant species in a series of nested quadrats in a secondary grassland community, southern Michigan (Evans and Cain, 190)

Species	Area in Square Decimeters																				
	0.25	0.50	1.0	2.0	4.0	8.0	16	32	64	100	200	400	800	1,600	3,200	6,400	12,800	25,600	51,200	102,400	204,800
Aristida purpurascens	x	x	x	x	x	x	x	x	x	x	x	x	x	x	x	x	x	x	x	x	x
Rumex acetosella	.	x	x	x	x	x	x	x	x	x	x	x	x	x	x	x	x	x	x	x	x
Cladonia verticillata	.	.	.	x	x	x	x	x	x	x	x	x	x	x	x	x	x	x	x	x	x
Cladonia cristatella	.	.	.	.	.	x	x	x	x	x	x	x	x	x	x	x	x	x	x	x	x
Poa pratensis	.	.	.	.	.	x	x	x	x	x	x	x	x	x	x	x	x	x	x	x	x
Poa compressa	.	.	.	.	.	.	x	x	x	x	x	x	x	x	x	x	x	x	x	x	x
Peltigera horizontalis	.	.	.	.	.	.	x	x	x	x	x	x	x	x	x	x	x	x	x	x	x
Cladonia cornuta	.	.	.	.	.	.	.	x	x	x	x	x	x	x	x	x	x	x	x	x	x
Oxalis stricta	.	.	.	.	.	.	.	.	x	x	x	x	x	x	x	x	x	x	x	x	x
Cladonia pyxidata	.	.	.	.	.	.	.	.	.	x	x	x	x	x	x	x	x	x	x	x	x
Antennaria fallax	.	.	.	.	.	.	.	.	.	x	x	x	x	x	x	x	x	x	x	x	x
Panicum meridionale	.	.	.	.	.	.	.	.	.	x	x	x	x	x	x	x	x	x	x	x	x
Gnaphalium obtusifolium	.	.	.	.	.	.	.	.	.	x	x	x	x	x	x	x	x	x	x	x	x
Ambrosia artemisiifolia	.	.	.	.	.	.	.	.	.	.	x	x	x	x	x	x	x	x	x	x	x
Aster sq. sterile	.	.	.	.	.	.	.	.	.	.	.	x	x	x	x	x	x	x	x	x	x
Solidago rigida	.	.	.	.	.	.	.	.	.	.	.	.	x	x	x	x	x	x	x	x	x
Liatris aspera	.	.	.	.	.	.	.	.	.	.	.	.	.	x	x	x	x	x	x	x	x
Antennaria neglecta	.	.	.	.	.	.	.	.	.	.	.	.	.	x	x	x	x	x	x	x	x
Polygonum tenue	.	.	.	.	.	.	.	.	.	.	.	.	x	x	x	x	x	x	x	x	x
Solidago nemoralis	.	.	.	.	.	.	.	.	.	.	.	.	.	x	x	x	x	x	x	x	x

	1	2	2	3	3	5	7	8	9	13	14	15	19	25	28	33	36	36	41	42	48
Polytrichum piliferum															x	x	x	x	x	x	x
Hieracium longipilum															x	x	x	x	x	x	x
Hieracium gronovii															x	x	x	x	x	x	x
Panicum oligodanthes															x	x	x	x	x	x	x
Hedeoma pulegioides														x	x	x	x	x	x	x	x
Lespedeza capitata																x	x	x	x	x	x
Ditrichum pallidum															x	x	x	x	x	x	x
Tragopogon pratensis																x	x	x	x	x	x
Cyperus filiculmis																x	x	x	x	x	x
Monarda fistulosa																x	x	x	x	x	x
Panicum depauperatum																x	x	x	x	x	x
Cladonia cariosa																x	x	x	x	x	x
Lactuca sp.																x	x	x	x	x	x
Polytrichum juniperinum																	x	x	x	x	x
Panicum sp.																	x	x	x	x	x
Oenothera biennis																	x	x	x	x	x
Crataegus crus-galli																		x	x	x	x
Prunus serotina																		x	x	x	x
Lechea villosa																		x	x	x	x
Lecidea sp.																		x	x	x	x
Asclepias syriaca																		x	x	x	x
Lespedeza virginica																		x		x	x
Setaria glauca																				x	x
Juniperus depressa																				x	x
Physalis heterophylla																					x
Potentilla argentea																					x
Crataegus sp.																				x	x
Cladonia alpestris																					x
Total species	1	2	2	3	3	5	7	8	9	13	14	15	19	25	28	33	36	36	41	42	48

is also true, but immaterial, that some species of little or no importance in the community may be sampled early (by the smaller areas) along with the more important species.

If the species-area relationship is to be a useful tool in plant sociology, one should be able to select, more accurately than has been the practice, some point on the curve which represents minimum adequate sampling or minimal area, as the case may be. Furthermore, the method of selecting this point should be mechanical, not visual, and equally applicable to any use of the curve. These considerations have given rise to the following proposal: to determine the point on the curve at which it has a certain percentile rise. For example, select arbitrarily the proposition to determine which point on the curve represents a rate of increase of 10 percent of the total number of species for an increase of 10 percent of the total sample area. This point can be found approximately by inspection, but it can be located easily and accurately by the following mechanical device. Place the edge of a triangle at the base of the chart so that its edge passes through zero (intersection of x and y) and through the point which represents 10 percent of the area and 10 percent of the species. A line parallel to this line (to the edge of the triangle) and tangent to the curve marks the point of the 1 : 1 ratio between rate of increase of species and rate of increase of area. If a ruler is placed along the right side of the triangle, which is placed as described above, the triangle can be slid up until its edge describes the tangent. Whatever the ratio of x to y axes, this method will indicate the same quadrat size. The investigator is free to select the ratio between rate of increase of species and rate of increase of area that he wishes to use.

In the multiple plot method, in which numerous sample units are employed in a single stand, the *minimum quadrat area* can be indicated by the species-area relationships, as illustrated in Figure 23. These data come from an old-field grassland in southern Michigan, dominated by *Aristida purpurascens* and *Poa compressa* (Evans, 188; Evans and Cain, 190; and Cain and Evans, 98). Sample units were of 0.05, 0.1, 0.25, 0.5, 0.75, and 1.0 sq. m. area and were used in sets of 20 each to make up the samples. One series of size-sets was arranged in a regularized pattern, and three series were random. The point of 1 : 1 ratio is indicated on the curve by the tangent line and arrow. This is the point in the species-area relationship where rate of sampling is equal to the rate of area increase. The quadrat size selected as minimum quadrat area is 0.25 sq. m. This is farther along the curve where the rate of area increase is about twice the rate of species in-

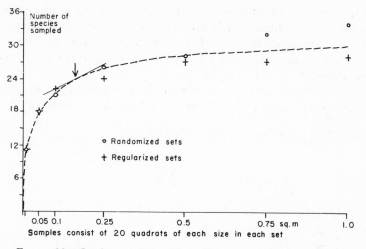

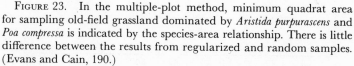

FIGURE 23.   In the multiple-plot method, minimum quadrat area for sampling old-field grassland dominated by *Aristida purpurascens* and *Poa compressa* is indicated by the species-area relationship. There is little difference between the results from regularized and random samples. (Evans and Cain, 190.)

crease. With this size of quadrat all the important species are being sampled rather regularly, with frequencies in Classes D and E.

The question of how many quadrats to use is handled in the same manner. The minimum quadrat area having been determined by the species-area relationship, a sample consisting of a series of such plots is taken and a new species-area curve is drawn. Figure 24 is taken from a study of a natural grassland on Long Island, New York, by Cain, Nelson, and McLean (102). The minimum quadrat area had been determined at 0.25 sq. m. Fifty such quadrats were analyzed. The shape of the curve of species plotted against number of quadrats indicates that 15 quadrats are adequate to sample this kind of vegetation. In order to provide a finer differentiation among the species with regard to their frequencies, 25 quadrats are adequate. This diagram reconfirms the point, for in addition to the curve plotted by using quadrats 1 to 50, points are shown for two series of 25 quadrats: numbers 1, 3, 5 . . . 49, and numbers 2, 4, 6 . . . 50 of the whole series. These points cluster around the curve and in no way suggest a minimum quadrat number larger than 15. Moreover, a comparison of species frequencies based on 50 quadrats with those based on 25 quadrats showed striking similarities in general. The only exceptions were a few highly gregarious species.

In the last few decades many investigators have been using the spe-cies-area relationships to help them plan their samples of vegetation for quantitative data because they indicate minimum area for single-plot samples and minimum quadrat area and number for multiple-plot samples.

It appears that the species-area relationships are similar for all com-munities, when drawn on arithmetic coordinates a sort of "law-of-

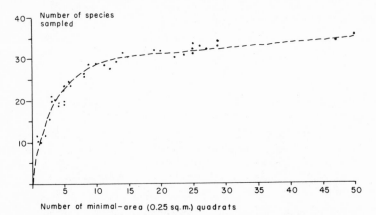

Number of minimal−area (0.25 sq.m.) quadrats

FIGURE 24.   In the multiple-plot method, when the minimal quadrat area has been determined, the species-area relationship can be used to suggest the minimum number of quadrats for an adequate sample. This figure, from Cain, Nelson, and McLean (102), shows the curve for 50 quadrats, and the dots which cluster about the curve for two sets of 25 quadrats. These data indicate that 25 quadrats are an ample number and that 15 would do, especially if several stands were to be examined.

diminishing-returns" curve results, but that the curves will differ according to the floristic richness of the communities and their relative homogeneity. But, communities can be compared as to this relation-ship more satisfactorily if the data are drawn on semi-log paper. Fig-ure 25 shows the same data as in Figure 22 for secondary grassland in southern Michigan. Although only three of the six cycles are repre-sented, apparently the species-area relationship plotted in this way results in a straight line. If this should prove to be true for communi-ties of all sorts, different ones could be compared directly in terms of the slope of the line. In this case it appears that the number of species added as area increases (extremely small areas being discounted) is about 11 per cycle, i.e., about 11 species sampled at 100 sq. dm., 22 at 1000 sq. dm., 33 at 10,000 sq. dm., and 44 at 100,000 sq. dm. If such a relationship were to continue to hold within this type of community, one would expect about 55 species on 1,000,000 sq. dm., 66 species on 10,000,000 sq. dm., etc.

The species-area relationship is a function not only of numbers of individuals in each local species population but also of their disper-

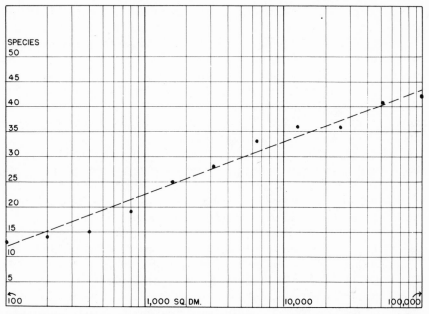

FIGURE 25. Three cycles of the same data as shown in Figure 22 plotted on semi-log paper. In such a graph the species-area relationship seems to be represented by a straight line. It is probable that this relationship is characteristic of the community here studied, and that other communities would have other characteristic relationships indicated by the slope of the lines.

sion. If we associate these results with those of Preston for populations, it seems likely that we are dealing with the same phenomenon. "In any association there are just as many very rare species as there are very common ones, but species of moderate abundance are vastly more numerous than either." From either sort of data, the species-population data of Preston or the species-area data discussed here, it is possible to estimate the total number of species within a stand of a given community type.

The Preston technique for estimating total number of species from species-population samples has been applied to tropical rain forest in the Amazon basin by Black, Dobzhansky, and Pavan (42); Pires,

Dobzhansky, and Black (320); and Cain *et al.* (103). In the last study the frequency of species of given densities on a 2-ha. plot indicated that the total flora of the vicinity of this plot and within the particular forest type is probably in the neighborhood of 200 species of trees with diameters of 10 cm. or more. The 2-ha. plot sampled about three-quarters of the tree species as defined here.

Returning again to the secondary grassland in southern Michigan discussed above, we find that an estimate of the total flora of the old field by projection from the species discovered on the nested sample plots falls far short of the known number of species. Referring to Figure 25, which shows about 44 species on 100,000 sq. dm., with about 11 species being added with each cycle, we see that there would be 55 species on 1,000,000 sq. dm. and 66 on 10,000,000 sq. dm. The field has an area of about 45,000 sq. m., so the projection suggests a flora of about 60 species, but the known number of species is 130!

The reason for the underestimation is that the data of Evans and Cain are derived from nested plots and the heterogeneity of the community was not adequately sampled. Evans and Dahl (191) later showed that there are several microassociations on the old field in addition to the *Aristida purpurascens-Poa compressa* community.

Evans, Clark, and Brand (192) made an estimation of the number of species present in this old-field grassland based on sets of randomly disposed quadrats. From the number of species sampled by eight different sets of 25 randomly located square-yard quadrats, an estimation of the number of species on the total area can be obtained by using the species-area relationship expressed by the formula proposed by Gleason (210):

$$S = \frac{s}{\log (n + 1)} \log (N + 1)$$

where S is an estimate of the number of species expected on an area consisting of N units, and s is the number of species encountered on n units selected at random. As Evans pointed out, the transformation using the logarithm of $n + 1$ causes the species-area line to pass through the intersection of the coordinates and thus permits a better estimate of S when this is based on relatively few samples.

The different sets of 25 quadrats sampled from 38 to 46 species and provided estimates of the total flora from 127.1 to 153.8 species. They also show the results of combining the 200 quadrats into sets of 50 and 100, and one set of 200. In the latter case the number of species sampled was 63 and the estimated number in the entire field was 129.5

—as the authors said, "an extraordinarily close fit to the known number of 130 species of vascular plants."

These two studies taken together serve to illustrate not the great discrepancy between the ability of the methods to estimate total flora but the necessity of using a sampling procedure appropriate to the ends desired and of not making a method serve an inappropriate function. The single-plot method breaks down immediately when any interpretation of the results from it is applied beyond the limits of the microassociation in which the single plot is located—in this case the portions of the old-field vegetation dominated by *Aristida* and *Poa*. The later study by Evans, Clark, and Brand, being based on numerous randomly disposed subplots, is able to encompass the heterogeneity in microassociations of the entire vegetation. The point is, of course, equally applicable to the estimations of Brazilian rain-forest tree species; these, however, were intended to be applied only to the local stand being studied, the limits of which were not known, and to have no meaning as soon as the type changed.

Chapter 8

THE PROBLEM OF DOMINANCE: COVERAGE

STUDENTS of vegetation have applied the term dominance to different phenomena. These differences are usually clear enough in context, so there is little to be gained by recommending the restriction of the term to a single meaning. In one sense dominance is the relative prevalence or predominance of individuals of a species that results from their numbers and massiveness. Each species of a community can be assigned some degree (percentage or class) of dominance according to the relative area or volume of the community that is occupied by it. Volume being extremely difficult to measure or even to estimate, the area of coverage of a species is generally the characteristic expressed in dominance. For vegetation this is usually done by measuring or estimating the area of coverage of the foliage of the species projected upon the ground. This is quite different from the actual, total foliage area and is best visualized as the area of ground that would be shaded if one imagined the sun directly overhead. Thus, because leaves overlap more or less and are seldom oriented horizontally, the coverage is usually considerably less than the total area of foliage.

Because there are usually as many different coverage values as there are species in a community, it is customary to group the species into a limited number of classes. Although these may be equal-value classes, they are often unequal. Three such systems of coverage classes are shown in Table 31. Plant sociologists commonly use the Braun-

TABLE 31. Comparison of the percentage values of three systems of coverage classes

Class	Braun-Blanquet	Hult-Sernander	Lagerberg-Raunkiaer
x	Less than 1%	. . .	. . .
1	1–5	Up to 6.25	Up to 10
2	6–25	6.5–12.5	11–30
3	26–50	13–25	31–50
4	51–75	26–50	51–100
5	76–100	51–100	. . .

Blanquet system, with an *x* class added for species that have a coverage value less than 1 percent.

In complex communities most investigators assign coverage class values to species separately for each stratum or synusia of the phytocoenosis. Thus species living in a single stratum will have a single value, but species of higher strata (except epiphytes) will have separate values for the layers in which they are transgressive as well as for the highest layer to which they attain. When handled in this way, coverage data can suggest much about community dynamics as well as present structure. In complex vegetation, such as humid temperate and tropical forests, the combined coverage of the several layers may exceed 100 percent and yet the ground may still receive some direct sunlight in spots. This occurs, of course, because the lower foliage exists in the partial shade of that above it.

Dominance is also used to express the phenomenon of actual predominance in a community of the individuals of a species. In this case the particular species is called the *dominant*. For example, in certain northern forests *Pinus banksiana* constitutes 80 to 100 percent of the tree layer, and in certain moor communities *Calluna vulgaris* may be the only species with a high degree of coverage. It is immediately apparent that we are confronted with two phenomena in this use of the term dominant. In most communities there are two or more synusiae and we can speak of the dominant of each layer. To return to the above examples, in the *Pinus banksiana* woods the low shrub layer might be dominated by *Vaccinium pennsylvanicum* and the ground layer by *Cladonia rangiferina*. In the *Calluna vulgaris* moor the moss layer may be dominated by *Sphagnum acutifolium*. In the other use referred to above, the term dominant has the sense of *community-dominant* which usually is the dominant of the superior stratum—*Pinus* and *Calluna* in the above examples.

Dominants in whatever layer are the species that have the largest total biomass (Odum, 301), but the dominant of the overstory differs from dominants of inferior layers, for it receives the full impact of the climate and reacts upon the climate and substratum as the most important modifier of them (Clements and Shelford, 130). We see, then, that in this sense the organisms that are the dominants are those that exert major control on the community. They do the most toward influencing the absence, presence, and success of other species, either through direct relations or indirectly in the formation of microhabitats. It is clear that some degree of physiological dominance or controlling influence is usually attributed to species which have high measured or estimated coverage. This means that they are dominant in both senses, that of physical coverage and that of influential role in the dynamism of the community ecology. This may be, but it may not be so, and mere determination of cover does not prove ecological dominance. A species of less coverage than another may yet play a more significant role in building and consolidating the community or, for that matter, in its ultimate disruption and succession by another community.

We have spoken thus far of single dominants, whether as synusial or community dominants, but it is probably more common for a small number of species to share in the dominance as *codominants*. Clarke (120) diagrams some of these relations (Figure 26). In the *Picea* forest

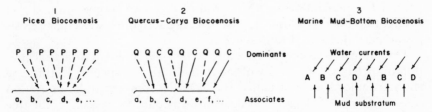

FIGURE 26.   In the spruce forest the sole dominant, *Picea*, influences the associated species of plants and animals, a, b, c. . . . In the oak-history forest codominants of the superior stratum, *Quercus* and *Carya*, influence the associated species, a, b, c. . . . The third diagram represents a marine mud-bottom situation in which elements of the environment directly influence the species. A, B, C. . . . (Clark, 120.)

there is a single community dominant. It is able to grow in great abundance because of its adaptation to the general conditions of climate and soil and, in turn, is primarily responsible for the conditions of light, heat, moisture, and air movement within the forest and for the physical and chemical conditions of the soil. The trees of *Picea* thus influence the associated species of plants and animals (a, b, c . . .). In the *Quercus-Carya* forest the same phenomenon occurs, but the control is by a small number of codominants which in this case might be

Quercus alba, Q. velutina, and *Carya glabra.* As Clarke points out, there is a second general situation in which the physical features of the environment directly exert major control over the principal species.

Further discussion of dominance will be facilitated by reference to the following outline of types of dominance and coverage:

I. Ecological (physiological) dominance
  A. In general ecology: Foliage coverage in each stratum
  B. In forestry
    1. Crown class
    2. Basal area
  C. In grassland studies: Basal area
II. Physiognomic dominance
  A. In open vegetation
  B. In closed vegetation
III. Family dominance

We have already pointed out that ecological dominance (I) in the various synusiae and community dominance in the principal layer are functions of the prevalence of one or a few species that are especially well adapted to the particular environments and hence have a superior competitive position in the community. There are, however, a few additional points to consider. The community dominants are commonly in the superior stratum of the phytocoenosis where the most control on the whole is exerted. These are the species that also have the ability to compete successfully in all strata of the community in stable vegetation, i.e., in various kinds of climax associations (Oosting, 303). But there are vegetation types in which the principal control is not in the superior stratum. In general, savanna vegetation is of this type (Beard, 35), for the real control is not in the scattered trees but in the grass-dominated field layer. A different kind of illustration is to be found in British woodlands that deteriorate because of water-logging of the soil by the action of *Sphagnum* (Tansley, 385). Another point is that there is a correlation between the number of dominants and the general favorableness of the environment. Communities (or synusiae) with single dominants tend, in any region, to be living on the less favorable sites, whereas communities with two or more dominants, or without dominants, tend to occupy the relatively more favorable sites. For example, although the flora of the state of Rio de Janeiro, Brazil, is a rich one, Magnanini (283), in his studies of the beach vegetation of Sernambetiba, had to deal with less than two dozen species of vascular plants and dominance was comparatively well marked. In studies of tropical rain forest Richards (344) said for different series of types

TABLE 32.   Variation in the composition of the *Dacryodes-Sloanea* rain-forest association with respect to dominance and floristic richness (Data from Richards, 344, after J. S. Beard)

Island	Percentage of Dacryodes excelsa	Number of Species per 10 Acres (4 Hectares)
Dominica	20	60
St. Lucia	11	41
St. Vincent	25	39
Grenada	40	23
St. Kitts	40	18

that "the degree of dominance of single species and the total number of species are related and vary inversely." This is illustrated in Table 32. In British Guiana he found both characteristics to be related to soil. At one end of a series of five forest types the forest has a single dominant and the soil is shallow and poorly aerated; at the other end of the series the soil is excessively porous and podsolized and the forest has a single dominant; and in the middle of the series, where soil conditions are most favorable and the flora richest, there is an absence of dominant species. In comparison with tropical and even temperate floras, high-latitude floras are relatively impoverished and single dominance is the rule in many communities living under comparatively submarginal conditions.

Although foresters sometimes use coverage as described above, estimating the foliage cover in the crown (canopy) and various layers of the forest, they more commonly use other approaches to the problem of dominance. Trees are classified in the woods as dominant, codominant, intermediate, and suppressed according to the position of the tree crown in the structure of the forest. Dominant trees, in this sense, are those whose crowns are definitely in the superior layer, irrespective of proportion of total cover. Codominants are simply those that share the superior canopy. Intermediate trees are transgressives whose crowns are partially overtopped. Suppressed trees are those whose crowns are definitely below the canopy. This sort of classification involves not only foliage or crown area, but also height and volume of crown and its relative exposure or shading. The forester is interested in crown classes because of their relation to growth rates.

In a classification of cover types of eastern United States, foresters (Hawley, 233) recognize 97 forest associations. In this work predominance is judged on the basis of the number of stems of the "dominant" species in the "dominant" and "codominant" crown classes. Foresters are usually interested in volume of wood or wood products, and all over the world they cruise (estimate and measure) certain tree characteristics in order to arrive at volume or piece statistics. Such work is very difficult in tropical rain forest, but it is being done currently in the Amazon under the auspices of the Food and Agriculture Organization (FAO). On the basis of 28 strips of 1 ha. each, Heinsdijk (237) found important species to have quite different patterns of occurrence; still it is feasible to cruise for individual species as well as for total volume of wood. One species averaged 21 cu. m. per ha., with a coefficient of variation of 43 percent; another species averaged 17 cu. m., with a coefficient of variation of 133 percent. Such measures are related to dominance, but the more direct manner of studying dominance in forest trees is to determine basal area.

Basal area is the cross-section area of trees, measured at 4.5 ft. above the ground, expressed in square feet per acre. The figure is easily arrived at from diameter breast high (d.b.h.). Basal area would be the area of stumps if all trees were cut down at a stump height of 4.5 ft. Although there are no careful data that we know of, there is general belief that there is a strong correlation between basal area and crown cover of the species of most forest types. Basal area provides a better measure of relative importance of tree species than simple stem counts because it incorporates size with number. An example of an interesting use of basal area is found in Korstian and Stickel's study (261) of *Castanea-Quercus* forest before and after the ravage of the chestnut, *Castanea dentata,* by the blight *Endothea parasitica* in eastern United States (Table 33). With the elimination of the chestnut, certain new

TABLE 33. Density and basal area in a *Castanea-Quercus* forest before and after ravages by the chestnut blight (Korstian and Stickel, 261)

Species	Density			Basal Area		
	1910–11	1924	Increase	1910–11	1924	Increase
Castanea dentata	153.3	0.0	. . .	64.18	0.0	. . .
Quercus rubra	22.0	38.0	72%	9.13	16.45	80%
Quercus montana	22.0	52.7	148%	5.25	14.48	176%
Quercus alba	9.4	9.4	0	1.97	2.07	5%
Quercus velutina	2.0	3.3		0.82	0.94	
Quercus coccinea	8.0	5.3		2.75	3.31	
Betula lenta	0.7	0.0		0.13	0.0	
Acer rubrum	0.0	0.7		0.0	0.82	
Fraxinus americana	0.0	6.7		0.0	0.32	
Carya sp.	0.0	6.0		0.0	0.29	
Acer saccharum	0.0	2.7		0.0	0.26	
Total	217.4	124.8		84.23	38.94	

species have been able to invade the forest *(Acer rubrum, Fraxinus americana, Carya* sp., and *Acer saccharum),* and two of the original species *(Quercus rubra* and *Q. montana)* have been able to take advantage of their opportunity by an increase in numbers and even more by an increase in growth rate, as shown by the higher percentage increase in basal area than in density.

TABLE 34.   Density by diameter classes and basal area of a *Fagus-Acer* climax forest in southern Michigan, sampled by 25 quadrats of 100 sq. m. (Cain, 86)

Species	Density by Diameter Classes, inches d.b.h.					Density Actual Relative		Basal Area	
	1–4	5–12	13–24	25–36	60	No.	%	Sq. ft.	%
Fagus grandifolia	50	16	29	2	...	97	38.3	70.5	50.7
Acer saccharum	77	1	2	2	...	82	32.4	16.7	12.0
Ulmus americana	3	...	1	1	1	6	2.4	27.4	19.7
Quercus rubra	...	2	1	1	...	4	1.6	7.5	5.4
Prunus serotina	3	3	...	...	...	6	2.4	1.7	1.2
Acer rubrum	2	1	...	2	...	5	2.0	14.0	10.0
Fraxinus americana	1	1	...	...	...	2	0.8	0.5	0.4
Tilia glabra	3	...	...	...	...	3	1.2	0.2	0.1
Carpinus caroliniana	25	...	...	...	...	25	9.9	0.5	0.4
Ostrya virginiana	23	...	...	...	...	23	9.1	0.5	0.4
Total in sample						253			
Total per acre						405		139.6 223	

Table 34 shows the results of a small sample of a climax *Fagus-Acer* forest in southwestern Michigan, with data for density by size classes and basal area (Cain, 86). Such data show well the differences between stem counts and basal area. Although *Fagus* and *Acer,* the dominants, are rather close in stem count, *Fagus* has more than four times the basal area of *Acer.* Although small in number, the large size of the trees of *Ulmus* and *Acer rubrum* brings up their proportion of basal area. There is no question that the dominant species are the ones that control the community, in this case especially *Fagus grandifolia.* The large number of small trees of *Acer* suggests that it is destined to increase in importance in the community, but this is not necessarily so, for the species happens to have a high mortality rate in the middle-sized classes in this area. The numerous small trees of *Carpinus* and *Ostrya* have no significance for the superior stratum of this forest, because their life form confines them to the inferior, small-tree layer.

In grassland research the term basal area has a completely different meaning than in forestry. Although total spread of foliage is the common basis for estimating coverage in herbaceous communities, for comparative studies of grasslands this has little meaning. With different degrees of utilization by grazing animals, with different weather conditions from season to season and year to year, and on different sites, the relative coverage of grass foliage is highly variable. As a consequence, in range research it has become common practice to estimate,

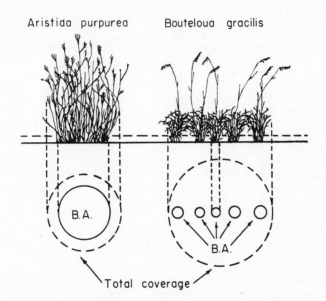

FIGURE 27. Differences between foliage cover and basal area of grasses. For the large compact clump of *Aristida* the difference is not great. When several small clumps occur, the difference may be considerable, as in the case of *Bouteloua*.

measure, and map grass clumps, on the basis of area at the height above the ground of normal utilization (Hanson and Love, 229). This is about 1 in. (2 to 3 cm.) above the ground, and the area at that height is called basal area. Changes that occur in basal area of a species, and differences in basal areas of different species, have much more meaning than total spread of foliage. The difference is illustrated in Figure 27, in which it can be seen that the basal area for a large, compact grass clump (such as *Aristida purpurea*) is not much different from total spread, but that when the mass is made up of several small clumps (as in *Bouteloua gracilis*) the total basal area is a relatively small part of the total foliage cover. Techniques of natural grassland and pasture analysis have been reviewed by Brown (65).

As well as on quadrats, coverage can also be determined from line transects. (See the discussion of the line-intercept method elsewhere in this *Manual.*) A good illustration of the measurement of basal area by means of line transects is given in the work of Anderson (15) on a tall-grass prairie in Kansas. He used 10-m. lines and measured the intercepts of the line to the nearest centimeter. As seen from the data in Table 35, only about $\frac{1}{10}$ of the line actually intercepted plants, but

TABLE 35. Basal coverage on a pasture near Manhattan, Kansas, based on measurements along 7 10-m. line transects (Data from Dice, 163, after Anderson, 15)

Species	Mean Length in cm. Along 7 x 1000-cm. Transects	Basal Area Index %
Andropogon furcatus	21.6	2.16
Bouteloua curtipendula	21.5	2.15
Buchloë dactyloides	19.5	1.95
Annual grasses	7.6	0.76
Sporobolus cryptandrus	7.5	0.75
Andropogon scoparius	6.8	0.68
Miscellaneous sedges	3.6	0.36
Miscellaneous perennial weeds	3.3	0.33
Chloris verticillata	3.1	0.31
Bouteloua gracilis	2.4	0.24
Miscellaneous annual weeds	2.2	0.22
Bouteloua hirsuta	1.8	0.18
Sorghastrum nutans	1.6	0.16
Additional perennial grasses	1.6	0.16
Sporobolus asper	1.2	0.12
Panicum virgatum	0.5	0.05
Poa pratensis	0.4	0.04
Sporobolus heterolepis	0.2	0.02
Total	106.3 cm.	10.63%

the technique gives good separation among the several species that are intercepted. Three species are seen to dominate the community: *Andropogon furcatus* (21.6 cm., or 2.16 percent), *Bouteloua curtipendula* (2.15 percent), and *Buchloë dactyloides* (1.95 percent).

Dice (163) uses what he calls a community coverage index that is actually based on a line transect. A rough approximation of the relative coverage in a region of different plant communities (when their areas are sufficiently large) can be obtained by noting mileage along a road through a region of interest (Dice 160). As shown in Table 36, considerable distances can be covered rapidly and the results tallied by 0.1-mile intercepts measured on the speedometer of an automobile. Dice recognizes the introduction of error by this method because where terrain is difficult the roads tend to avoid mountains, cliffs, lakes, swamps, bogs, rivers, etc., at least in a proportionate amount; and as a consequence communities of such situations are underrepresented in any measures derived.

In grazing studies, especially in the United States, the term "density" unfortunately is employed in the sense of coverage rather than of num-

TABLE 36. Community coverage based on line transects along roads. Original data in 0.1-mile units measured by automobile speedometer (Data from Dice, 160, 163)

Vegetation Type	Community Coverage Index	
	Canadian Province: 10–20 miles North of North Bay, Ontario 10 Miles	Hudsonian Province: Cochrane to Swastika, Ontario 94.7 Miles
Northern hardwoods-white pine: Acer saccharum Betula allegheniensis Pinus strobus	0.72	. . .
Black spruce bog: Picea mariana	0.22	0.49
Jack pine forest: Pinus banksiana	. . .	0.11
Aspen second-growth Populus tremuloides Populus spp.	. . .	0.26
Mixed types of forest	0.06	0.11
Clearings	. . .	0.03
Total	1.00	1.00

ber. For example, in the *Range Management Handbook* of the U.S. Soil Conservation Service (398) we find the following description of methods. Density of upright plants is based directly on the amount of ground covered, but for spreading weeds and grasses it is recommended that the shoots be raised or gently pressed together so that all the normal interstices between the leaves are completely filled and a 10/10 density (100 percent) is produced. The relative or actual amount of area with 10/10 coverage is then estimated for the whole stand. In passing through the stand the examiner mentally carries with him a "moving average" of plant density and composition. Such reconnaissance methods are extremely rough, but they permit the examination of large areas in a brief period; and if the examiners are experienced, valid comparisons of composition and condition can be made.

For more intensive work range examiners use the *square-foot density* method. In this method the investigator lays out random and repli- cated plots, each one of 100 sq. ft. in area (a circle of 5.64 ft. radius). On each plot the coverage of each species is expressed in square-foot units of 10/10 density In other words, 1 sq. ft. of ground completely covered by plants of a species is the unit of estimation. For example, if all the plants of a species were visually brought together and were found to occupy fully 1 sq. ft. of area, it would have a 1 percent cov- erage. The number of square feet of 10/10 density recorded for a given species on a given plot represents the total ground-cover percentage of that species. On the basis of the whole sample (the series of 100 sq. ft. plots), conclusions are drawn as to the grassland community as a whole. More exact methods of grassland analysis depend on small quadrats that are listed, counted, clipped, or charted, and on tran- sects, line intercepts, and point contacts. Other techniques are dis- cussed in the *Manual.*

In many communities there is no dominance by a single species or by a small number of codominant species. Allan (9) has pointed out that in many alpine communities and on rocks, fell-fields, and screes all species may have very low percentages of actual coverage. In such instances he speaks of *physiognomic dominance* (II in our outline) of the open communities by plants of certain life form that give the com- munity its characteristic appearance. Often in a desert the trees and shrubs that give the community its physiognomy are rather widely and evenly spaced. This is the case in the Sonoran desert of Arizona where the tree cactus, *Carnegie gigantea,* is in an open arrangement of low cov- erage. Another example is in certain cerrados of Minas Gerais, Brazil, where the trees may be widely spaced through the grass-dominated layer.

This type of physiognomic dominance may be deceptive and in- volve actual ecological dominance. It may be that the community is really closed, not above ground by shoot competition, but below ground, by root competition. In open desert communities the subter- ranean living space may be fully occupied, the plant roots in com- petition, and true ecological dominance expressed just as it is in communities with competing shoots. If this were not so, it would be difficult to explain the regular spacing of such plants as *Carnegie.* In other types of situations, such as an alpine fell-field (Cain, 92), al- though the total surface of the terrain may be very incompletely occupied by plants, all the living space for vascular plants may be occupied and actual competition and true dominance may take place. The open character of the plant cover in general is due to the small scattered pockets of soil that occur only among the boulders.

Another kind of physiognomic dominance has been described for visually closed communities. In his studies of certain brush communities of South Africa, Adamson (3) pointed out that in successional stages after fire and even to a certain extent in the climax no one species exerts strict dominance, but collectively several species, all of the same life form, dominate a community. He has termed this *life-form dominance,* and has emphasized that such species have a high degree of interchangeability within any particular community. This seems to mean that such species are essentially ecologically equivalent and no one species is able to become predominant with a high degree of coverage. This phenomenon also occurs in grasslands (Clements, 127), is common in tropical forests (Richards, 344), and can occur in one stratum but not another of various communities. Life-form dominance is more likely to occur in communities in regions of a rich flora, and in any region is more likely to be present on the most favorable sites than in regions of impoverished floras and on sites with extreme conditions where ordinary dominance tends to prevail.

Richards (344) has introduced the term *family dominance.* In the rain forest of the Mt. Dulit region that is typical of the primary forest of Malaya, the outstanding features of its floristic composition are the extremely large number of tree species and the small proportion of the stand formed by any one of them, according to Richards. He adds, "It is noteworthy that, though no single species formed more than a very small proportion of the whole stand, one family, the Dipterocarpaceae, forms at least 17% of trees 8 in. dia. and over at least 44% of those 16 in. and over. There is thus a 'family dominance' of the Dipterocarpaceae in the upper stories. . . . 'Family dominance' seems to be a rather common feature of tropical forests, both with and without single dominance species." It is also possible to speak of family dominance of the Meliaceae in some West African forests and of the Leguminosae in some South American rain forests. In the British Guiana wallaba forest the Leguminosae form 53 percent of the whole stand (Davis and Richards, 159). In some stands of the mixed rain forest of the Amazon there is a tendency toward family dominance without its being attained. At Castanhal, Pará, Pires, Dobzhansky, and Black (320) studied 3.5 ha. of terra firme forest and found 1482 trees of 179 species of 10 cm. dia. or over. The Leguminosae with 30 species composed 12 percent of the stand (174 trees); the Sapotaceae

with 25 species composed 18 percent of the stand (266 stems); and
the Lecythidaceae with only 5 species composed 18 percent of the
stand (273 stems).

Although we do not have the appropriate statistics, it appears that
the Lauraceae approach family dominance in the mountain rain forests, the Vochysiaceae in the cerrados, and the Leguminosae in the
semi-arid vegetation of Brazil.

In conclusion we would emphasize that dominance is one of the
most important analytic characteristics of communities. In many cases
it is unnecessary to determine number if coverage is estimated. Estimations of number and distribution (frequency) need to be supple-
mented by coverage data. Coverage can often be obtained simultaneously with other data.

Chapter 9

SIZE OF SAMPLE
UNITS

SOME DIFFICULTIES WITH THE QUADRAT METHOD

We have already dealt at some length with the necessity for sampling vegetation and have given examples of some sampling methods for analytic data. It has also become apparent that the quadrat, as a sample unit, has some shortcomings and imperfections. One must face not only the questions of what size, shape, and arrangement of quadrats are suitable for obtaining data concerning a given community, and what number of the selected sample units should be used, but also the question of what limits of accuracy are required in the investigation. These are partly matters of efficiency and economy. It may be a question of balancing one's resources, in money and time, between intensive local analysis, the results of which may have a relatively high degree of probable accuracy, against more extensive general studies of a type of vegetation or a regional vegetational complex. But there is the more important question of the validity of the data themselves. We can ask, for example, whether Raunkiaerian frequency data are meaningful. Under what conditions are they meaningful? Under what conditions are data on density, frequency, arrangement, etc., comparable for a species in different communities, for the different species in a community, etc.?

Since the early questioning of the quadrat method by Gleason (209), many investigators have concerned themselves with methodology. Some, like McGinnies (287), Penfound (313), and Curtis and McIntosh (146), have studied the problems of sampling artificially constructed

191

populations. Important studies have been made by Archibald (16) and Williams (419); and in these papers, especially that by Curtis and McIntosh, much of the literature has been reviewed. At this point, however, we wish to consider in some detail the important paper by Evans (188) on the influence of quadrat size on ecological data, because his studies were made against fully known natural local populations.

Cain and Evans (98) had prepared a map showing the location on 6864 sq. m. of all plants of *Lespedeza capitata, Liatris aspera,* and *Solidago rigida* in a portion of an old-field grassland in southern Michigan (Evans and Cain, 190), the numbers of which were, respectively, 696, 298, and 388. Within the mapped area the arrangement of individuals of these species and their densities were known, the latter being 0.1014 *Lespedeza,* 0.0434 *Liatris,* and 0.0565 *Solidago* per square meter. By means of a transparent overlay, the map was divided into 429 contiguous quadrats, each of which represented 16 sq. m. (4 × 4 m.). These quadrats were halved and their number doubled (858 quadrats of 8 sq. m. area). The process was repeated until there were 109,824 quadrats of 0.0625 sq. m. area. Each of the nine sample sets of necessity constituted a 100 percent sample of the populations under study. This being so, any effects of quadrat size on ecological data involve no sampling errors. It has been seen that these densities are relatively low, at least in comparison with the grass species that form the community dominants, and Thomson (387) has shown that their distributions depart radically from random patterns, but in both respects these species represent conditions commonly encountered in community studies.

With respect to density, it is seen that quadrat size does not influence density values. From Table 37 we see that the density per quadrat 1 sq. m. in area for *Lespedeza,* for example, is 0.1014 plant, and that the density per quadrat 2 sq. m. in area is double. In comparing the different

TABLE 37.   The relation of density (number of plants per quadrat examined) to quadrat size (Evans, 188)

Quadrat Size in sq. m.	Quadrat Number	Lespedeza	Liatris	Solidago
0.0625	109,824	0.0063	0.0027	0.0035
0.125	54,912	0.0127	0.0054	0.0071
0.25	27,456	0.0254	0.0109	0.0141
0.5	13,728	0.0507	0.0217	0.0283
1.0	6,864	0.1014	0.0434	0.0565
2.0	3,432	0.2028	0.0868	0.1131
4.0	1,716	0.4056	0.1737	0.2261
8.0	858	0.8111	0.3473	0.4522
16.0	429	1.6224	0.6947	0.9044

SIZE OF SAMPLE UNITS

TABLE 38. The relation of relative abundance (number of plants per occupied quadrat) to quadrat size, (Evans, 188)

Quadrat Size in sq. m.	Quadrat Number	Lespedeza	Liatris	Solidago
0.0625	109,824	1.06	1.02	1.01
0.125	54,912	1.11	1.05	1.02
0.25	27,456	1.23	1.09	1.03
0.5	13,728	1.40	1.18	1.07
1.0	6,864	1.74	1.35	1.14
2.0	3,432	2.26	1.61	1.22
4.0	1,716	3.12	1.96	1.33
8.0	858	4.09	2.40	1.60
16.0	429	5.80	3.24	2.11

species, it is seen that their density relationships remain the same whatever the quadrat size, as, in fact, they must.

Looking now at the effect of quadrat size on *relative abundance,* here defined as the number of individuals per occupied quadrat, we find that for the smallest quadrat ($\frac{1}{16}$ sq. m.) the three species are nearly the same, being close to the minimal value of one plant per occupied quadrat (Table 38). As progressively larger quadrats are used, the three species retain their order of relative abundance, each increasing with increased size of sample units, but the differences are greater. This is to be expected for species that have different degrees of departure from randomness in their distribution. In conclusion it is clear that although quadrat size does not affect unit-area density calculations, it does affect the data on relative abundance or density in occupied quadrats.

When Evans determined the frequency percentages for the species in sets of quadrats of different size, he found that quadrat size has a strong influence on frequency data. Doubling quadrat size does not produce a doubling of frequency, as it does with density. Furthermore, the different species (Table 39) change their relationships as the area of the sample unit is changed. As Evans points out, *"Solidago,* for example, which is only slightly more frequent that *Liatris* and roughly half as frequent as *Lespedeza* in the smallest quadrats, is twice as frequent as *Liatris* and one-and-one-half times as frequent as *Lespedeza* in the largest quadrats."

Several investigators have been concerned with the departure from randomness in the distribution of individuals of a species in nature and have made efforts to measure it (Preston, 330; Thomson, 387; Curtis and McIntosh, 146; McGinnies, 287; Fracker and Brischle, 199; Whitford, 414; and Blackman, 44). Evans has applied several of these measures to his data and arrives at the conclusion that they are all

TABLE 39.   The relation of frequency (percentage of quadrats occupied) to quadrat size (Evans, 188)

Quadrat Size in sq. m.	Quadrat Number	Lespedeza	Liatris	Solidago
0.0625	109,824	0.60	0.27	0.35
0.125	54,912	1.14	0.52	0.72
0.25	27,456	2.06	1.00	1.38
0.5	17,728	3.62	1.84	2.67
1.0	6,864	5.84	3.22	4.95
2.0	3,432	8.97	5.39	9.27
4.0	1,716	13.05	8.86	16.96
8.0	858	19.81	14.45	28.32
16.0	429	27.97	21.45	42.89

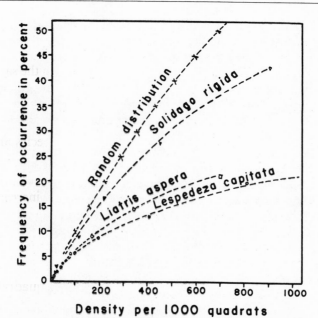

FIGURE 28.   Frequency-density curves derived from series of quadrats of different sizes (Evans, 188). These data suggest the value of using sets of quadrats of different sizes rather than of a single size in the study of a community as it permits comparisons among species and with randomness.

influenced by the size of the quadrat used to obtain the basic data. According to him, "It seems likely that disagreement in the results of various authors stems in part from differences in the sizes of their quadrats, and that success or failure in the application of these measures depends upon a fortunate or unfortunate choice of quadrat size."

It seems to us that Evans' most important conclusion is that field ecologists, in sampling populations, should not follow the usual practice of using a single size of quadrat, but should utilize several sizes in order to put frequency-density relationship to practical use. He says, "If quadrats of several sizes are employed in collecting data, the frequency-density curve that can be derived will enable one to determine, qualitatively at least, the degree to which the observed distributions depart from randomness and by extrapolation or interpolation to compare two or more sets of data obtained by quadrats of different size." This is illustrated in Figure 28.

THE LINE-INTERCEPTION METHOD: ULTIMATE REDUCTION OF THE TRANSECT

The *line intercept* is a special form of the transect often employed for the analysis of certain quantitative characteristics of a stand of more or less low and compact vegetation such as a natural grassland or pasture. The line intercept was introduced by Canfield (107) and is now being used in several grassland investigations in the United States. It has been employed by Canfield (108, 109, 110) in further studies, by Anderson (15) in tall-grass prairie, by Hormay (241) on California bunch-grass communities, and by Parker and Savage (309) on southern Great Plains vegetation. A recent testing of it against point-contact methods by Whitman and Siggeirsson (416) will illustrate the method.

In an apparently uniform piece of upland, native, ungrazed, mixed-grass range in southwestern North Dakota, Whitman and Siggeirsson laid out an experimental plot 300 x 500 feet. This tract was then subdivided into 30 plots each 50 x 100 feet. To each of these minor plots were assigned four line transects for testing the line-interception method. Each "line," a stretched wire along the ground, was 10 m. long and was given a width of 1 cm.; i.e., any plant was considered "intercepted" if its base was within 0.5 cm. on either side of the wire, except that single-stalked species were arbitrarily considered intercepted if they lay within 1 cm. of the line. All intercepts were measured along the line to the nearest 0.5 cm. The positions of the lines within each of the 30 subplots were determined by random selection using an imaginary grid with a 2.5-ft. interval. In the statistical analysis of data four line transects were considered to constitute a sample of the vegetation.

The large experimental plot contained 57 species. The line intercepts picked up 12 out of 13 species of grass, all 3 species of sedge, and 36 out of 41 species of forbs, or a total of 51 of the 57 species. The authors state that the principal species of the cover are *Stipa comata* Trin.

& Rupr., *Bouteloua gracilis* (HBK) Lag., *Carex filiforma* Nutt., *Carex eleocharis* Bailey, *Agropyron smithii* Rydb., and *Calamagrostis montanensis* Scribn. The principal miscellaneous grasses are *Koeleria cristata* (L.) Pers. and *Stipa viridula* Trin. Among the many kinds of forbs present in relatively low numbers, the most important are *Sphaeralcea coccinea* (Pursh) Rydb., *Erysimum asperum* (Nutt.) DC., and *Lygodesmia juncea* (Pursh) DiDon. The line-intercept method gave density percentages as follows:

Stipa comata	5.40
Bouteloua gracilis	5.84
Agropyron smithii	1.28
Calamagrostis montanensis	0.73
Miscellaneous grasses: 8 other species	1.39
Sedges: all 3 species together	4.33
Forbs: all 36 species encountered	1.73
Total	20.70

Despite the uniform appearance of the vegetation, variability of *Stipa comata, Bouteloua gracilis,* and *Carex* spp., which together made up more than 70 percent of the vegetation, was in excess of 30 percent of their mean density. The authors concluded that for survey work in vegetation of this type and density 23 line transects would provide for estimates of the three major components of the vegetation with sampling errors of 10 percent or less, and between 10 and 20 percent for essentially all other components. They also found that practical field working rates for two men in vegetation of this type was about 20 line transects per day.

Evans and Cain (190), in a comparative study of sampling techniques on old-field grassland vegetation in southern Michigan, used a single long-line transect, formed by a steel tape 50 m. long and 1 cm. wide, stretched along the ground through the vegetation. The position of each plant rooted under the tape was recorded to the nearest centimeter. The intercepts are shown in Table 40. *Poa compressa* L. had an average spacing of 18.1 cm. along the line transect; 65.3 percent of the culms were closer together than the average spacing; and on the basis of 1-m. units it had a frequency of 96 percent. *Aristida purpurascens* Poir. had an average spacing of 19.3 cm.; 65.2 percent of the culms were closer than the average; and frequency was 100 percent. These frequencies compare favorably with those obtained from regularized and random sets of 0.25 sq. m. quadrats. The number of culms compared favorably with data obtained from clipped quadrats. For most purposes of stand analysis the shorter, replicated, randomly located

TABLE 40. Number of individual culms or plants and average distances between adjacent individuals encountered along a 50-meter transect through the *Poa-Aristida* community, southern Michigan (Evans and Cain, 190)

Species	Number of Culms or Plants	Average Distance Between Adjacent Individuals (cm.)
Poa compressa L.	276	18.1
Aristide purpurascens Poir.	259	19.3
Rumex acetosella L.	125	40.0
Antennaria nèglecta Greene	28	178.6
A. fallax Greene	25	200.0
Poa pratensis L.	16	312.4
Solidago nemoralis Ait.	11	454.5
Hedeoma pulegioides (L.) Pers.	10	500.0
Krigia virginica (L.) Willd.	5	1000.0
Panicum sp.	4	1250.0
Gnaphalium obtusifolium L.	3	1666.7
Erigeron canadensis L.	3	1666.7
Liatris aspera Michx.	2	2500.0
Hieracium longipilum Torr.	2	2500.0
Panicum oligosanthes var. scribnerianum (Nash) Fern.	2	2500.0

line transects of Whitman and Siggeirsson are preferable to the single long transect used by Evans and Cain. In any case, the method is relatively satisfactory for many purposes; it is compared with point-intercept and other methods elsewhere in this *Manual*.

In the strict sense, the line transect is a "line" and not an unusually long and narrow rectangular plot; but even in the strict sense it has some width because it consists of a tightly stretched cord, wire, or tape. Plants with which it makes contact can be described in terms of *number* and spacing, and *frequency* according to subunits of length or replicated lines; and in terms of the proportion of length of line intercepted or shaded by the plant species, or *dominance*. Bauer (29, 30) used the transect as a line in studies of chaparral, and in a comparative study found it more efficient than quadrats. Canfield (110) used the line intercept both for botanical analysis and for measuring forage utilization by stock. Anderson (15) in tall-grass pastures used only vegetation in contact with the line because it was difficult to decide just which culms of grasses were within a strip 1 cm. wide. This difficulty was obviated by Evans and Cain (190), who used a steel tape 1 cm. wide which not only defined the narrow strip but automatically provided a means of horizontal measurement. In the work of Parker and Savage (309) the width of the belt was 1 cm. for herbs and 10 cm. for shrubs,

and the data recorded were area of coverage. The wire determining
the line was stretched between stout steel pins; after the cover of shrubs
was determined, the line was dropped to ground level for analysis of
herbs. Roe (348) used the method to record small changes in basal
cover by adequate markers that provided for the almost exact reloca-
tion of the line when needed. (See also Brown 65).

In summary, it seems that the line, or very long and narrow rectangle, is a sampling device that provides fewer opportunities for error
in measuring or estimating cover than the isodimensional quadrat,
and that it is also more rapid. Great caution is necessary to avoid bias
resulting from any consistent tendency of an investigator to count or
not count problematical intercepts. Such a bias is more likely to show
up in the results of different observers than in the different results of
one observer. As to length, each individual line intercept (or subsample) should be long enough to cross the several phases of any mosaic
that exists within a stand of a community type. The mosaic may be
easily seen in bog and heath vegetation, in pastures and natural grassland, etc., but it may have to be detected by studying the initial results
from what proves to be an unnecessarily long line unit. Whereas there
is some evidence that the point-contact method is not of much use in
open vegetation such as that of deserts, the line-intercept method may
be very useful. On the other hand, in very dense vegetation the line
intercept may be difficult to use unless it is laid on the ground and
employed only for basal hits. An effort to judge a vertical plane of interception above the line may be difficult in complex vegetation and
yield results with low reliability. Line sets can be employed for samples within stands and for comparison between stands of the same
type of vegetation by use of a 2 x 2 contingency table. Because of its
length, the line-intercept method is especially adapted to the study of
ecotones between communities and for correlations between changes
in botanical composition and structure and changes in environmental
conditions such as slope, exposure, soil moisture, etc.

THE POINT-CONTACT METHOD: ULTIMATE REDUC-
TION OF THE QUADRAT

Many methods of quadrat analysis of vegetation are tedious and
in some ways unsatisfactory statistically. It was a logical development
not only that investigators would examine the question of quadrat
size and number in relation to efficiency, to the end that both would
be reduced as much as possible, but that in size the sampling unit
would be reduced to a point. Levy and Madden (271) seem to have
introduced the modern point-contact method in quantitative analysis

of vegetation. Several investigators have employed the method on natural grassland vegetation and pastures. Among them are Hanson (228); Tinney, Aamodt, and Ahlgren (388); Arny and Schmid (18); Clarke, Campbell, and Campbell (121); Arny (17); Drew (167); Crocker and Tiver (141); Coupland (139); and Whitman and Siggeirsson (416).

The theoretical basis of the point sampling method is simple. As the sampling unit is reduced in size it becomes more probable that it is completely covered by the foliage of one plant or not covered at all. The ultimate is reached, of course, with the point that is too small to be "partially" covered. As Greig-Smith (221) says, "At the limit, when the sample area becomes a point, the proportion which is covered of the infinitely large total number of sample areas equals the cover of the species. The points actually examined in an investigation, if properly selected, are an unbiased sample of the infinitely large number of possible points and give an estimate of the true value of cover, the accuracy of which can be increased to any desired degree of precision by increasing the sample size."

In practice, however, the sample unit is not a point in the mathematical sense (unless cross hairs are used in an optical instrument) but the end of a pin traveling through space, and the pin has the cross-sectional area of a small plot. Goodall (219) has shown the influence of pin diameter on the frequency of the pin's contact with foliage. He used pins of 1.84 and 4.75 mm. diameter and a cross-hair arrangement for observations of a true point given as zero diameter. From among his results we note, for example, that foliage of the grass *Ammophila arenaria* was hit with a frequency of 60.5 percent for the true point (zero diameter), 74.5 percent for the pin 1.84 mm. in diameter, and 82.0 percent for the larger pin of 4.75 mm. diameter in one set of 200 points. No hits, or bare ground, had a reverse relationship to size in a set of 200 points, dropping from 53.0 to 42.5 and 38.5 percent in the same sequence of sizes as above.

In common practice the points are located in sets of 10 by dropping metal pins through a wooden frame containing 10 guide holes spaced 2 in. apart. Tinney, Aamodt, and Ahlgren (388) found that better records were obtained by dropping the pins at an inclination of 45° rather than vertically, as this gave more comparable results for plants of different life form. The point-contact method has been used in both regularized and random samples, and has been compared with other sampling techniques. Whitman and Siggeirsson (416) for example, compared the point-contact (or intercept) method with the line-intercept method. In the same study they also compared statistics resulting from all intercepts with those resulting only from basal intercepts by the inclined point-contact method. In the first system all contacts of the point of the pin with the vegetation are recorded by species as the pin is projected downward, irrespective of the number of times any plant is hit. Bare ground was recorded whether or not plants were intercepted above. Species density was calculated by expressing the number of hits on any one species per 100 points as a percentage of the total number of vegetation hits per 100 points and multiplying this by 100 minus the percentage of hits on bare ground. This can be expressed as follows:

$$\frac{H}{P} \times 100 \times (100 - B) = D$$

where H equals hits on a species, P equals points (100), B equals hits on bare ground, and D equals density. In the second system only basal contacts with vegetation are recorded. In their study of mixed-grass vegetation, 10 frames or 100 points were taken in each of 30 subplots 50 x 100 ft. of a major 300 x 500 ft. plot. All samples were random in the subplots.

When used to secure density estimates of equal accuracy, Whitman and Siggeirsson found that point-contact methods are not much more rapid than the line-intercept method for the major components of the vegetation. The all-contacts analysis does have an advantage with the single-stalked grasses and forbs. The lower variability in the density estimates for such species permits analyses of equal precision with less effort. Whitman and Siggeirsson found that 1400 points for the all-contact method and 3600 points for the basal-contact method would provide estimates for major components of the vegetation with sampling errors of 10 percent or less, which might be taken as a reasonable minimum working basis for the analysis of vegetation of the type studied. Also, it was their experience that two investigators familiar with the vegetation could record about 1500 all-contact points and 3000 basal contact points per day.

The exact application of the point-contact method to a particular problem will depend upon the nature of the vegetation—such as its height, density, richness in species and life forms, etc.—and the objectives of the study. Instead of using sets of points, Blackman (43), Eden and Bond (175), and Goodall (219) have used single points. This system is probably more accurate for species with highly contagious (clumped) distributions because they do not tend to be overrepresented; but it is more time-consuming, if the points are random, and allows more subconscious influence in point (or plant) selection. Several workers, such as Hanson (228), Ellison (178), and Drew (167), used regularized locations for points or point sets, but there are strong theoretical arguments for randomization.

Vertical pins distort positively the results for broad-leaved species relative to grasses, and pins inclined at 45° have the additional advantage of recording more interceptions and improving visibility of the pin's progress downward. As the pin moves downward, different investigators have recorded only the first plant hit, only basal hits, or all hits including bare ground. When only first hits are recorded, there is an overemphasis on tall plants; when only ground-level hits are recorded, creeping plants are overrepresented. West (412) has shown that the more open the vegetation, the larger the size of the sample must be; and Osborn, Wood, and Paltridge (306) concluded that the method was useless in vegetation in arid regions. For extensive surveys in Australia, Tiver and Crocker (389) found 300 to 500 points per stand adequate for definition of pasture types and studies of species relations to climate and soil, and the method is sufficiently sensitive for studies of pasture changes under fertilization, different intensities of grazing, and seasonal changes. Brown (65), who reviewed the technique thoroughly, as well as other methods of analyzing vegetation—and to whom the authors of this *Manual* are much indebted—concluded that the point method has every prospect of becoming the accepted one for large-scale surveys as well as for exact field analysis of low-growing vegetation.

The point-contact method gives cover results that are generally comparable for different samples of the same species; but because such differences as species with small leaves or much dissected and compound leaves or linear leaves give exaggerated cover results, comparisons among species are less reliable. Because individuals of a species are commonly not randomly distributed but more or less clumped, the method of setting points in frames of 10 does not yield observations with statistical independence, and there is a tendency to exaggerate the number of species with high and low values. Goodall (219) has shown that random points are more efficient than frame-blocked points, but the greater speed of grouped points may offset the disadvantage and allow a larger number of point samples, thereby producing the same efficiency. Greig-Smith (221) concluded that the vertical set of points encounters fewer variables resulting from different plant forms than inclined points and that the only advantage of inclined points is found when the interest is in species of very low cover.

Chapter 10

THE COMBINATION
OF COMMUNITY
CHARACTERISTICS

TOTAL ESTIMATE

We have made it clear that the characteristics of number, coverage, and pattern (frequency, aggregation) are separate and distinct attributes of community structure. There are, however, different ways in which these and other characteristics may be combined to facilitate or enhance description. One example is *total estimate* as employed by plant sociologists of the Braun-Blanquet school, which is a combination of abundance and coverage in one scale, as follows:

x   Individuals of a species very sparsely present in the stand; coverage very small
1   Individuals plentiful, but total coverage small
2   Individuals very numerous, if small; or covering at least 5 percent, if large
3   Individuals few or many, but collectively covering 25 to 50 percent of the area
4   Coverage 50 to 75 percent of the area
5   Coverage 75 to 100 percent of the area

The smaller classes of total estimate have more to do with abundance; the larger classes (3 to 5) are straight coverage classes on the Braun-Blanquet scale (58). Braun-Blanquet says that sociability should also be estimated when the above system of total estimate is used for species; that separate estimates should be made for the species of each stratum; and that whereas coverage alone may be adequate for estimating numerous small quadrats, the combined or total estimate should be used for larger samples such as a single 100 sq. m. plot. A somewhat more elaborate scale for total estimate has been used by Evans and Dahl (191). See page 142.

ASSOCIATION TABLES: BRAUN-BLANQUET METHOD

The construction of association tables of a definite type is one of the conspicuous practices of plant sociologists of the Braun-Blanquet persuasion. Such association tables are composed of data from several stands (association individuals, concrete examples of the association type). The tables are usually organized on a basis of fidelity. This means that the species are arranged in the table by groups according to fidelity classes. The "characteristic species" of the association form the first group; this is followed by characteristic species of the alliance to which the association belongs, and then by one or more groups of associated species of lower fidelity. Thus the species that have indicator value for the association and the hierarchical classification of associations into alliances and orders and classes are distinguished and set first in the table. For each species, whatever its fidelity group, the association table customarily shows two further data as paired class assignments, as, for example, *3.4 Asperula odorata* or *x.2 Carex silvatica*. The first of these figures is the assignment of the species to a class in the scale of total estimate (combined abundance-coverage); the second figure is the assignment of the species to a sociability class. Each entry in the association table—the data for each association individual—is customarily obtained from a single plot for the stand. This plot must be at least as large as the minimal area of the association. Additional information for the species may be appended; for example, symbols may be added for life form, for constancy class, for dynamic role of the species, etc. Also there should be data for the stands, such as altitude, slope and exposure, soil type, etc. In Table 41 we have abstracted part of the data from a much fuller table given in illustration by Braun-Blanquet (58). This table is for the association of *Elyna myosuroides* from the central Alps, East Grisons. From this table we see that certain species are of high fidelity, although this is not revealed by data concerning only a single association, and that species of high fidelity for the association are not necessarily of high total estimate, high sociability, or even high constancy. *Elyna*, however, not only is a characteristic species but also rates high in total estimate and constancy. It

TABLE 41. Part of an association table for the Elynetum of the East Grisons, Central Alps (Braun-Blanquet, 58)

	Association Individuals (Stands)													Constancy Classes
	1	2	3	4	5	6	7	8	9	10	11	12	13	
Characteristic Species of the Association														
Elyna myosuroides	4.3	4.3	3.3	4.3	4.3	4.3	3.3	4.3	4.3	4.3	4.3	4.3	4.3	V
Dianthus glacialis	:	:	:	:	:	:	:	:	:	:	:	:	1.2	I
Draba siliquosa	:	:	:	:	x	x	x	:	:	x	x	x	x	IV
Carex capillaris var. minima	x	1.2	1.2	:	x	x	:	1.2	1.1	x	x	x	x	V
Carex atrata	:	:	x	x	x	1.1	:	1.1	x	x	x	:	:	IV
Cerastium alpinum var. lanatum								x						II
Arenaria ciliata ssp. tenella	1.2	x.2	x.2	x	x	x	:	x	x	1.1	1.1	:	:	V
Saussurea alpina	x	:	1.1	x	1.1	:	x	2.1	1.1	1.1	1.1	1.1	x	IV
Erigeron uniflorus	x	:	x	x	x	:	:	x	:	x	x	x	x	V
Gentiana tenella	:	:	:	:	:	1.1	x	x	x	x	:	:	:	III
Viscaria alpina	:	:	:	:	:	:	x	:	:	:	:	:	:	I
Characteristic Species of the Alliance														
Festuca pumila	2.2	1.2	x.2	2.2	1.2	1.2	2.2	2.2	1.2	1.2	2.2	2.2	1.2	V
Sesleria coerula var. calcarea	1.2	1.2	2.3	x	1.2	x	x.2	x.2	x.2	x.2	:	1.2	:	V
Carex rupestris	x	x	1.2	x	1.1	x	x	:	1.1	x	x	x	x	V
Minuartia verna var.?	1.1	x	x.2	x	x	x	:	:	x	x	:	x	x	V
Gentiana verna var.?	x	x	x	:	x	x	:	:	x	:	:	:	:	IV
Leontodon podium	:	x	x	:	x	:	:	:	:	x	:	:	:	II
Helianthemum alpestre	x	:	x	:	:	:	:	:	:	:	:	:	:	I

Characteristic Species of the Order												
Potentilla crantzii	1.1	..	1.1	x	x	x	1.2	1.1	x	x	1.1	V
Oxytropis campestris	..	1.2	1.2	x	.	.	x	.	.	x	1.2	IV
Indifferent and Companion spp.												
Polygonum viviparum	x.2	x	1.1	x	x	x	x	1.1	:	x	x	V
Silene acaulis	x.2	x.2	x.2	x	:	:	:	:	x.2	x.2	1.2	V
Antennaria carpatica	1.1	x	x	x	:	x	x.2	x	:	x	x	V
Agrostis alpina	:	2.2	x.2	x	:	:	x.2	x	x	1.2	:	IV
Gentiana brachyphylla	x	1.1	:	x	:	x	:	x	x	x	:	III
Carex sempervirens	:	:	:	:	1.2	:	:	:	:	:	:	II
Festuca halleri	:	:	:	:	:	:	:	:	1.2	x	x	II
Moss Layer												
Cetraria islandica var. crispa	1.1	1.2	1.1	x	1.1	1.2	1.1	x	x	x	1.1	V
Cladonia pyxidata	x	x	x	x	:	x	x	x	x	x	x.2	V
Cetraria cucullata	1.1	:	1.1	1.2	x	1.2	1.2	:	:	:	2.2	IV
Cladonia silvatica	:	x	2.2	x	x	:	:	:	x	:	1.2	II
Polytrichum juniperinum	:	:	x	x	x	:	:	x	:	x	x	III

Total species 72, only selected ones shown in this table. Two stations omitted, and all the descriptive data for the stands.

In the data for each species in each stand the first of the paired symbols (separated by the dot) is for the total estimate class, and the second is for the sociability class. When only the symbol x is present, sociability was not assigned to the species.

is for these reasons that the community is named after it, the *Elynetum*. Many of the same comments apply to species characteristic of the alliance; they are various as to other characteristics.

"LOCAL ABUNDANCE"

A rapid working method for the examination of numerous stands of several different associations is that employed by Dansereau (151) and variously described as "local abundance" or "local coverage." In this method a fairly large single plot is used (seldom less than 100 sq. m. and usually about the size of the estimated minimal area) on which all species are examined. Separate lists of the species of each stratum are kept, and each species is assigned a single index symbol. The classes and their description are as follows:

-     Plants without sociability
- x   Distribution unequal, but concentration little notable
- 1   Individuals isolated; local abundance 1 to 20 percent
- 2   Groups or tufts (clumps) dispersed; local abundance 21 to 40 percent
- 3   Few concentrated colonies, but each one of little extent; local abundance 41 to 60 percent
- 4   Colonies of large concentration, but generally without the individuals touching; local abundance 61 to 80 percent
- 5   Colonies pure, of touching individuals; local abundance 81 to 100 percent

Dansereau (see also Magnanini, 283) considers this a method of determining sociability, which seems to be equated with "local abundance or coverage." On the large plot the first element of the class definitions is considered, and then where the species occurs the local coverage is estimated. It sometimes happens that a single symbol cannot be used to satisfy the two elements of a class definition, in which case two symbols are used, the first referring to the manner of occurrence of individuals or groups and the second to the abundance or coverage in the local areas where the plants occur.

It seems to us that this method blurs the distinctions between number (whether estimated abundance, or density), manner of distribution (frequency, or sociability), and coverage (dominance). This is somewhat like a subjective DFD index. We know, however, that with this method Dansereau produces comparable and consistent data in his association tables, and that persons who have worked with him (as have the authors of this *Manual*) can do likewise. But it is not a method that can be recommended generally because of the high content of personal opinion and experience that goes into the assignment of values to the species. For most investigators the somewhat more tedious distinction and separate consideration of abundance, coverage, and sociability are to be recommended.

COMBINED FREQUENCY

Basically frequency is the percentage occurrence of a species in a series of units of a sample taken in an association individual or stand. When comparable sampling is done in each of a series of stands of the same association, the results can be put together as combined frequency. For example, Species a may have the following frequency percentages as a result of sampling 10 stands of an association type by means of 10 quadrats in each stand: 100, 100, 80, 70, 90, 100, 100, 100, 90, 90. Its combined frequency will be 92 percent. Such a species is consistently of high frequency in all stands. Species b might have the following frequencies on the basis of the same samples: 60, 40, 10, 80, 90, 100, 20, 30, 10, 70. It would have a combined frequency of 51 percent. Species c might have the following frequencies: 0, 0, 10, 30, 90, 100, 0, 90, 100, 100, with a combined frequency of 52 percent. In these hypothetical but quite realistic examples Species b and c have almost identical combined frequencies, but they are different in another regard. Species b has a constancy of 100 percent, whereas Species c has a constancy of 70 percent. Species a has high constancy as well as high frequency. These two characteristics can be combined by writing combined frequency as an exponent of constancy, as follows: Species a, 100^{92}; Species b, 100^{51}; Species c, 70^{52}. In this notation the figures are percentages of constancy and frequency. Perhaps a more revealing system is to write index numbers rather than percentages, as follows: Species a, 10^{92}; Species b, 10^{51}; Species c, 7^{52}, thus indicating the number of stations on which the constancy and frequency are based. A still more precise notation would be, for Species a, $10/10^{92/100}$, indicating both the number of stations and the number of quadrats, but orthographically this is horrible.

DFD INDEX

The DFD index based on the sum of the percentage density, percentage frequency, and percentage dominance (coverage) was introduced by Curtis (144). Our illustration of the DFD index (Tables 42, 43, 44) is from Cottam (134), who studied the plant sociology of a *Quercus* woods near the prairie-forest border of southwestern Wisconsin. Density is the number of individuals per unit area; frequency is

TABLE 42.   The DFD index of trees 4 in. d.b.h. and over in a *Quercus* woods in south-western Wisconsin (Cottam, 134)

Species	Frequency %	Density %	Dominance Based on Basal Area %	DFD Index
Quercus alba	83.0	62.99	61.03	207.02
Quercus spp. (Q. velutina group)	53.0	27.97	35.29	116.26
Quercus macrocarpa	8.0	2.82	2.12	12.94
Prunus serotina	14.0	4.52	0.99	19.51
Carya ovata	2.0	0.56	0.24	2.80
Acer rubrum	1.0	0.28	0.03	1.31
Understory trees				
Populus grandidentata	1.0	0.56	0.23	1.79
Ostrya virginiana	1.0	0.28	0.07	1.35
Total values per acre		143	105.1 sq. ft.	
Total values per hectare		345	259.6 sq. ft.	

TABLE 43.   Frequency, density, and abundance of shrub species in a *Quercus* woods in southwestern Wisconsin (Cottam, 134)

Species	Frequency 4 × 4 m. Quadrats %	Density per 1600 sq. m.	Abundance Occupied 4 × 4 m. Quadrats
Rubus allegheniensis	88.0	3306	37.5
Cornus femina	88.0	1496	17.0
Corylus americana	86.0	2740	31.9
Parthenocissus vitacea	59.0	2216	37.6
Amelanchier interior	35.0	75	2.1
Rubus idaeus	23.0	499	21.7
Vitis riparia	22.0	107	4.9
Rosa sp.	21.0	170	8.1
Prunus virginiana	21.0	99	5.0
Rhus radicans	17.0	406	23.9
Rubus occidentalis	15.0	145	9.7
Salix sp.	9.0	15	1.7
Amorpha canescens	7.0	20	2.9
Sambucus canadensis	6.0	26	4.3
Ceanothus americanus	5.0	32	6.8
Vitis aestivalis var. argentifolia	5.0	34	6.8
Rhus glabra	5.0	27	5.4

the number of quadrats in which a species is represented; dominance for trees is computed from basal area; abundance is the average number of individuals of a species computed on a basis of occupied quadrats. Note that this definition differs from "abundance" in the sense of Braun-Blanquet and this *Manual*. The sample consisted of 100 quadrats 10 × 10 m., or a total of 1 ha. (2.5 acres), laid out on a grid

TABLE 44.   Frequency, density, and abundance of herb species in a *Quercus* woods in scouthwestern Wisconsin (Cottam, 134)

Species	Frequency 1 × 1 m. Quadrats %	Density per 1600 sq. m.	Abundance Occupied 1 × 1 m. Quadrats
Carex pensylvanica	63.0	6663	105.8
Galium concinnum	62.0	884	14.2
Geranium maculatum	58.0	459	7.9
Smilacina racemosa	54.0	130	2.4
Desmodium acuminatum	50.0	262	5.2
Circaea latifolia	46.0	389	8.4
Osmorhiza claytoni	36.0	423	11.8
Phryma leptostachya	26.0	140	3.9
Amphicarpa bracteata	33.0	166	5.0
Aralia nudicaulis	27.0	127	4.7
Poa pratensis	25.0	4535	181.6
Pteridium aquilinum	21.0	79	3.8
Lysimachia quadrifolia	18.0	24	1.3
Anemona quinquefolia	17.0	90	5.3
Smilacina stellata	15.0	36	2.4
Pyrola elliptica	12.0	112	9.3
Desmodium nudiflorum	8.0	102	12.7
Arenaria lateriflora	5.0	70	14.0

system dispersed throughout the stand. Each 10 × 10 m. quadrat contained one 4 × 4 m. quadrat and one 1 × 1 m. quadrat, always located in the same corner of the largest quadrats. The large quadrats were used for trees only, which were tallied by diameters, and from which density, frequency, and dominance (basal area) were computed. The 4 × 4 quadrats were used for frequency, density, and abundance of shrubs and trees under 1 in. d.b.h.; the 1 × 1 m. quadrats were used for herbaceous plants.

Trees 4 in. d.b.h. and over have a density of 143 per acre (345 per ha.) and a dominance of 105.1 sq. ft. basal area per acre (259.6 sq. ft. per ha.). The *Quercus* spp. are distinctly dominant, with *Quercus alba* nearly twice as important as the black-oak group *(Q. velutina)*.

Four shrub species make up nearly 85 percent of the total density: *Rubus allegheniensis, Cornus femina, Corylus americana,* and *Parthenocissus vitacea.* Because of their small size and the method of counting each ascending culm, the grass *Poa pratensis* and the sedge *Carex pensylvanica* are conspicuously of greatest density; but the important herbaceous species in this woods, according to frequency, density, and ground cover, are *Galium concinnum, Geranium maculatum, Smilacina racemosa, Desmodium acuminatum, Circaea latifolia, Osmorhiza claytoni, Phryma leptostachya,* and *Amphicarpa bracteata.* The DFD index for trees and the simultaneous use of frequency, density, and abundance for shrubs and herbs makes possible a revealing description of composition and structure. There are, of course, other analytic characteristics that can be added to these for a still fuller description.

A novel and promising use of the DFD index has been reported by the director of the Tropical Forest Experiment Station (392). Strong differences in DFD index of species occurring in different forest types within the rain-forest complex have been used as indicators of the types concerned. The elements of the index are defined as follows: Density is the number of individuals of each species per unit of area; frequency is the number of plots on which each species occurs; dominance is the percentage of the total basal area of a species. In Table 45 we see that certain species have high DFD indexes in the rain for-

TABLE 45.   DFD indexes used as indicators of types in rain forest (392)

Species	DFD Index	
	Rain Forest	Montane Thicket
Alchorneopsis portoricensis Urban	53	3
Cecropia peltata L.	109	58
Dacryodes excelsa Vahl.	130	30
Didymopanax morototoni (Aubl.) Scne.	72	33
Inga vera Willd.	46	3
Inga laurina (Sw.) Willd.	74	26
Sloanea berteriana Choisy	89	34
Cyrilla racemiflora L.	34	124
Micropholis chrysophylloides Pierre	12	86
Micropholis garcinifolia Pierre	83	121
Ocotea spathulata Mez.	47	83

est proper and low indexes in the montane thicket rain forest, and other species have the converse relationship. The presence of such species as *Alchorneopsis portoricensis* and *Dacryodes excelsa* in rain forest with a high DFD index and a low index in montane thicket rain forest makes them good indicators of the former type. Conversely, such species as *Micropholis chrysophylloides* and *Ocotea spathulata,* having high indexes in montane thicket rain forest, make them good indicators of that type.

It will be noticed that density and dominance are expressed on a unit-area basis and are essentially unaffected by the size, shape, and arrangement of the quadrats, except for the probable accuracy of the means; but that frequency is decidedly influenced by quadrat characteristics. Since frequency percentages of the species participate equally in the DFD index with density and dominance, the nature of this variable must be kept in mind.

IMPORTANCE VALUE INDEX (IVI)

As an index, "importance value" has one difference from the DFD index. The importance value index was introduced by Curtis and McIntosh (147) in a paper on the upland forest continuum in southwestern Wisconsin. Relative density (the proportion of the density of a species to that of the stand as a whole) and relative dominance (the proportion of the basal area of a species to the stand as a whole) are computed as in the DFD index. The difference lies in frequency, which is also calculated so as to be relative, rather than the usual simple, direct expression. This change puts frequency on the same basis as the other characteristics and gives the summation of the indexes a constant value of 300. The authors claim that this index is an excellent indication of the vegetational importance of a species within a stand. In their study of 95 stands of upland hardwoods, they held no preconceptions as to forest associations but studied any stand that met the following specifications: (1) The stand had to be natural and of adequate size; (2) it had to be free from disturbances such as fire, grazing, or excessive cutting; (3) it had to be on an upland site on which run-off water never accumulated. Table 46 shows the importance value indexes for the major trees of the region as determined in the above manner.

Confronted with a mass of data, Curtis and McIntosh sought an objective system of classification of the 95 forest stands. If the single leading dominant were used for classification, there would be 9 types; the use of two codominants in order would require 30 types; the use of the first three codominants in order would require 75 types; and if a type were required to have all four of its leading species in the same order there would be 95 types, i.e., each stand would be a "type." There would appear to be no natural groups involved in this series of nonselected stands of the region, unless the regional forest as a whole

TABLE 46.   Importance value indexes for the major forest trees of southwestern Wisconsin based on a study of 95 stands (Curtis and McIntosh, 147)

Species	Number of Stands of Occurrence in 95 Stands (Constance)	Average Importance Value	Maximum Importance Value Total: 300
Quercus rubra	80	90.4	228
Acer saccharum	45	82.8	201
Quercus alba	86	64.1	202
Quercus velutina	40	62.8	206
Tilia americana	63	39.6	179
Ulmus rubra	53	33.4	140
Quercus macrocarpa	25	24.8	170
Fraxinus americana	28	20.0	94
Prunus serotina	56	17.3	114
Ostrya virginiana	48	16.2	42
Carya ovata	39	15.7	61
Acer rubrum	18	13.3	58
Juglans nigra	21	12.5	30
Carya cordiformis	43	12.2	44
Juglans cinerea	23	12.1	53

is one heterogeneous type. Making use of the importance value index they could, however, develop a rational arrangement of stands.

In Table 47 are shown the four species that were leading dominants in 80 of the 95 stands, placed in groups according to the single leading dominant: 7 stands with *Quercus velutina* as leading dominant, 18 stands with *Q. alba,* etc. The data for IVI and constancy showed that the most logical arrangement of stands was in the order of *decreasing* IVI from stands dominated by *Q. velutina* to *Acer saccharum* (reading down in the first column of figures), and that such an arrangement produced a series of *increasing* values for *A. saccharum* (reading downward in the last column). Such a ranking of stands was in agreement with general observation of forest composition in the region, so the next step was to treat the other trees, which are of intermediate "importance potential" (capable of attaining a high IVI in one or more stands), in the same manner. Then studies of the quantitative characteristics of understory shrubs and herbs showed that they could be arranged in rational patterns according to forest stands, with given species of trees as leading dominants. This was also true of available potassium and calcium in the A_1 horizon of the soils of the stands. This was suggestive of the fact that the upland forest ecosystems could be arranged in one continuous series by means of the IVI. On the basis of this method the species with high IVI potential form the following series: *Quercus macrocarpa—Quercus velutina—Prunus serotina—Quercus alba —Carya ovata—Juglans nigra—Quercus rubra—Acer rubrum—Fraxinus americana—Tilia americana—Juglans cinerea—Carya cordiformis—Ulmus rubra— Ostrya virginiana—Acer saccharum.* Figure 29 shows bar graphs of IVI for some of the species arranged in the sequence of two leading dominants from the combination of *Quercus macrocarpa—Quercus velutina* at one end to the combination *Acer saccharum—Tilia americana* at the other end. The graphs clearly show the graduated series of various patterns the species display according to the IVI. The leading-dominants method produced a rational phytosociological arrangement, but it did not demonstrate the existence of any discrete forest associations in the region. The relation of the leading species to the continuum is shown in Figure 30. These curves are smoothed by running averages of five stands according to the formula $(a + 2b + c)/4$ (Curtis and McIntosh, 147). The IV curves of species such as *Quercus macrocarpa* and *Q. velutina* are truncated at the left; those of *Acer saccharum, Ostrya virginiana,* and *Tilia* are truncated at the right; *Quercus rubra* seems to be contained within the series. However, in other regions the species may have other values.

Being a relatively new concept, the importance value index has not yet received wide application, but Cain, Castro, *et al.* (103), have applied it to equatorial rain forest near Belém, Pará. The Amazonian

TABLE 47.   Average IVI (importance value index) and constancy percentage of trees in stands with the four species of highest importance potential as leading dominant (Curtis and McIntosh, 147)

| | The Following Species as Leading Dominants in | | | |
| | 7 Stands | 18 Stands | 34 Stands | 21 Stands |
Species	*Quercus velutina*	*Quercus alba*	*Quercus rubra*	*Acer saccharum*
Quercus velutina				
Average IV	165.1	39.6	13.6	0
Constancy %	100.0	72.3	38.3	0
Quercus alba				
Average IV	69.9	126.8	52.7	13.7
Constancy %	100.0	100.0	97.1	66.7
Quercus rubra				
Average IV	3.6	39.2	152.3	37.2
Constancy %	25.0	94.5	100.0	76.3
Acer saccharum				
Average IV	0	0.8	11.7	127.0
Constancy %	0	5.6	29.4	100.0

TABLE 48.   Leading tree species of tropical rain forest of terra firme, Mucambo, Instituto Agronômico do Norte, Belém, Pará, arranged according to their importance value indexes

Species	Family	IVI
Vochysia guianensis	Vochysiaceae	23.42
Eschweilera odora	Lecythidaceae	21.61
Goupia glabra	Celastraceae	15.14
Protium trifoliolatum	Burseraceae	13.08
Eschweilera krukovii	Lecythidaceae	12.90
Protium sp., "Breu mescla"	Burseraceae	9.29
Tovomita stigmatosa	Guttiferae	6.45
Iryanthera juruensis	Myristicaceae	6.38
Protium nodulosum	Burseraceae	6.33
Trattinikia sp.	Burseraceae	5.62
Vantanea cupularis	Humiriaceae	5.54
Anacardium giganteum	Anacardiaceae	5.03
Protium carnosum	Burseraceae	5.00
Vouacapoura americana	Leguminosae	4.67
Theobroma subincana	Sterculiaceae	4.63
Piptadenia suaveolens	Leguminosae	4.26
Sapotaceae, Gen. sp.	Sapotaceae	4.20
Parkia pendula	Leguminosae	4.05
Micropholis acutangula	Sapotaceae	4.04
Sterculia pruriens	Sterculiaceae	4.01
Osteophloeum platyspermum	Myristicaceae	3.40
Protium polybotryum v. blackii	Burseraceae	3.30
Chimarrhis turbinata	Rubiaceae	3.29
Protium puncticulatum	Burseraceae	3.27
Eschweilera blanchetiana	Lecythidaceae	3.26
Pourouma myrmecophila	Moraceae	3.24
Poraqueiba guianensis	Icacinaceae	3.17
Pithecolobium jupunba	Leguminosae	3.15
Helicostylis pedunculata	Moraceae	3.11
Tapura singularis	Dichapetalaceae	2.90
Caryocar microcarpum	Caryocaraceae	2.82
Thyrsodium paraensis	Anacardiaceae	2.72
Qualea albiflora	Vochysiaceae	2.66
Ptychopetalum olacoides	Olacaceae	2.63
Couepia hoffmanniana	Rosaceae	2.61
Pouteria caimito	Sapotaceae	2.52
Iryanthera paraensis	Myristicaceae	2.46
Manilkara huberi	Sapotaceae	2.43
Dendrobangia boliviana	Icacinaceae	2.31
Pouteria sp.	Sapotaceae	2.06
Trattinickia rhoifolia	Burseraceae	1.93
Caryocar villosum	Caryocaraceae	1.91
Neea sp.	Nyctaginaceae	1.37
Enterolobium shomburgkii	Leguminosae	1.35

rain forest is exceedingly rich in tree species; and although there may be local concentrations of a species, over vast areas the forest is generally without dominance by one or a few species. The Mucambo study was made on a 2-ha. sample plot of upland forest which had 39 families, 100 genera, and 157 species of trees 10 cm. or more in diameter on it. Including slightly smaller forms, there were 173 species

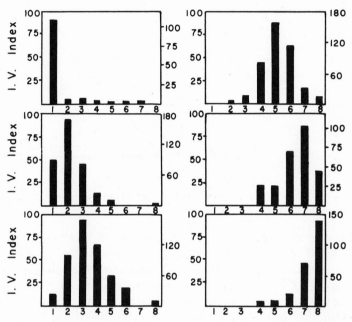

FIGURE 29.   Bar graphs of importance value indexes (IVI) of selected species along the continuum from *Quercus macrocarpa* and *Q. velutina* at the xerophytic end to *Acer saccharum* and *Tilia americana* at the mesophytic end of the forest continuum. Species clearly show consistent patterns of IVI along the continuum according to their ecological tolerances.

of trees. Inspection alone would not permit even an approximate rating of the leading species of the forest. The plot was divided into 20 strips 10 X 100 m., on which each tree was identified and measured so it was possible to determine relative density, relative frequency, and relative dominance (calculated from basal area) for each species—in other words, the IVI for the tree flora. The results are shown in Table 48 for the 44 leading species. These are all of the species that obtained a relative measure of 1 percent or more for at least one of the characteristics entering into the index. In other words, no other one of more than 100 species attained as much as 1 percent for any measure. The

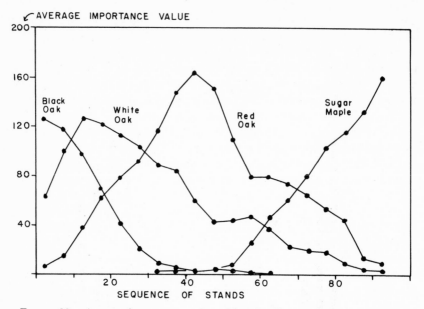

FIGURE 30. Average importance value of four leading species in the ecological sequence of the upland forest continuum.

leading species, *Vochysia guianensis,* has an IVI of 23.42 out of the total value of 300 (the sum of all indexes). The five leading species have a combined value of 86.15 out of 300, and the 44 leading species together total 229. There is obviously no clear dominance, nor even an approach to it, yet the use of the IVI permits the alignment of *every* species in the flora and brings considerable description and understanding of the community.

CLIMAX ADAPTATION NUMBER AND THE CONTINUUM INDEX

Further development of the techniques of combining community characteristics was a logical outcome of the work of Curtis and his colleagues. In their studies of importance values they found that each species reaches its optimum development (at least for the region under study) in stands whose position bears a definite relationship to that of other species, somewhat as colors form an orderly sequence in the spectrum. This sequence has correlations with other phenomena of interest in ecology, such as (1) stages in forest succession from pioneer to climax, (2) the mesophily sequence of Dansereau (149), (3) the shade tolerance sequence in common use by foresters (Baker,

23), (4) clinal series based on soil, etc. Furthermore, similar patterns are being revealed for shrubs, herbs, and many groups of animals associated with, or an integral part of, the upland forest complex of the region. As a consequence of the above, Curtis and McIntosh (147) established a 10-part scale of *climax adaptation numbers* in which *Acer saccharum,* at one end of the series because of its high IVI, was assigned the value 10, and *Quercus macrocarpa,* at the other end of the series, was assigned the value 1. Other species took their places because of their demonstrated positions in the "spectrum." The authors settled on the term "climax adaptation number" because the numbers show the "relative degree of climaxness" of the species, *Acer saccharum* being the species best adapted to maintain itself in the ecosystem of terminal forests of the region. On the basis of the same reasoning, *Quercus macrocarpa* is least adapted to the climactic ecosystem of the region, and other species fall in between, as shown in Table 49.

Rightly enough, Curtis and McIntosh do not seem too happy with

TABLE 49.   Climax adaptation numbers of tree species of the upland forest continuum of southern Wisconsin. (Curtis and McIntosh, 147)

Scientific Name	Common Name	Climax Adaptation Number
Quercus macrocarpa Michx.	Bur oak	1.0
Populus tremuloides Michx.	Trembling aspen	1.0
Acer negundo L.	Box elder	1.0[a]
Populus grandidentata Michx.	Large-tooth aspen	1.5
Quercus velutina Lam.	Black oak	2.0
Carya ovata (Mill.) K. Koch	Shagbark hickory	3.5
Prunus serotina Ehrh.	Black cherry	3.5
Quercus alba L.	White oak	4.0
Juglans nigra L.	Black walnut	5.0
Quercus rubra L.	Red oak	6.0
Juglans cinerea L.	Butternut	7.0
Ulmus thomasi Sarg.	Rock elm	7.0[a]
Acer rubrum L.	Red maple	7.0[a]
Fraxinus americana L.	White ash	7.5
Gymnocladus dioica (L) Koch	Kentucky coffee tree	7.5[a]
Tilia americana L.	Basswood	8.0
Ulmus rubra Muhl.	Slippery elm	8.0
Carpinus caroliniana Walt.	Blue beech	8.0[a]
Celtis occidentalis L.	Hackberry	8.0[a]
Carya cordiformis (Wang.) K. Koch	Yellowbud hickory	8.5
Ostrya virginiana (Mill.) K. Koch	Ironwood	9.0
Acer saccharum Marsh	Sugar maple	10.0[a]

[a] The climax adaptation number of these species is tentative, because of their low frequency in this study.

their choice of the expression "climax adaptation number," but what they lacked was "a word to encompass all of those adaptive physiological and morphological characters that differentiate plants of initial stands from plants of terminal stands." They are, however, still thinking in terms of succession, and in that frame of reference their term is satisfactory. The matter is more complex. In other regions such species as *Quercus macrocarpa* and *Q. velutina* may—in fact are—dominants of the terminal communities, and thus there they would have a "climax adaptation number" of 10, rather than 1 and 2. But even more confusing than this, within a single region there may be a mosaic of climaxes; and the stands that represent the climax in one ecosystem, as shown by leading dominants, may represent successional stages to a different climax. Thus the oaks mentioned above may be "preclimax" relics of a xerothermic period (according to the terminology of Clements) in a region where they are also dominants in a successional stage to a northern hardwoods climax. We propose, therefore, that the terms *ecological sequence index* and *ecological sequence number* would avoid the commitment to a particular climax that is implicit in the term "climax adaptation number."

A few data (Table 50) are now available for the comparison of climax adaptation numbers (Brown and Curtis, 66). The minor differ-

TABLE 50.   Comparison of climax adaptation numbers of some species in three regions of the United States (Brown and Curtis, 66)

	Great Smoky Mts. (Whittaker)	Wisconsin	
		Southwestern (Curtis and McIntosh)	Northeastern (Brown and Curtis)
Pinus strobus	3.3	. . .	5.0
Quercus velutina	3.9	2.0	. . .
Quercus alba	4.1	4.0	4.0
Acer rubrum	6.4	7.0	6.0
Quercus rubra	6.8	6.0	6.0
Fagus grandifolia	7.8	. . .	10.0
Tsuga canadensis	8.6	. . .	8.0
Betula lutea	9.3	. . .	8.0
Acer saccharum	9.4	10.0	10.0

ences in the values for these species are not as remarkable as their high degree of similarity. It must be remembered that two populations in different regions going under the same name may be considerably different genetically, and hence ecologically. This may be the case for *Fagus grandifolia*, which is the sole instance in the table of an important difference in climax adaptation numbers between the Great Smoky Mountains and Wisconsin, regions that are at least 1000 km. apart.

The *vegetation continuum index* is the product of the climax adaptation number multiplied by the importance value, as determined for each species of each stand from the sampling data. The climax adaptation number of each species in a stand is multiplied by the importance values and the products are added to give the stand a rating. All species play a role in this summation, and each stand can thereby be located in the vegetation continuum with the maximum utilization of the available data. The maximum possible value in the vegetation continuum index is, of course, 3000 (IVI 300 × CAN 10); and the minimum possible value is 300 (IVI 300 × CAN 1). Importance values for species in different stands can be plotted against the continuum index, from 300 to 3000.

Several factors in the environment have been studied in connection

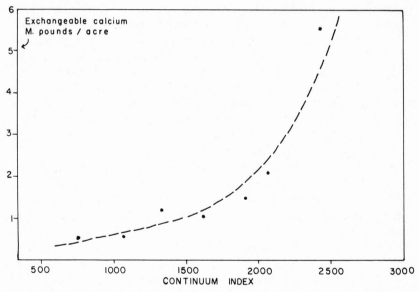

FIGURE 31.   Correlation between exchangeable calcium in the soil and the continuum (Curtis and McIntosh, 147).

with the investigation of the continuum. Figure 31 illustrates one such correlation, that of exchangeable calcium in thousands of pounds per acre plotted against the continuum index (Curtis and McIntosh, 147).

The concept of the continuum and the techniques of arriving at a continuum index are an important contribution to the science of vegetation analysis, and they bring into question several traditional concepts of formal plant ecology, such as that of the objective reality of the usual associations. The work of Curtis and Cottam and their associates is, in fact, a demonstration in support of Gleason's individualistic association hypothesis (Gleason, 212; Cain, 96). It is similar to the "sylvan continuum" of Darling (156).

LUTZ PHYTOGRAPHS

Lutz (281) introduced a polygonal figure for the purpose of diagraming simultaneously four characteristics of the structure of a forest. As shown in Figure 32 (1), four equiangular radii are used to graph the following data: (a) the percentage of total density of trees 10 in. d.b.h. and over that the given species composes; (b) frequency percentage of the species of the above size (this will vary with the quadrats used in sampling); (c) the occurrence of the species in five designated size classes (described below); (d) the dominance of the species, as measured by basal area and expressed as a percentage of the total. Lutz used the following five size classes: (1) reproduction up to 1 ft. high; (2) reproduction 1 to 12 ft. high; (3) saplings 1 to 3 in. d.b.h., (4) poles 4 to 9 in. d.b.h., (5) trees 10 in. d.b.h. or over. Later investigators either have used Lutz' original data basis or have revised the distribution through size classes by expressing this as a percentage figure of the maximum size of the species in the stand, thus placing the data of all four radii on an equivalent basis. Several workers—Cain (82, 86), Daubenmire (158), Eggler (176), etc.—found this device useful and applied it to their analyses of woods, for the phytograph gives a visual impression of the relative importance of the various species in a woods. Whitford (415) pointed out that the area within a phytograph is roughly comparable with the DFD value which we discussed earlier.

Figure 32 shows the schematic basis of the phytograph (1) and provides a few illustrations. In (2) the larger phytograph (QA) is that of *Quercus alba*, the dominant of a virgin forest in southern Indiana (Cain, 82); (QR) is the next most important species, *Quercus rubra*. In (3) there are phytographs of the two most important species of a virgin forest in southern Michigan: (FG) *Fagus grandifolia*, the dominant, and (AS) *Acer saccharum*, the next most important species (Cain, 86). The phytographs in (4) are (AS) *Acer saccharum*, the dominant, and (TA) *Tilia americana*, the next important species, in a woods in Minnesota (Buell and Cantlon, 71).

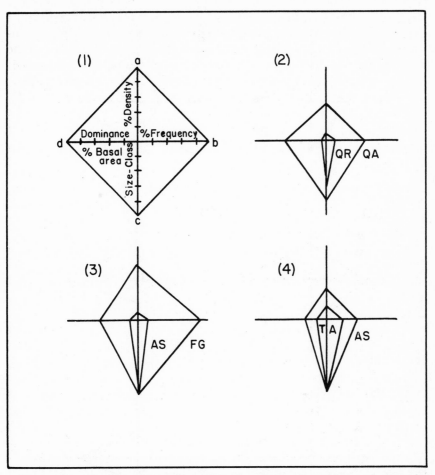

FIGURE 32.   (1) shows the radii used in the construction of Lutz phytographs. (2) Phytographs for *Quercus alba* (QA) and *Q. rubra* (QR) in a virgin forest in southern Indiana (Cain, 82). (3) Phytographs for *Acer saccharum* (AS) and *Fagus grandifolia* (FG) in a virgin forest in southern Michigan (Cain, 86). (4) Phytographs for *Acer saccharum* (AS) and *Tilia americana* (TA) in a hardwood forest in Minnesota (Buell and Cantlon, 71).

Figure 33 shows the phytographs for spruce and fir species in widely separated forests, as studied by Oosting and Billings (304) in the eastern United States, and by Oosting and Reed (305) in the western United States. (1) is the phytograph for *Picea rubens* in the southern Appalachians, and (3) is the same species in the northern Appalachians. (2) is *Abies fraseri,* the endemic fir of the southern Appalachians, and (4) is *Abies balsamea,* its widespread counterpart in the Northeast. For the

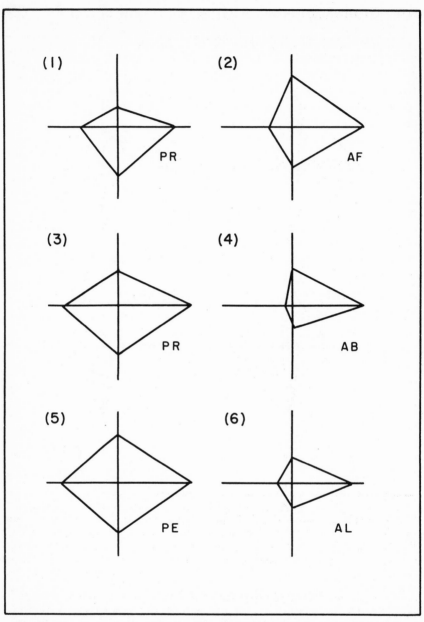

FIGURE 33.   Lutz phytographs for *Picea* and *Abies* codominants in United States forests (1) *Picea rubens* from the southern Appalachian Mountains; (3) *Picea rubens* from the northern Appalachians; (5) *Picea engelmanni* from the Rocky Mountains; (2) *Abies fraseri* from the southern Appalachians; (4) *Abies balsamea* from the northern Appalachians; (6) A*bies lasiocarpa* from the Rocky Mountains. (Data from Oosting and Billings, 304, and Oosting and Reed, 305.)

spruce-fir forests of the Rocky Mountains of Wyoming, phytograph (5) is for *Picea engelmanmi,* the leading dominant of the formation there, and (6) is *Abies lasiocarpa,* its common associate. Merkle (290) and Roach (347) have made good use of phytographs in comparative studies of conifer-dominated forests of Oregon, as have many investigators in other regions.

COVERAGE-STRATIFICATION DIAGRAM

A second graphic scheme of considerable interest is the simultaneous diagraming of the horizontal strata (layers) of vegetation and the total or combined coverage in each layer. Coverage of a layer is expressed either as the average total coverage in percentage or according to standard cover classes; the layers can be diagramed to scale according to height, except that the proportion of the ground layer

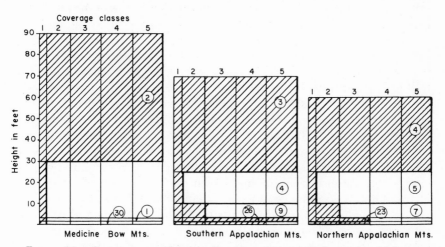

FIGURE 34. Coverage-stratification diagrams of spruce-fir forests in widely separated regions of the United States. Circled figures show the number of species and shaded areas the cover class in each stratum.

may have to be exaggerated. Figure 34 shows coverage-stratification diagrams for *Picea-Abies* forests in the southern and northern Appalachian Mountains (eastern United States) and in the Medicine Bow Mountains (western United States) (Oosting and Billings, 304; Oosting and Reed, 305). The circled figures are the number of species in each layer. In addition to the generalized structure that is indicated by the coverage-stratification diagram, there are several possible refinements that are illuminating. It is possible, for example, to divide the coverage within a layer in order to show the proportion of the leading species making up the coverage, as shown in a *Taxodium* woods (Cain, 84). The role played by transgressives of the dominant species can be shown in the coverage of the inferior strata (Cain, 86), as for example in woods dominated by *Acer saccharum* that have heavy *Acer* reproduction. These diagrams are related to profiles, as shown by Richards (344) for tropical rain forests, but each has its own special uses. The profile can show exactly the structure of one woods at a single intersect; the coverage-stratification diagram can generalize a regional pattern.

On the grounds of the Instituto Agronômico do Sul, Pelotas, Rio Grande do Sul, there is a primitive woods of about 8 ha. that has been carefully studied as to floristic composition and is being preserved for ecological study (Luis and Bertels, 278). In July, 1955, Cain and José da Costa Sacco, Chief of the Botany Section of the Instituto, made a preliminary analysis of the woods, assigning the species of the published list to strata. Since then Dr. Sacco has carefully revised the table by eliminating adventives and species not properly in the woods, adding others not previously listed, and reassigning species to synusiae where necessary, so that in Table 51 each species is listed according to the tallest stratum it attains. In this very dense woods time did not permit quantitative analysis, but species have been divided into two groups, those that appear to be definitely important in each stratum and the remainder that are less important because of low numbers, coverage, or spotty occurrence. As in the case of most tropical and subtropical woods, the strata often are not readily seen. But they do exist as can be shown by the maximum mature heights of various life forms. The predominance of woody plants in the flora and the abundance of seedlings of woody plants in the lower layers and of transgressives[1] in the intermediate layers tend to obscure the natural existence of layers. Furthermore, it is characteristic for the upper limits of strata to be irregular, whereas in temperate woods the strata often are remarkably uniform in height.

Our coverage-stratification diagram for Horto Botânico (Figure 35) attempts to illustrate some of these features. Maximum heights of trees in the superior stratum (A) vary from about 15 to 20 m.; and, not shown in the diagram, occasional trees emerge to about 25 m. We endeavor to suggest this irregularity in stratum A, and in B and C as well, by lighter shading in the upper parts of these layers in the coverage-stratification diagram. The coverage percentage shown for each

[1] In this sense, a "transgressive" is a species that must pass through (vertically) one or more layers as it develops from seedling to its mature life-form stature.

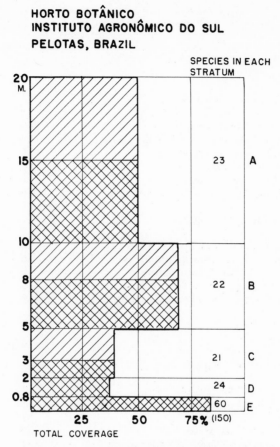

FIGURE 35.   Modified coverage-stratification diagram of virgin woods, Horto Botânico Instituto Agronômico do Sul, Pelotas, Rio Grande do Sul. Strata
A–C have lighter shading at the top to indicate that
they are variable in height between the limits indicated. See the text for details.

layer, however, is the total coverage for the layer. The table also shows
symbols for the life form[2] and leaf-size class of each species. These are
discussed elsewhere in this *Manual,* and also by Cain, Castro, *et al.* (103).

Taking further advantage of the complete species list for this woods,
we have organized Table 52 by plant families. Not only is there no

[2] The term "annual" as used by the botanists at the Instituto does not mean "therophyte" or
true annual in which all plant parts die each year except the seeds, but is applied to all herbaceous forms dying back to the ground. Hence the statistics in Figure 34 for "annuals" do not
match the life-form data for therophytes in Table 51.

TABLE 51.   Composition and structure of the natural forest of the Horto Botânico do Instituto Agronômico do Sul, Pelotas, Rio Grande do Sul. Species are arranged by strata, life-form[a] and leaf-size classes,[b] with a distinction between those more and those less important. (Basic data by Dr. José da Costa Sacco, with the assistance of the authors)

	Life Form	Leaf Size
A. *Tall tree stratum:* 15–20 (25) m. Total coverage 50%		
More Important Species		
Luehea divaricata Mart. & Zucc. Tiliaceae	Ms	Ms
Arecastrum romanzoffianum (Cham.) Becc. Palmae	Ms	Ms
Sorocea illicifolia Miq. Moraceae	Ms	Ms
Patagonula americana L. Borraginaceae	Ms	Mi
Ficus subtriplinervia Mart. Moraceae	Ms	Mi
Allophylus edulis (St. Hil.) Radlk. Sapindaceae	Ms	Mi
Less Important Species		
Quillaja brasiliensis (St. Hil.) Mart. Rosaceae	Ms	Mi
Citharexylum montevidense (Spreng.) Moldenke Verbenaceae	Ms	Mi
Xylosma salzmanni Eichl. Flacourtiaceae	Ms	Mi
Ocotea pulchella Mart. Lauraceae	Ms	Mi
Phyllocalix involucratus (DC). Berg. Myrtaceae	Ms	Mi
B. *Intermediate tree stratum:* (7) 8–10 m. Total coverage 70%		
More Important Species		
Pircunia dioica (L.) Moq. Phytolaccaceae	Ms	Ms
Myrsine umbellata Mart. Myrsinaceae	Ms	Ms
Pisonia nitida Mart. Nyctaginaceae	Ms	Ms
Trichilia catigua A. Juss. Meliaceae	Ms	Ms
Maba inconstans (Jacq.) Griseb. Ebenaceae	Ms	Mi
Acanthosyris spinescens (Mart. & Eichl.) Griseb. Santalaceae	Ms	Mi
Vitex montevidensis Cham. Verbenaceae	Ms	Mi
Actinostemon caribaeus Griseb. Euphorbiaceae	Ms	Mi
Cupania vernalis Cambess. Sapindaceae	Ms	Mi
Lithraea brasiliensis March. Anacardiaceae	Ms	Mi
Less Important Species		
Solanum swartzianum Roem. & Schult. Solanaceae	Ms	Ms
Myrsine ferruginea Spreng. Myrsinaceae	Ms	Ms
Trema micrantha (L.) Blume Ulmaceae	Ms	Ms
Campomanesia aurea Berg. Myrtaceae	Ms	Ms
Chuquiraga spinescens Baker Compositae	Ms	Mi
Fagara rhoifolia (Lam.) Engl. Rutaceae	Ms	Mi
Iodina rhombifolia Hook. & Arn. Santalaceae	Ms	Mi
Sebastiana klotzchiana Muell. Arg. Euphorbiaceae	Ms	?

Table 51—*(Continued)*

	Life Form	Leaf Size
C. *Low tree and high shrub stratum:* 3–5 m. Total coverage 40%		

More Important Species

	Life Form	Leaf Size
Myrcianthes gigantea Legrand. Myrtaceae	Mi	Ms
Basanacantha spinosa (Jacq.) K. Sch. Rubiaceae	Mi	Ms
Erythrina crista-galli L. Leguminosae	Mi	Ms
Celtis spinosa Spreng. Ulmaceae	Mi	Mi
Casearia silvestris Sw. Flacourtiaceae	Mi	Mi
Sambucus australis Cham. & Schlecht. Caprifoliaceae	Mi	Mi
Schinus polygamus (Cav.) Cabrera Anacardiaceae	Mi	Mi
Eugenia uniflora L. Myrtaceae	Mi	Mi
Fagara hiemalis (St. Hil.) Engl. Rutaceae	Mi	N
Cereus peruvianus (L.) Mill. Cactaceae	Mi	A

Less Important Species

	Life Form	Leaf Size
Scutia buxifolia Reiss. Rhamnaceae	Mi	Mi
Styrax leprosum Hook. & Arn. Styracaceae	Mi	Mi
Berberis laurina Thunb. Berberidaceae	Mi	Mi
Dodonaea viscosa Jacq. Sapindaceae	Mi	Mi
Cestrum parqui L'Herit. Solanaceae	Mi	Mi
Myrrhinium rubiflorum Berg. Myrtaceae	Mi	Mi

	Life Form	Leaf Size
D. *Low shrub stratum:* 0.8–2.0 m. Total coverage 30–40%		

More Important Species

	Life Form	Leaf Size
Abutilon molle (Ort.) Sweet. Malvaceae	N	Ms
Daphnopsis racemosa Griseb. Thymelaeaceae	N	Ms
Dianthera nodosa Benth. & Hook. f. Acanthaceae	N	Ms
Solanum auriculatum Ait. Solanaceae	N	Ms
Baccharis spicata (Lam.) Baillon Compositae	N	Mi
Eupatorium buniifolium Hook. & Arn. Compositae	N	Mi
Pavonia communis St. Hil. Malvaceae	N	Mi
Baccharis dracunculifolia DC. Compositae	N	N
Baccharis articulata (Lam.) Pers. Compositae	N	Le
Calliandra tweedii Benth. Leguminosae	N	Le
Opuntia monacantha Haw. Cactaceae	N	A

Less Important Species

	Life Form	Leaf Size
Abutilon pauciflorum St. Hil. Malvaceae	N	Ma
Eupatorium inulaefolium HBK. Compositae	N	Ms
Lantana camara L. Verbenaceae	N	Ms
Buettneria urticifolia K. Sch. Sterculiaceae	N	Mi
Guadua trinii (Nees) Rupr. Gramineae	N	Mi

TABLE 51—*(Continued)*

	Life Form	Leaf Size
Guttarda uruquensis Cham. & Schlecht. Rubiaceae	N	Mi
Discaria longispina Miers. Rhamnaceae	N	Le

E. *Herb stratum:* 0–0.8 m.
Total coverage 80–90%

Perennial plants, normally evergreen

More Important Species

Clidemia hirta (L.) D. Don Melastomaceae	N	Ms
Baccharis anomala DC. Compositae	N	Mi
Solanum gracile Dun. Solanaceae	N	Mi
Baccharis ochracea Spreng. Compositae	N	Le
Bromelia antiacantha Bertol. Bromeliaceae	Ch	Ma
Tradescantia fluminensis Vell. Commelinaceae	Ch	Mi
Oplismenus hirtellus (L.) Beauv. Gramineae	Ch	Mi
Chaptalia nutans (L.) Polak. Compositae	H	Ms
Elephantopus tomentosus L. Compositae	H	Mi
Paspalum inaequivale Raddi Gramineae	H	Mi
Paspalum paniculatum L. Gramineae	H	Mi
Paspalum mandiocanum Trin. Gramineae	H	Mi
Panicum helobium Mez. Gramineae	H	Mi
Panicum missionum Ekman Gramineae	H	Mi
Panicum laxum Sw. Gramineae	H	Mi
Canna indica L. Cannaceae	G	Ms
Pharus glaber HBK. Gramineae	G	Ms
Oxalis sellowiana Zucc. Oxalidaceae	G	Mi
Solanum sisymbrifolium Lam. Solanaceae	?	Ms

Less Important Species

Begonia semperflorens Link & Otto Begoniaceae	N	Ms
Solanum ciliatum Lam. Solonaceae	N	Ms
Heimia salicifolia (HBK.) Link & Otto Lythraceae	N	N
Solanum capsicastrum Link. Solanaceae	N	N
Baccharis gaudichaudiana DC. Compositae	N	A
Baccharis sagittalis (Less.) DC. Compositae	N	A
Baccharis trimera (Less.) DC. Compositae	N	A
Baccharis usterii Heering Compositae	Ch	Mi
Blechnum brasiliense Desv. Polypodiaceae	Ch	Mi
Doryopteris pedata (L.) Fee Polypodiaceae	H	Ms
Polygonum hydropiperoides Michx. Polygonaceae	H	Mi
Blechnum auriculatum Cav. Polypodiaceae	H	N

TABLE 51—*(Continued)*

	Life Form	Leaf Size
Plants normally dying back to the ground, or nearly so		

More Important Species

	Life Form	Leaf Size
Stipa megapotamica Spreng. Gramineae	H	Ms
Alternanthera pilosa Moq. Amaranthaceae	H	Mi
Urtica urens L. Urticaceae	H	Mi
Salpichroa origanifolia (Lam.) Thell. Solanaceae	H	N
Piptochaetium montevidense (Spreng.) Parodi Gramineae	H	N
Piptochaetium bicolor (Vahl.) E. Desv. Gramineae	H	N
Hyptis mutabilis (Rich.) Briq. Labiatae	G	Mi
Oenothera longiflora L. Onagraceae	G	Mi
Bidens pilosa L. Compositae	Th	Mi
Silene gallica L. Caryophyllaceae	Th	Mi
Senecio brasiliensis (Spreng.) Less. Compositae	Th	N
Sida rhombifolia L. Malvaceae	Th	N

Less Important Species

	Life Form	Leaf Size
Aristida altissima Arech. Gramineae	H	Mi
Conyza notobellidiastrum Griseb. Compositae	H	Mi
Paspalum plicatum (Michx.) Pers. Gramineae	H	Mi
Vernonia polyanthes Less. Compositae	H	Mi
Piptochaetium lasianthum Griseb. Gramineae	H	N
Stipa melanosperma J. Presl. Gramineae	H	N
Borreria centranthoides Cham. & Schlecht. Rubiaceae	G	Mi
Geranium albicans St. Hil. Geraniaceae	G	Mi
Briza subaristata Lam. Gramineae	Th	Mi
Bromus uruguayensis Arech. Gramineae	Th	Mi
Bromus unioloides HBK. Gramineae	Th	Mi
Verbena dissecta Willd. Verbenaceae	?	N
Iresine celosioides L. Amaranthaceae	?	Mi
Rivina humilis L. Phytolaccaceae	?	Mi
Acanthospermum australe (Loefl.) O. Ktz. Compositae	?	?
Polycarpon tetraphyllum (L.) L. Caryophyllaceae	?	?
Jussieua fruticosa DC. Onagraceae	?	?

F. *Lianas,* listed according to the highest stratum attained, notation as above

A stratum

	Life Form	Leaf Size
Passiflora suberosa L. Passifloraceae	Li	Ms
Passiflora elegans Mast. Passifloraceae	Li	Mi
Bignonia unguis-cati L. Bignoniaceae	Li	Mi

TABLE 51—(Continued)

B stratum	Life Form	Leaf Size
Pithecoctenium echinatum (Aubl.) K. Sch. Bignoniaceae	Li	Ms
Smilax campestris Griseb. Liliaceae	Li	Ms
C stratum		
Cissampelos pareira L. Menispermaceae	Li	Mi
Clematis bonariensis Juss. Raunuculaceae	Li	Mi
Canavalia bonariensis Lindl. Leguminosae	Li	Mi
Phaseolus adenanthus G.F.W. Mey. Leguminosae	Li	Mi
Orthosia aphylla (Vell.) Malme Asclepiadaceae	Li	Le
D stratum		
Passiflora caerulea L. Passifloraceae	Li	Ms
Janusia guaranitica (St. Hil.) A. Juss. Malpighiaceae	Li	Mi
Urvillea uniloba Radlk. Sapindaceae	Li	Mi
Muehlenbeckia sagittifolia Meissn. Polygonaceae	Li	Mi
Chymocarpus pentaphyllus (Lam.) D. Don Tropaeolaceae	Li	N
Solanum boerraviaefolium Sendt. Solanaceae	Li	?

G. *Vascular epiphytes,* listed according to the highest
   stratum attained

A stratum		
Aechmea legrelliana Baker Bromeliaceae	E	Ms
Aechmea gamosepala Wittm. Bromeliaceae	E	Ms
Phoradendron sp. Loranthaceae (Hemiparasite)	E	Mi
Polypodium vacciniifolium Langsd. & Fisch. Polypodiaceae	E	Mi
Tillandsia aeranthos (Loisel) L. B. Smith Bromeliaceae	E	Mi
Tillandsia usneoides L. Bromeliaceae	E	Le
Rhipsalis aculeata Weber Cactaceae	E	A
Rhipsalis sarmentacea Otto & Dietr. Cactaceae	E	A
Rhipsalis saglionis Otto Cactaceae	E	A
B stratum		
Gen. sp. Orchidaceae	E	Mi
Peperomia deppeana Schlecht. & Cham. Piperaceae	E	N

[a] Symbols used for life-form classes:
  Ms—Mesophanerophyte
  Mi—Microphanerophyte
  N—Nanophanerophyte
  Ch—Chamaephyte
  H—Hemicryptophyte
  G—Geophyte (Cryptophyte)
  Th—Therophyte
  Li—Liana
  E—Epiphyte (vascular)

[b] Symbols used for leaf-size classes:
  Ma—Macrophyll
  Ms—Mesophyll
  Mi—Microphyll
  N—Nanophyll
  Le—Leptophyll
  A—Aphyllus

TABLE 52. Floristic composition of the synusiae of the Horto Botânico, Pelotas, as shown by the number of species in each family

Families	Tall Tree Stratum A	Intermediate Tree Stratum B	Low Tree Stratum C	Low Shrub Stratum D	Herb Stratum E	Lianas F	Epiphytes G	Total
Compositae	..	1	..	6	13	..	..	20
Gramineae	..	..	..	1	18	..	..	19
Solanaceae	..	1	1	1	5	1	..	9
Bromeliaceae	..	..	..	..	1	..	4	5
Cactaceae	..	..	1	1	..	..	3	5
Myrtaceae	1	2	2	..	..	..	..	5
Leguminosae	..	..	1	1	..	2	..	4
Malvaceae	..	..	..	3	1	..	..	4
Verbenaceae	1	1	..	1	1	..	..	4
Passifloraceae	..	..	..	..	..	3	..	3
Polypodiaceae	..	..	..	..	2	..	1	3
Rubiaceae	..	..	1	1	1	..	..	3
Sapindaceae	1	1	..	..	..	1	..	3
Amaranthaceae	..	..	..	..	2	..	..	2
Anacardiaceae	..	1	1	..	..	..	..	2
Bignoniaceae	..	..	..	..	..	2	..	2
Caryophyllaceae	..	..	..	..	2	..	..	2
Euphorbiaceae	..	2	..	..	..	..	..	2
Flacourtiaceae	1	..	1	..	..	..	..	2
Moraceae	2	..	..	..	..	..	..	2
Myrsinaceae	..	2	..	..	..	..	..	2
Onagraceae	..	..	..	..	2	..	..	2
Phytolaccaceae	..	1	..	..	1	..	..	2
Polygonaceae	..	..	..	..	1	1	..	2
Rutaceae	..	1	1	..	..	..	..	2
Santalaceae	..	2	..	..	..	..	..	2
Ulmaceae	..	1	1	..	..	..	..	2
Acanthaceae	..	..	..	1	..	..	..	1
Asclepiadaceae	..	..	..	..	..	1	..	1
Begoniaceae	..	..	..	..	1	..	..	1
Berberidaceae	..	..	1	..	..	..	..	1
Boraginaceae	1	..	..	..	..	..	..	1
Cannaceae	..	..	..	..	1	..	..	1
Caprifoliaceae	..	..	1	..	..	..	..	1
Commelinaceae	..	..	..	..	1	..	..	1
Ebenaceae	..	1	..	..	..	..	..	1
Geraniaceae	..	..	..	..	1	..	..	1

TABLE 52—*(Continued)*

Families	Tall Tree Stratum	Intermediate Tree Stratum	Low Tree Stratum	Low Shrub Stratum	Herb Stratum	Lianas	Epiphytes	Total
	A	B	C	D	E	F	G	Total
Labiatae	..	..	..	..	1	..	..	1
Lauraceae	1	..	..	..	..	..	..	1
Liliaceae	..	..	..	..	..	1	..	1
Lythraceae	..	..	..	..	1	..	..	1
Malpighiaceae	..	..	..	..	..	1	..	1
Melastomaceae	..	..	..	..	1	..	..	1
Meliaceae	..	1	..	..	..	..	..	1
Menispermaceae	..	..	..	..	..	1	..	1
Nyctaginaceae	..	1	..	..	..	..	..	1
Oxalidaceae	..	..	..	..	1	..	..	1
Palmae	1	..	..	..	..	..	..	1
Piperaceae	..	..	..	..	..	..	1	1
Ranunculaceae	..	..	..	..	..	1	..	1
Rosaceae	1	..	..	..	..	..	..	1
Sterculiaceae	..	..	..	1	..	..	..	1
Styracaceae	..	..	1	..	..	..	..	1
Tiliaceae	1	..	..	..	..	..	..	1
Thymelaeaceae	..	..	..	1	..	..	..	1
Tropaeolaceae	..	..	..	..	..	1	..	1
Urticaceae	..	..	..	..	1	..	..	1
Totals (57)	11	19	13	18	59	16	9	145

dominance in this woods by one or a few species in a layer, but there is no family dominance. For the whole flora the average is about 2.5 species per family; if we omit the Compositae and Gramineae, which do not give physiognomic dominance, the average is 2.

DANSEREAU'S STRUCTURAL-PHYSIOGNOMIC CLASSIFICATION

Schimper (360), Warming (409), Rübel (353), Schimper and Faber (361), and others have developed systems of classifying vegetation that do not depend on floristic characteristics but represent an appreciation of the structure of the vegetation. Dansereau (152) has carried this evolution to its furthest development, building on the idea of a flexible system that is embodied in the climatic classification of Köppen (259) and the geographical system of Küchler (262, 263, 264, 265). In subsequent publications (153, 155) Dansereau has further developed his system and applied it variously to vegetation of the world, according to Schimper and Faber (361), and to various regions. His recent *Biogeography* (155) should be sought for illustrations, especially matched drawings and symbolic representations that are highly readable in their simpler forms and somewhat more difficult when an attempt is made to show many features of the vegetational structure and the life forms of the plants.

Dansereau's system employs six categories of criteria, symbolized in sequence by letters: (1) *Life form:* T—trees, F—shrubs, H—herbs, M—bryoids, E—epiphytes, L—lianas; (2) *size:* t—tall, m—medium, l—low (with size limits for T, F, H, and M); (3) *coverage:* b—barren, i—discontinuous, p—in tufts or groups, c—continuous; (4) *function:* d—deciduous, s—semi-deciduous, e—evergreen, j—evergreen succulent or evergreen-leafless; (5) *leaf shape and size:* n—needle or spine, g—graminoid, a—medium or small, h—broad, v—compound, q—thalloid; (6) *leaf texture:* f—filmy, z—membranous, x—sclerophyll, k—succulent. Categories 1, 4, 5, and 6 have corresponding diagrammatic symbols that are combined according to the structure of the vegetations; hence any stand can be represented by both letters and diagrams in a flexible system.

This is a nonquantitative system for the description and recording of vegetation on a structural basis. It has no concern with floristics. Number, cover, and pattern are given only general estimates, yet the system can be handled by an investigator in an objective, if nonquantitative, manner. It permits useful discriminations. The results are mappable. It is rapid. If it were not for Dansereau's new book (155) and the numerous and handsome illustrations it contains, we would devote more space to this system that simultaneously employs a wide combination of vegetational characteristics.

Chapter 11

CONCEPTS IMPORTANT IN SYNTHESIS

PRESENCE AND CONSTANCY

As we have seen, floristic geography is basically a systematization of the various combinations of species that characterize various regions; and the units of territory in floristic geography are variously defined political units (county, state, province), geographical units (island, mountain, continent), or natural area determined jointly by some aspect of the environmental complex and the limits of occurrence of selected species. In plant sociology floristic composition is naturally related to communities; i.e., territories are defined by their occupancy by a stand of a community, by the combination of the several stands of a community type, by alliances of communities, by formations, etc. As soon as botanists commenced making more or less complete lists of the species of communities and comparing these lists, certain concepts began to crystallize that are very useful in the analysis of vegetation: presence, constancy, fidelity.

The *presence* of a species is the degree of regularity with which a species reoccures in different examples of a community type. According to Braun-Blanquet (58), Lorenz (276) meant by "presence" the more or less persistent occurrence of a species in all the stands of a certain plant community; but the concept became established only after Cajander (104) presented tabular comparisons of the species lists from stands of an association, and Brockmann-Jerosch (63) compared the lists from different kinds of associations.

No community type occurs in a single continuous stand, but is represented in nature by more or less scattered examples of various sizes occurring throughout its range along with examples of other kinds of associations. Under primitive conditions such a pattern results from heterogeneity of the environment produced by the areal patterns of occurrence of topographic, geologic, edaphic, and other complexes. Deforestation, agriculture, and other activities of man produce a further heterogeneity by the artificial fragmentation of once continuous stands into more or less isolated remnants with unnatural boundaries. It thus happens that in many regions of the earth a stand of a community type is a comprehensible unit from which a more or less complete list of species can be obtained, the *floristic relevé*. When lists from different stands of a community type are compared, it is found that certain species occur in all or most of the lists, others in only a few, etc. Thus developed the idea of degree of presence which is expressed in percentage or, following Braun-Blanquet, by assignment of each species to one of a limited number of presence classes, as follows:

Presence Class 1: Species found in 1 to 20 percent of the concrete examples of the association studied
Presence Class 2: Species of 21 to 40 percent presence
Presence Class 3: Species of 41 to 60 percent presence
Presence Class 4: Species of 61 to 80 percent presence
Presence Class 5: Species of 81 to 100 percent presence

Employment of the concept of presence is illustrated in Table 53, describing the heath bald association of the Great Smoky Mountains (Cain, 80). This subalpine community dominated by broadleaf evergreen shrubs occurs naturally in isolated stands, on ridges like islands in the sea of the *Picea-Abies* forest. Although the list includes only woody plants, the significance of the comparison is not lost, for herbaceous species are extremely few in number. The tabular comparison shows some correlation between species (number and presence) and altitude, and some variability is introduced by differences in stand size that are not shown in the table. As is quite typical, some species have a high degree of presence, some are intermediate, and a relatively large number belong to Classes 1 and 2. There are two readily apparent weaknesses in presence if employed alone for the characterization of associations. (1) Different stands are of different sizes, and on the average the larger the stand the larger the species list; and (2)

TABLE 53. The presence of 34 species of woody plants in 17 stands of the heath bald association of the Great Smoky Mountains, Tennessee (Cain, 80)

Species	6500 Ft.						5000 Ft.						4000 Ft.				
	1	2	3	4	5	6	1	2	3	4	5	6	1	2	3	4	5
Rhododendron catawbiense	(X)	x	x	x	x	x	(X)	x	x	x	(X)	(X)	x	x	x	(X)	x
Vaccinium corymbosum	x	x	x	(X)	x	x	(X)	(X)	x	x	x	(X)	x	x	(X)	(X)	x
Rhododendron punctatum	(X)	(X)	(X)	(X)	(X)	(X)	x	x	x	x	(X)	x					
Dendrium prostratum (Leiophyllum)	(X)		(X)	(X)		(X)	x	(X)	x	x	(X)	(X)					
Vaccinium erythrocarpum	x	x	x	x	x	x	x										
Menziesia pilosa	x	x	x	x		x											
Pyrus americana (Sorbus)	x	x	x	x													
Prunus pensylvanica	x	x															
Picea rubens	x			x	x	x											
Abies fraseri	x			x	x	x											
Ribes prostratum			x														
Rubus canadensis		x	x					x		x	x	x				x	
Diervilla sessilifolia			x							x	x	x				x	
Kalmia latifolia							(X)	(X)	(X)	(X)	x	x	(X)	(X)	(X)	(X)	(X)
Pyrus melanocarpa (Aronia)							x		x		x	x	x				x
Lyonia ligustrina							x			x	x						x
Gaylussacia baccata							x				x	x					x
Nyssa sylvatica							x				x	x					x

Species														
Ilex monticola									x	x		x	x	x
Clethra acuminata								x	x	x	x	x	x	x
Viburnum cassinoides							x	x	x		x		x	x
Smilax rotundifolia						x	x			x	x	x	x	x
Acer rubrum						x		x		x	x	x	x	x
Robinia pseudoacacia						x							x	x
Andromeda floribunda						(X)					x	x	x	x
Amelanchier canadensis					x		x			x	x	x	x	x
Rhododendron maximum					x		x		x	x	x	x	x	x
Leucothoë catesbaei					x				x	x	x	x		x
Oxydendrum arboreum					x							x		x
Pinus pungens							x	x		x	x			x
Sassafras variifolium											x			x
Gaylussacia ursina													x	x
Castanea dentata													x	x
Hammamelis virginiana														x
Average number of species for each altitudinal group of stands	9				11					14				

(X) = Species is dominant in the stand.
x = Species is present, but not dominant.

no distinction is made between species represented by only a few plants
and those that are large in number. Finally, tabular comparisons of
floristic lists must be based on truly comparable stands, for differences
in maturity of the community, in altitude of the stands (as in Table
53), in geographical occurrence (distance) etc., are likely to introduce
heterogeneity that diminishes the validity of presence statistics. On
the other hand, comparisons against such variables make clear the
role of the factor. For example, in the heath bald association table
there are only 2 species of Class 5 presence out of a total of 34; but
for the stands occurring in the highest altitudinal belt there are 4 out
of 9 species that are of Class 5 presence. *Rhododendron catawbiense* and
Vaccinium corymbosum (complex) have Class 5 presence in all altitudinal
belts; *Rhododendron punctatum* and *Vaccinium erythrocarpum* are also Class
5 in the high-altitude belt; *Rhododendron punctatum, Dendrium prostratum,*
and *Kalmia latifolia* are Class 5 in the intermediate belt; and *Kalmia
latifolia, Clethra acuminata, Ilex monticola, Smilax rotundifolia,* and *Rhododendron maximum* are Class 5 in the low-altitude belt.

Rather extensive employment of the presence method of comparing
stands of a community type or of related types has been made by Dansereau (149) on the Laurentian forests of *Acer saccharum* and by Curtis
and Greene on Wisconsin prairies (145). The latter authors point out
that quick methods of comparison, such as the determination of presence, permit wide-ranging studies of a type of vegetation and might
well precede local intensive analyses of "typical" stands. In fact, it is
difficult to know what a "typical" stand is until after broad reconnaissance studies have been made. Curtis and Greene studied 65 relic
prairie stands that occurred on four distinct land types, and although
they did not use exactly delimited constant sample areas, they usually prepared their species lists from tracts of not less than 4 acres
(16,000 sq. m.) and eliminated any stands as "fragmentary" that had
lists smaller than 30 species. All the stands had a total of 237 species.
The low prairie, on poorly drained flatlands, had 179 species of the total;
the high prairie, on internally well-drained uplands, had 172 species;
the dry lime prairies, on thin soils over limestone with excellent surface
drainage, had 126 species. No perfect indicator species was found in
these prairies, i.e., a species present in all stands of one type of prairie
and absent from the stands of all other types. If the critical level of presence is lowered to include species that have a presence above 66.7
percent for one prairie type and below 33.3 percent for all other types,
then 8 species qualify as indicators of the low prairie, 2 species for the
dry lime prairie, 1 species for the high prairie, and 0 for the sand prairie
type. Curtis and Greene finally prepared a table of 84 species, each

of which attains at least 50 percent presence in one prairie type, regardless of their occurrence in other types. These are the constant species of Brockmann-Jerosch (63). From the Curtis and Greene table we reproduce in Table 54 only the species designated as preferential because they occurred with a presence in one type at least 10 percent greater than in any other type.

Although there are several apparent weaknesses in the use of presence data alone, certain interesting points can be brought out, as illustrated in Figure 36. Some species occur in the different prairie types

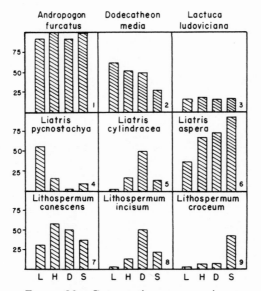

FIGURE 36. Comparative presence, in percentage, of certain species in relic prairie stands. L = low, poorly drained prairie; H = high, internally well-drained prairie; D = dry prairie on thin soil over limestone; S = sand prairie.

with about the same presence; but in one case the percentage is high *(Andropogon furcatus)* and in another it is low *(Lactuca ludoviciana)*. Some species occur in all types but have a decided preference for one type *(Liatris pycnostachya, Lithospermum croceum)*. Congenors may have—in fact, are likely to have—sharply different ecological preferences, as indicated by their different degrees of presence in the various prairie types. Another point brought out by the complete presence lists, not shown in our abbreviated table, is that five families (Compositae, Gramineae, Leguminosae, Asclepiadaceae, Umbelliferae) together

TABLE 54. Presence percentages of "preferential" species in four types of relic prairie in Wisconsin (Curtis and Greene, 145)

Species	Low Prairies	High Prairies	Lime Prairies	Sand Prairies
Coreopsis palmata	50.0	(89.5)	68.8	71.5
Liatris aspera	37.5	68.4	75.0	(93.0)
Helianthus rigidus	68.8	(84.3)	56.2	21.4
Petalostemum purpureum	56.2	52.6	(93.8)	50.0
Asclepias syriaca	68.8	(84.3)	43.7	35.7
Aster ericoides	43.7	(84.3)	62.5	14.3
Andropogon scoparius	43.7	26.3	75.0	(85.8)
Rhus glabra	37.5	63.1	(75.0)	28.6
Rudbeckia hirta	(93.8)	42.1	18.7	35.7
Lespedeza capitata	50.0	52.6	18.7	(78.6)
Potentilla arguta	25.0	57.9	(68.8)	35.7
Anemone cylindrica	31.2	52.6	(68.8)	21.4
Aster laevis	50.0	(79.0)	31.2	. . .
Helianthus grosseserratus	(75.0)	57.9	25.0	7.1
Solidago nemoralis	31.2	36.8	(68.8)	42.9
Eryngium yuccifolium	(75.0)	47.4	18.7	21.4
Lactuca canadensis	(68.8)	47.4	37.5	14.3
Physalis virginiana	18.7	47.4	(62.5)	28.6
Sisyrinchium campestre	56.2	31.6	43.7	28.6
Aster sericeus	. . .	36.8	(75.0)	42.9
Desmodium canadense	(68.8)	57.9	6.2	14.3
Elymus canadensis	(68.8)	52.6	18.7	14.3
Erigeron ramosus	(56.2)	42.1	32.1	28.6
Phlox pilosa	(68.8)	47.4	12.5	21.4
Ceanothus americanus	25.0	(68.4)	12.5	35.7
Fragaria virginiana	(75.0)	47.4	. . .	21.4
Silphium integrifolium	(56.2)	36.8	42.9	14.3
Bouteloua curtipendula	. . .	21.0	93.8	35.4
Pycnanthemum virginianum	(100.0)	21.0	6.2	14.3
Asclepias verticillata	18.7	36.8	(68.8)	14.3
Heuchera richardsoniana	(56.2)	31.6	31.2	14.3
Koeleria cristata	31.2	10.5	43.7	(57.1)
Panicum leibergii	37.5	(52.6)	25.0	14.3
Solidago missouriensis	43.7	(63.1)	25.0	. . .
Thalictrum dasycarpum	(93.8)	31.6	. . .	7.1
Lathryus venosus	(50.0)	36.8	6.2	28.6
Zizia aurea	(87.5)	15.8	. . .	21.4
Desmodium illinoense	18.7	(57.9)	12.5	21.4
Kuhnia eupatorioides	6.2	21.0	(75.0)	14.3
Veronicastrum virginicum	(81.3)	21.0	6.2	14.3
Baptisia leucantha	(62.5)	26.3	6.2	14.3
Hypoxis hirsuta	(50.0)	26.3	12.5	21.4
Galium boreale	(62.5)	26.3	. . .	14.3
Spartina pectinata	(75.0)	15.8	. . .	14.3
Equisetum laevigatum	(56.2)	21.0	6.2	14.3

TABLE 54—(Continued)

Species	Low Prairies	High Prairies	Lime Prairies	Sand Prairies
Lobelia spicata	(56.2)	21.0	12.5	7.1
Aster novae-angliae	(75.0)	10.5	. . .	7.1
Convolvulus sepium	18.7	(57.9)	. . .	7.1
Artemisia caudata	6.2	15.8	(50.0)	14.3
Calamagrostis canadensis	(62.5)	15.8	. . .	. . .
Gentiana andrewsii	(62.5)	10.5	. . .	7.1
Liatris pycnostachya	(56.2)	15.8	. . .	7.1
Oxypolis rigidior	(81.3)	5.3	. . .	. . .
Liatris cylindracea	. . .	15.8	(50.0)	14.3
Lithospermum incisum	. . .	10.5	(50.0)	21.4
Solidago graminifolia	(62.5)	15.8	6.2	. . .
Spiraea alba	(68.8)	. . .	. . .	7.1
Equisetum arvense	(62.5)	5.3	. . .	. . .
Helianthus strumosus	. . .	(52.6)	. . .	7.1
Krigia biflora	(50.0)	5.3	. . .	14.3
Scutellaria parvula	6.2	10.5	(50.0)	7.1
Cicuta maculata	(50.0)	5.3	. . .	7.1
Prenanthes racemosa	(50.0)	15.8	. . .	. . .
Hieracium longipilum	. . .	. . .	12.5	(50.0)

The species in this table are arranged in descending order of presence percentage for all stations in Wisconsin. This table is abbreviated from the original and includes only those species of 50 percent or more presence in at least one prairie type that are also "preferential" because they occur with at least 10 percent greater presence in one prairie type, indicated by ( ), than in any other type.

comprise more than 50 percent of the species, whereas 24 of the remaining 47 families were monotypic in the prairies.

Our third illustration of the use of presence data is taken from a very different type of vegetation, the floodplain rain forest of Araparí Island in the lower Amazon near Belém, Pará. Time did not permit detailed studies of this forest, but it was possible to make landings at six widely spaced points where tree identifications were made with the assistance of local woodsmen (Cain, Castro, et al., 103). At each stop paths used for rubber gathering were traversed and all trees were examined until over 50 species had been encountered. The results are given in Table 55, in which six presence classes are used, one for each station. The species are arranged in the table according to phanerophytic life-form classes. Within each height class the species are further grouped by presence, as follows: 6/6, 5/6 . . . 1/6. From the total of 109 tree species encountered, 14 had 6/6 presence. Five of them were megaphanerophytes, 8 mesophanerophytes, and 1 microphanero-

TABLE 55. Phanerophytes of the varzea of Araparí Island, Pará, arranged according to the life-form classes of Raunkiaer

Species	Presence at 6 Stations					
	I	II	III	IV	V	VI
MEGAPHANEROPHYTES: taller than 30 m.						
Emergent						
Sumaúma—*Ceiba pentandra* (L.) Gaertn.	x	x	x	x	x	x
Merití—*Mauritia flexuosa* L.f.	..	..	x	..	..	..
Not Emergent						
Seringueira—*Hevea brasiliensis* (HBK.) Muell. Arg.	x	x	x	x	x	x
Andiroba—*Carapa guianensis* Aubl.	x	x	x	x	x	x
Iperana—*Crudia bracteata* Benth.	x	x	x	x	x	x
Tanimbuca—*Terminalia guyanensis* Eichl.	x	x	x	x	x	x
Jatobá—*Hymenaea courbaril* var. *subsessilis* Ducke	x	x	x	x	..	x
Patacheiro—*Dimorphandra* sp.?	x	x	x	x	..	x
Ucuuba—*Virola surinamensis* Warb.	x	x	..	x	x	x
Taperebá—*Spondias mombim* L.	..	x	x	x	x	x
Cabeça de macaco—*Pouteria* aff. *paraensis* (Standl.) Baehni	..	x	x	x	x	x
Paracuuba—*Mora paraensis* Ducke	..	x	x	x	x	x
Guajará—*Chrysophyllum* sp.?	..	x	x	x	x	x
Matamata giboia—*Eschweilera subglandulosa* (Steud.) Miers	x	..	..	x	x	x
Matamata commun—*Eschweilera odora* (Poepp.) Miers	x	x	..	x	..	x
Faveiro—*Vantanea guianensis* Aubl.	x	x	x	..	..	x
Rim de paca—*Crudia oblonga* Benth.	..	x	x	x	x	..
Tacacazeiro—*Sterculia elata* Ducke	..	x	x	x	x	..
Apuí—*Ficus* sp.?	..	..	x	x	x	x
Tatapiririca—*Tapirira guianensis* Aubl.	x	..	x	x	..	..
Parapará—*Jacaranda copaia* (Aubl.) D. Don	x	x	..	x	..	..
Jutairana—*Cynometra bauhiniaefolia* Benth.	x	..	..	..	x	x
Açacu—*Hura crepitans* L.	x	..	..	..	x	x
Envira pe d'anta—*Sterculia pruriens* (Aubl.) K. Sch.	..	..	..	x	x	x
Comida de pombo—*Citharexylon poeppigi* Walp.	x	..	x	..	..	..
Cajú acu—*Anacardium giganteum* Engl.	..	x	..	x	..	..
Caxinguba—*Ficus radula* Willd.	..	x	..	x	..	..
Cedra—*Cedrela odorata* L.	..	..	..	x	x	..
Buiuçu—*Ormosia coutinhoi* Ducke	x	..	..	..	..	..
Macaranduba—*Manilkara huberi* (Ducke) Standley	x	..	..	..	..	..
Pitaicá—*Swartzia acuminata* Willd.	x	..	..	..	..	..
Parimarí—*Parinarium rudolphi* Huber	x	..	..	..	..	..
Sapucaia—*Lecythis paraensis* (Huber) Ducke	x	..	..	..	..	..
Pajurá—*Couepia bracteosa* Benth.	..	x	..	..	..	..
Mutamba—*Guazuma ulmifolia* Lam.	..	..	x	..	..	..
Guaruba bacuri—*Qualea albiflora* Warm.	..	..	x	..	..	..
Mamorana—*Bombax spruceanum* (Dcsne.) Ducke	..	..	..	x	..	..
Tauarí—*Couratari pulchra* Sandwith	..	..	..	..	x	..
Nectandra pichurim Mez.	..	..	..	..	x	..
Anani—*Symphonia globulifera* L.f.	..	..	..	..	x	..
Munguba—*Bombax munguba* Mart. & Zucc.	..	..	..	..	x	..
Maparajuba—*Manilkara amazonica* (Huber) Standley	..	..	..	..	..	x

TABLE 55—(Continued)

Species	Presence at 6 Stations					
	I	II	III	IV	V	VI
MESOPHANEROPHYTES: Group A, 20–30 m.						
Mututí—*Pterocarpus amazonicus* Huber	x	x	x	x	x	x
Jatuaúba—*Guarea guedesii* C. DC.	x	x	x	x	x	x
Inga nobilis Willd.	x	x	x	x	x	x
Pracaxi—*Pentaclethra macroloba* (Willd.) O. Ktze.	x	x	x	..	x	x
Ipê—*Macrolobium angustifolium* (Benth.) Cowan	x	..	x	x	x	x
Maúba—*Licaria mahuba* (Samp.) Kosterm.	x	x	x	x	..	x
Cupurana—*Matisia paraensis* Huber	..	x	x	x	x	x
Areuareu—*Protium* sp.?	x	x	..	x	..	x
Ingá-açu—*Inga cinnamomea* Spruce	x	..	..	x	x	x
Marupá—*Simaruba amara* Aubl.	x	x	x	..	..	x
Ingá cipó—*Inga edulis* Mart.	..	x	x	x	..	x
Ventosa—*Hernandia guianensis* Aubl.	..	x	..	x	x	x
Aroeirá—*Licania macrophylla* Benth.	x	..	..	..	x	x
Cumarúrana—*Taralea oppositifolia* Aubl.	x	x	..	x	..	..
Pente de macaco—*Apeiba burchellii* Sprague	..	x	x	..	x	..
Imbaúba branca—*Cecropia leucocoma* Miq.	..	x	..	x	x	..
Jutaí pororoca—*Dialium guianense* (Aubl.) Sandwith	..	..	..	x	x	x
Bacaba—*Oenocarpus bacaba* Mart.	x	..	x	..	..	..
Patauá—*Oenocarpus bataua* Mart.	x	x	..	..	..	..
Uchirana—*Saccoglottis guianensis* Mart.	..	x	..	..	x	..
Açacurana—*Erythrina glauca* Willd.	..	x	x	..	..	..
Taxirana—*Coccoloba latifolia* Lam.	..	..	..	x	..	x
Jacareuba—*Calophyllum* aff. *brasiliense* Camb.	..	x	..	..	..	..
Cordia nodosa Lam.	..	x	..	..	..	..
Paliteira—*Clitoria racemosa* Benth.	..	..	x	..	..	..
Chapeu de sol—*Cordia tetrandra* Aubl.	..	..	x	..	..	..
Helicostylis pedunculata R. Ben.	..	..	..	x	..	..
Mucucú—*Licania heteromorpha* Benth.	..	..	..	..	x	..
Caneleira do igapo—*Toulicia* sp.?	..	..	..	..	x	..
Cordia exaltata Lam.	..	..	..	..	x	..
Pouteria sp.?	..	..	..	..	..	x
MESOPHANEROPHYTES: Group B, 8–20 m.						
Mututí duro—*Swartzia racemosa* Benth.	x	x	x	x	x	x
Breu—*Protium pinesii* Swart.	x	x	x	x	x	x
Assaí—*Euterpe oleracea* Mart.	x	x	x	x	x	x
Geniparana—*Gustavia calycaris* Miers	x	x	x	x	x	x
Bacurirana—*Rheedia macrophylla* (Mart.) Planch. & Triana	x	x	x	x	x	x
Ingárana—*Pithecolobium huberi* Ducke	x	x	x	x	..	x
Murumuru—*Astrocaryum murumuru* Mart.	x	x	x	x	x	..
Inajárana—*Quararibea guianensis* Aubl.	..	x	x	x	x	x
Cupuí—*Theobroma subincana* Mart.	x	x	..	x	..	x
Ubuçu—*Manicaria* sp.?	x	x	..	..	x	x
Cacauí—*Theobroma speciosa* Spreng.	x	..	x	x	..	x
Paxiuba—*Iriartea exorrhiza* Mart.	..	x	x	x	x	..
Meraúba—*Mourira grandiflora* DC.	..	x	..	x	x	x

TABLE 55—*(Continued)*

Species	Presence at 6 Stations					
	I	II	III	IV	V	VI
Trichilia paraensis C. DC.	..	x	x	x	..	x
Canela de garca—*Rinorea martini* (Turcz.) Blake	..	..	x	x	..	x
Janaú—*Trichanthera multijuga* Rich.	x	..	..	..	x	x
Inaja—*Maximiliana regia* Mart.	..	..	x	..	x	x
Tamaquaré—*Caraipa grandifolia* Mart.	x	..	..	..	..	x
Mamorana—*Bombax aquaticum* (Aubl.) K. Sch.	x	..	x	..	..	..
Urucurí—*Attalea excelsa* Mart.	..	..	x	..	x	..
Mangarana—*Tovomita stigmatosa* Planch. & Triana	x	..	..	..	..	..
Jupatí—*Rhaphia taedigera* Mart.	x	..	..	..	..	..
Guadua glomerata Munro	..	x	..	..	..	..
Envira preta—*Guatteria atra* Sandwith	..	x	..	..	..	..
Cassia multijuga Rich.	..	..	x	..	..	..
Marajá—*Bactris* sp.?	..	..	..	..	x	..
Caripê—*Couepia* sp.?	..	..	..	..	..	x
Mouriria sagotiana Triana	..	..	..	..	..	x
MICROPHANEROPHYTES: 2–8 m.						
Cacau—*Theobroma cacao* L.	x	x	x	x	x	x
Ubim—*Geonoma* sp.?	x	..	..	..	..	..
Sororoca—*Ravenala guyanensis* Petersen	x	..	..	..	..	..
Seringarana—*Elvasia elvasioides* (Planch.) Gilg	x	..	..	..	..	..
Pitomba—Gen. sp.?	x	..	..	..	..	..
Capitiú—*Siparuna guianensis* Aubl.	..	..	x	..	..	..
Tabernaemontana angulata Muell. Arg.	..	..	..	x	..	..
Heisteria sessilis Ducke	..	..	..	..	..	x

Summary by stations and total for Araparí:

		I	II	III	IV	V	VI
Megaphanerophytes	(42)	21	20	20	24	22	20
Mesophanerophytes	(59)	28	33	30	29	30	34
Mircrophanerophytes	(8)	5	1	2	2	1	2
Totals:	(109)	54	54	52	55	53	56

phyte. At the other end of the scale are 39 species found at a single station only. It should be pointed out that the entire forest of Araparí Island in one sense represents a single stand and that the stations studied are merely selected points for examination. This fact, however, is not of great significance, for studies of presence in temperate vegetation are usually made on relic areas of formerly continuous stands under virgin conditions.

Investigators at the Tropical Forest Experiment Station have reported on the "presence" of species in mixed rain forest that is very similar to the type elsewhere in tropical America. The sampling was based on 40 plots each 0.25 acre in three rain-forest types: Tabonuco type, lower montane rain forest; Colorado type, montane thicket rain forest; and the Palm type. The results are shown in Table 56, where it is seen that both Classes D (61 to 80 percent) and E (81 to 100 percent) tend to be relatively small and of about the same size. The report does not explain the distribution of the sample plots; but since the data are based on equal-sized plots they should be referred to as constancy (not presence) unless they are subsamples within single stands, in which case the data are properly referred to as frequencies. In any case such sampling is rare in rain forest and hence of considerable interest.

TABLE 56.   The occurrence of species on 40 plots of 0.25 acre each in rain forest at the Tropical Forest Experiment Station

Frequency Class "Presence"	Tabonuco Lower Montane	Rain-Forest Type Colorado Montane Thicket	Palm
81 to 100%	3 species	4 species	4 species
61 to 80%	4 "	4 "	5 "
41 to 60%	7 "	3 "	8 "
21 to 40%	15 "	6 "	11 "
2.5 to 20%	44 "	34 "	36 "
Less than 2.5%	95 "	No data	No data

Following Brockmann-Jerosch, the species of Class 5 presence are often referred to as the "constants" of the community. Although Braun-Blanquet employed the term in the same way, he proceeded to give it a different meaning, which we prefer. This meaning is as follows: When the tabular comparison of species lists is based on exactly equivalent areas from different stands of the same community type, the percentage occurrence of a species in stands surveyed is its degree of *constancy*. Constancy, then, is comparable to presence except that the variability introduced by differences in area of stands (larger stands having longer lists of species) has been eliminated.

In producing stand lists for presence determination there was always the problem of stand boundary and, with it, the problem of whether or not to include certain peripheral species in the list. This has been eliminated by using the arbitrarily bound sample of definite size employed for constancy determination; but two new problems are thereby introduced: (1) the size of the sample area, and (2) the selection of its location so that it will be representative of the stand. As in the case of presence, constancy can be given directly as percentage or can be expressed by the use of a limited number of constancy classes, as follows:

Constancy Class 1: Species found on 1 to 20 percent of the lists for stands of an association, each list being based on a unit area of the stands
Constancy Class 2: Species of 21 to 40 percent constancy
Constancy Class 3: Species of 41 to 60 percent constancy
Constancy Class 4: Species of 61 to 80 percent constancy
Constancy Class 5: Species of 81 to 100 percent constancy

The *constants* of an association are commonly the species of Class 5 constancy, but some investigators use 10 equal classes and speak of constants only when species occur in 90 percent or more of the samples. A high degree of constancy together with a high degree of dominance produces species that are called *constant-dominants*. For many plant sociologists, especially of northern Europe, the constant-dominants are the species that characterize associations and provide the key to their ecology, classification, etc.

The distinctions that have been made between presence and constancy are illustrated in Figure 37. Areas 1a, 1b . . . 1f are different stands of an association occurring in the region; areas 2a, 2b . . . 2f are different stands of another association. If separate species lists are prepared for the complete stands 1a to 1f and these lists are compared, each species can be assigned a presence percentage or class. The same is true of 2a to 2f or any other association represented by a series of discrete stands. Stand 1f being much larger than 1e, it would undoubtedly have a much larger species list; i.e., several species found in Stand 1f would be absent from 1e, possibly because of the small area of the latter and the vicissitudes of chance and competition. Area 1e, relatively small though it may be, may still be large enough to contain the characteristic composition and structure of the association (as determined by experience with other, larger stands) and may be included in the tabular comparison used to describe the association. If, however, it does not contain the characteristic combination of species, it will be discarded as a fragmentary stand.

If instead of using the total area of each stand for the preparation of lists, a single sample area from each stand is used (as indicated by the equivalent quadrats in 1a, 1b . . . 1f) for the preparation of species lists, the resulting percentage occurrences are called constancy.

The association represented by Stands 2a, 2b . . . 2f is sampled in a different way—by numerous, small, scattered quadrats, one set of 25 quadrats in each stand. Within any one stand the percentage occurrence of a species in the quadrats of the set is the frequency of the

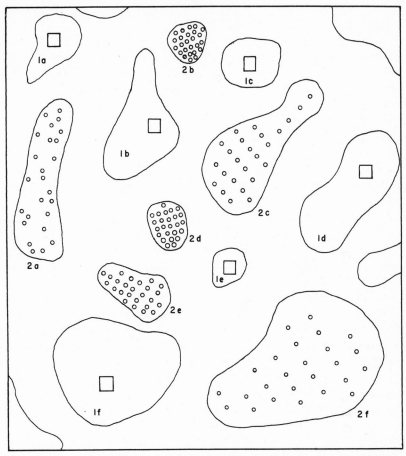

FIGURE 37. Diagram to illustrate the differences between presence, constancy, and frequency. Areas 1a to 1f are stands of an association type; areas 2a to 2f are stands of a different type of vegetation. These two associations are considered as being scattered through the matrix of a more or less continuous third association. See the text for explanation of the concepts.

species. Frequency is to a stand what constancy is to an association type, sample data on a unit-area basis; but the former is analytic and the latter is synthetic. Constancy for an association type can be determined from sets of scattered quadrats as well as from a single quadrat in each stand, the only requirement being comparability of total area.

Finally, Figure 37 also suggests visually the nature of fidelity. Any species confined to a given association, such as 1a, 1b . . . , would have a high degree of fidelity. Any species occurring in Associations 1 and

2 (and others elsewhere) would be of low fidelity to any of the associations.

Data on frequency and constancy can be used together as a partial measure of the floristic homogeneity of an association. Frequency is concerned with the homogeneity of dispersion of individuals of a species within a stand; constancy is concerned with its regularity of occurrence in several stands. (This is a complex problem; the reader should refer also to the discussion of spacing.) Data for the two can be combined, with constancy written as a superscript to frequency. Let us suppose that a set of 25 quadrats, each 1 sq. m., is used as a sample in each of 10 stands of a community type. In any one set of quadrats a given species can occur in from none to all 25 of the quadrats and have a frequency from 0 to 100 percent. The *combined frequency* of a species is the sum of its frequencies in the different sets, which for the 10 stands in our hypothetical case might be 100, 100, 96, 40, 92, 0, 80, 100, 96, 100. The species would have a combined frequency of 804 out of a possible 1000, and it would have an *average frequency* of 80.4 percent. Since the species occurred in 9 of the 10 sets, it would have a constancy of 90 percent. As a measure of homogeneity we could write $90^{80.4}$. Romell (350) suggests the following definition: "*Homogeneity* consists of a *repetition of variations,* sufficiently frequent on a given surface, in the composition of the plant cover." Obviously, homogeneity is a relative matter, and no mechanical method of obtaining data (quadrats of a given size and number scattered in a given manner over a territory) can really resolve the problem, for the repetitive pattern of variation that is normal within a community as interpreted by one investigator is sufficient to produce a mosaic of different communities in the interpretation of another investigator. (This is a problem of the type that we return to again and again, as in the discussion of fidelity, natural areas, the continuum, etc.)

FIDELITY, EXCLUSIVENESS

Fidelity is the concept in plant sociology of the relative exclusiveness of occurrence of a species in an association or a group of related associations. Some species seem never or seldom to be found except within the "fabric" of a particular plant association. At the other extreme are some species that are able to flourish as members of several different associations. Two different phenomena are involved in this concept: (1) the degree of exclusiveness or fidelity, and (2) the relative success of the species as expressed in numbers, vigor, etc. Fidelity has to be expressed for a species, if the species occurs as a member of more than one community, as its fidelity to a particular community; this means that the same species may have a high fidelity for one community and a low fidelity for another within the general area of its occurrence.

Braun-Blanquet (58) employs five fidelity classes which he describes as follows:

Fidelity Class 1: Strange species: species that are rare and accidental intruders from another plant community or relics of a community that has previously occupied the same station

Fidelity Class 2: Indifferent species: species without pronounced affinities for any community

Fidelity Class 3: Preferential species: species present in several communities more or less abundantly, but predominantly or with better vitality in one certain community

Fidelity Class 4: Selective species: species found most frequently in a certain community but also, though rarely, in other communities

Fidelity Class 5: Exclusive species: species completely or almost completely confined to one community

Species of Class 1 are referred to as *accidentals,* of Class 2 as *companions,* and of Classes 3 to 5 as *characteristic species.* Relative fidelity is useful in classifying associations in a hierarchy. For example, species that can be used to distinguish subassociations (not being exclusives for the association) are called *differential species.* In a similar sense, other species may be diagnostic (exclusive) for categories higher than the association, such as alliances and orders. As a matter of fact, the crux of the Braun-Blanquet system of plant community taxonomy (so far as floristic characteristics are concerned) is his use of fidelity data.

Braun-Blanquet ascribes high value in plant sociology to characteristic species as furnishing a connecting link between studies of the composition and structure of communities and their ecological relations. He wrote:

1. The characteristic species are primarily decisive for the floristic individuality of a community.

2. They are collectively the best indicators of the ecological condition of a community.

3. They permit an estimate of the stage of development attained by the community.

4. They permit the drawing of conclusions as to the present and former distribution of certain communities.

5. They are of special value in determining the natural affinities of plant communities, thus making possible a classification of communities on a floristic basis.

We see, then, that characteristic species are of importance in the floristics, ecology, succession (dynamism), historical chorology, and taxonomy of communities.

In many studies of vegetation, fidelity is expressed in general terms based on nonquantitative observation, whether or not the term "fidelity" is used for the concept. For example, Sampson (356) presents diagrammatically the two aspects involved in the concept of fidelity: exclusiveness and abundance.

Under ideal conditions the assignment of fidelity rank to a species can be made only when all communities of a region are equally well known and, furthermore, when quantitative data are available, because the concept involves not only exclusiveness but also such matters as abundance and vitality. The basic or primary requirement is representative floristic lists for each community which, alone, indicate degree of presence within stands of each community type. If the lists are prepared on the basis of sample units rather than whole stands, constancy data are available. Other data that may be available include abundance or density, coverage, frequency or combined frequency, homogeneity or combined frequency and constancy, and vitality. Braun-Blanquet gives an example in which presence classes and abundance classes, in the given association and in other associations, form the basis for assignment to fidelity classes.

As difficult as it is to obtain adequate data for assigning fidelity classes to species (the fidelity-class assignment of a nonexclusive species changing from community to community), we face another serious problem. Fidelity is essentially a local or provincial phenomenon. A wide-ranging species, for example, may in one area be an exclusive of a given association and in another area be an exclusive of an entirely different association. In general, the farther one goes geographically from the location of a particular study, the less fidelity have "fidelity data."

Gaussen (207), Cain (96), and others have pointed out the weakness of defining associations on a basis of character species (fidelity classes 3 to 5). For the association Piceetum excelsae Braun-Blanquet gives as characteristic species *Listera cordata*, *Pirola uniflora*, and *Lycopodium annotinum*. An examination of the total areas of the spruce and these three herbs shows that they are by no means the same. Furthermore, *Listera cordata* is associated with *Pinus uncinata* in the Pyrenees, with *Pseudotsuga mucronata* in Vancouver, with *Abies balsamea* and *Pinus strobus* generally in northeastern America, as well as with peat bogs. *Pirola uniflora* is associated with *Picea alba* in Alaska and with *Picea engelmanni* and *Pinus aristata* in Arizona. *Lycopodium annotinum* is associated with *Pinus strobus* in New Brunswick, with *Tsuga canadensis* in the Appalachians, and with *Picea stichensis* in the Pacific Northwest. As Gaussen says, these species do not have any direct bond with *Picea excelsa*. They are as characteristic of other associations as of Piceetum excelsae. To believe that they define the *Picea excelsa* association, except possibly in a comparatively small area, seems illusory.

Numerous examples of the same type can be found in Lippmaa's study (274) of the *Galeobdolon-Asperula-Asarum* union dominated by cryptophytes and hemicryptophytes, and in its widest expression essentially coextensive with the temperate broad-leaf deciduous forests. This union (or unistratal association) of Lippmaa is the characteristic herbaceous layer community of the Baltic deciduous forest region where his studies were centered. The following list shows the plants he defined as character species (Classes 3 to 5 of fidelity) and constant species (Classes 4 to 5 of constancy):

Both character and constant species
  Hepatica triloba Gilib.
  Pulmonaria officinalis L.
  Orobus vernus L.
  Asperula odorata L.
  Viola mirabilis L.
  Milium effusum L.

Character species but not constant species
  Actaea spicata L.
  Mercurialis perennis L.
  Sanicula europaea L.
  Dentaria bulbifera L.
  Lamium galeobdolon (L.) Crantz
  Stellaria holostea L.
  Asarum europaeum L.
  Lathraea squamaria L.
  Bromus beneckenii (Lge.) Syme.
  Allium ursinum L.

Constant species but not character species
  Majanthemum bifolium (L.) F. W. Schm.
  Fragaria vesca L.
  Rubus saxatilis L.
  Melica nutans L.
  Oxalis acetosella L.
  Carex digitata L.

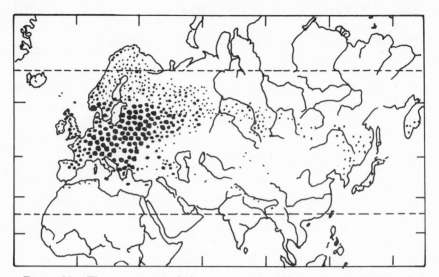

FIGURE 38. The occurrence of character species (Classes 3 to 5 fidelity) of the *Galeobdolon-Asperula-Asarum* union of cryptophytes and hemicryptophytes of the broad-leaf temperate forests of Eurasia (Lippmaa, 274). Smallest dots are areas with 1 to 4 species; second size, 5 to 8 species; third size, 9 to 12 species; and largest dots, 13 to 16 species.

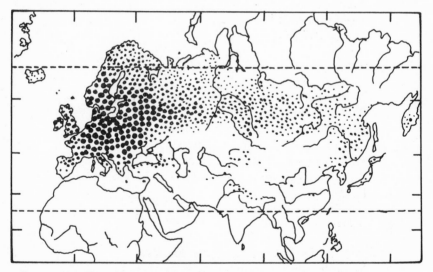

FIGURE 39. The occurrence of constant species (Classes 4 and 5 constancy, 61 to 100 percent) of the *Galeobdolon-Asperula-Asarum* union of cryptophytes and hemicryptophytes of the broad-leaf temperate forests of Eurasia (Lippmaa, 274). Smallest dots are areas with 1 to 3 species; second size, 4 to 7 species; third size, 8 to 11 species; and largest dots, 12 to 14 species.

Anemone nemorosa L.
Paris quadrifolia L.
Trientalis europaea L.
Aegopodium podagraria L.

Figure 38 shows the frequency distribution of the character species, the largest dots showing the places of occurrence of 13 or more of the character species. Figure 39 shows the distribution of the constant species, the largest dots indicating the places where 12 or more of them occur. Both maps show the greatest concentration of species in Eurasia south of 55° N. and west of 50° E., but with numerous species in Scandinavia, southward in the Mediterranean and several of the extending eastward completely across Asia. Lippmaa's detailed study of the distributions of these species led him to recognition of a series of 11 facies of the *Galeobdolon-Asperula-Asarum* union: Middle Balkan, Pontine, Tauric (S.E. Asia Minor), Colchian (Georgia, Transcaucasia), Middle European, Atlantic, Balto-Kassubian, Podolian (W. Ukraine), Sarmatian (Poland and Russia west of the Volga), Ural-Siberian, and Altaian. Lippmaa recognized also a somewhat larger series of varieties of the union and said that in Atlantic North America and in East Asia there were cryptophytic-hemicryptophytic unions that stand very close to the Eurasian *Galeobdolon-Asperula-Asarum* union.

It seems to us that in Lippmaa's work we find not a strengthening of the significance of the concept of fidelity but a weakening of it, for the following reason. If one were to make a study corresponding to that of Lippmaa centered on the region of any one of the facies of the above described union, a new set of characteristic and constant species would be found. Then, extending the study to the ultimate range of these species, he would find a set of facies related to the community upon which the original study was concentrated. To make the point another way, in reference to the maps taken from Lippmaa's study (Figures 37 and 38), the large dots for the greatest concentrations of character and constant species would now be centered in a new location and the numbers of species would diminish in all directions from that center.

The fact remains, however, that the Swiss-French school of plant sociologists, with its intensive use of fidelity data, has been very successful, attracting followers in many lands and making fine concurrent investigations of community ecology as well as floristics. These possibilities lie mainly in the fact that exclusive species are good indicators of *local* ecological and syngenetic conditions. Some species have narrow ecological tolerances; others have broad tolerances. Ecological amplitude may or may not be tied in with the relative richness in biotypes of the species population. Some relic species with biotype de-pauperization appear to have small ecological amplitude (Anderson, 14; Cain, 90). In any case, the species that are closely adapted to a particular environmental situation cannot range far from it and are likely to be exclusive species of the community that occupies the particular environmental situation.

Chapter 12

LIFE FORM AND
LEAF SIZE

THE life form of a plant is the vegetative form of the plant body that is thought usually to be a hereditary adjustment to environment. Life form has nothing to do with the sexual reproductive structures which constitute the principal basis for the classification of plants into species, genera, and families. The organisms that show the same general vegetative features belong to the same life form whatever their systematic position in the plant families. Man has always recognized certain major life-form differences among plants in such groups as herbaceous and woody plants, trees and shrubs, broad-leaf and needle-leaf trees, lianas, grasses, mosses, etc.

It was probably by Humboldt (244) that the concept of life form was formalized. He attempted to group vegetative types on a physiognomic basis with some implicit effort to express relations between environment and certain life-form groups. Humboldt named 15 groups of plants whose physiognomy was important in the study of landscapes:

1. The banana form: *Musa, Heliconia, Strelitzia*
2. The palm form: *Cocos, Mauritia*
3. The tree-fern form: *Alsophila, Cyathea, Cibotium*
4. The aroid form: *Arum, Pothos, Dracontium*
5. The conifer form: *Taxus, Pinus, Picea*
6. All the sharp-leaf forms: *Araucaria, Juniperus*
7. The tamarisk form: *Mimosa, Gleditschia, Porlieria*
8. The mallow form: *Sterculia, Hibiscus, Ochroma*

   9. The liana form: *Vitis, Paullinia, Bauhinia*
  10. The orchid form: *Epidendrum, Serapias, Cattleya*
  11. The cactus form: *Opuntia, Cereus, Carnegia*
  12. The casuarina form: *Casuarina, Equisetum*
  13. The grass form: *Andropogon, Panicum, Scirpus*
  14. The moss form: *Bryum, Sphagnum, Polytrichum*
  15. The lichen form: *Cladonia, Parmelia, Gyrophora*

Following Humboldt's work, many systems of life-form classification have been introduced, with or without the presumption of a direct relation between vegetative form and environment, and with or without dependence upon taxonomic entities for their characterization— Kerner (255), Grisebach (222), Drude (169, also 170), Warming (409), Schimper (360), Pound and Clements (328; also Clements, 126), Raunkiaer (331, 337), Brockmann-Jerosch and Rübel (64; also Rübel, 352, 353), Vahl (399), Gams (204), Hayek (234), DuRietz (174). DuRietz may be consulted especially for a review of the literature and for a system, never completed, that abandons all suggestions of epharmonic adaptation. Cain (97) reviewed the world literature on life forms and phytoclimates according to Raunkiaer.

The only system that has received world-wide use during the past half-century is that of Raunkiaer, and it will be presented here in some detail. Nearly all life-form systems tacitly assume the following broad principles: (1) Plants have different ecological amplitudes or tolerances; (2) in a plant's successful existence it makes an automatic physiological integration of the total environment; and (3) there is often a correlation between morphology and adaptation. In addition to these assumptions, Raunkiaer employed three guiding rules in his selection of life-form characteristics for the recognition and classification of relationships between plant life form and climate: (1) The characters used must be structural and essential, i.e., they must represent important morphological adaptations; (2) the characters must be sufficiently obvious so that one can see in nature to which life form a plant belongs; and (3) the life forms collectively must constitute a homogeneous system. It is this last requirement, especially, that has made Raunkiaer's system usable and popular; its simplicity and unitary theme have made possible statistical treatment of floras and communities and consequently facilitated comparative studies.

Except for certain climates that are constantly warm and humid, all show a certain amount of seasonal rhythm with alternating periods that are more or less favorable or unfavorable for growth. In comparing two climates the differences between them in their favorable seasons may be relatively insignificant, whereas the differences between them in their unfavorable seasons may be considerable and of great importance. Unfavorable seasons due to insufficient available water may be short or long and there may be one or more such periods each year. Adaptations have a combined physiological-morphological basis. In many cases there are apparent morphological features that correlate with environments and can be used as indices of them. Upon these facts Raunkiaer developed his life-form classification based upon the degree of protection to the perennating buds. When growth is slowed and dormancy is forced upon a plant by drought or cold, the most critical tissues are the meristematic ones; therefore the amount of protection provided embryonic growing tissues and their success in enduring the unfavorable period represent a critical adaptation. It is for this reason that Raunkiaer selected the protection afforded the perennating buds as the principal basis of his life-form system.

The percentage of each life-form class in a flora can be compared with a "standard" percentage. All the percentages together constitute a *biological spectrum,* according to Raunkiaer; and the more or less arbitrary standard that he developed as a base line for comparison is called the *normal spectrum.* The normal spectrum is the result of a sampling procedure in which 1000 species were selected from the world flora in such a manner as to constitute a random sample of it and, presumably, of the various life forms. Whether or not the normal spectrum is truly representative is of no great moment; it can still be used as a base line against which deviations can be measured in relative terms.

RAUNKIAER'S LIFE-FORM CLASSIFICATION

Raunkiaer's system consists of five principal life-form classes, arranged according to increased protection of the *perennating buds:* phanerophytes, chamaephytes, hemicryptophytes, cryptophytes, and therophytes.

CLASS I, PHANEROPHYTES (PH). Members of Class I have their bud-bearing shoots in the air and are mostly woody trees and shrubs. Since these buds are elevated and exposed to the atmosphere during the unfavorable season, and since the severity of conditions generally increases with height above the ground, the phanerophytes are logically divided into subclasses according to height: tall, medium, and low trees, and shrubs. The boundaries of these subclasses are more or less arbitrary, yet they fit pretty well with maximum statures of woody plants under different climates. *Megaphanerophytes* (Mg) are trees over 30 m. tall; *mesophanerophytes* (Ms) are trees between 8 and 30 m. tall; *microphanerophytes* (Mi) are trees and shrubs between 2 and 8 m. tall; and *nanophane-*

rophytes (N) are shrubs between 25 cm. and 2 m. tall. Sometimes the two tallest classes are combined and indicated by the symbol (MM). Although most phanerophytes have some ecological plasticity, growing taller the more favorable the site, there are also hereditary limits beyond which they cannot grow. In assigning height classes it thus becomes necessary to determine the maximum height of the species for the flora or community under study. Its height elsewhere is irrelevant.

For further refinement in the classification of phanerophytic life-forms, Raunkiaer suggested the separation in each height class of the plants whose buds are protected by bud scales from those which do not have such structures. Departing from the unitary theme of protection of embryonic tissues, Raunkiaer also provided for subdivision on a basis of evergreen and deciduous leaves because they are the principal transpiring organs and make the greatest demand on water during the unfavorable season. All the height classes may have these same subdivisions.

The above broad categories are inadequate for detailed considerations, especially in tropical regions. Forms common in the tropics that deserve separate treatment are (1) the lianas (phanerophytia scandentia) that can be handled in the regular height classes; (2) the herbaceous phanerophytes *(Musa, Piper, Impatiens, Begonia,* certain Euphorbiaceae); (3) the stem succulents (certain Cactaceae, Euphorbiaceae, Compositae, Bombacaceae, Sterculiaceae); and (4) the vascular epiphytes (certain Bromeliaceae, Orchidaceae, Pteridophyta, Araceae, Gesneraceae, etc.).

Others interested in the structure of vegetation have erected height classes that differ from those of Raunkiaer. The systems of Küchler (264) and Dansereau (152) are illustrated in Figure 40, in which height is given in meters. No scheme devised for world-wide use and employing a limited number of height classes could be expected to fit every given situation. For example, in the Brazilian equatorial rain forest the principal canopy may exceed 30 m., and above that occur the much taller, scattered, emergent trees, such as *Ceiba pentandra* in varzea and *Bertholletia excelsia* in terra firme; but both strata have to be classified as megaphanerophytes. For purposes of statistical comparisons of vegetation, Raunkiaer's system seems to us to be worth adhering to. Beyond that use, however, the description of any community should include the actual heights of the various layers, whatever they may be.

CLASS II, CHAMAEPHYTES (CH). The members of Class II are also woody or semi-woody perennials. They are separated from the phanerophytes because they are so low (perennating buds are definitely

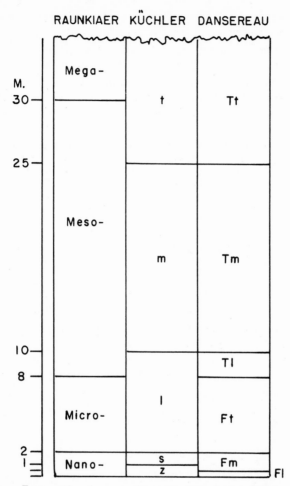

FIGURE 40. A comparison of height classes of phanerophytes according to Raunkiaer (337), Küchler (264),
and Dansereau (152).

above the ground surface but less than 25 cm. high) that their buds
often receive protection from fallen leaves and, in suitable climates,
from snow cover. Raunkiaer recognized four principal subdivisions of
the chamaephytes: (1) suffrutescent or semi-shrubby forms, (2) pas-
sively decumbent forms, (3) actively creeping or stoloniferous forms,
and (4) cushion or polster plants. The cushion plants undoubtedly
provide their buds with the greatest protection in the class, the often
compact mass of stems, leaves, and litter giving the buds shelter. In
addition to such subclasses as have been mentioned, there may be

separate groups for hard grasses of the tussock form, succulent-leaved perennials *(Sedum, Sempervivum, Mesembryanthemum)*, creeping herbs *(Thymus, Veronica, Cerastium*, certain grasses), carpet mosses *(Thuidium, Hylocomium, Hypnum)*, and fruticose lichens *(Cladonia, Cetraria)*, although these last two classes do not have buds in the usual sense. Some plants have shoots that rise to greater heights than 25 cm. above the ground, but these shoots die back to low levels; hence, on the basis of perennating buds, such plants must be classified as chamaephytes, or in other cases as hemicryptophytes or geophytes. Some rank undergrowth in rain forests is of these types.

CLASS III, HEMICRYPTOPHYTES (H).   Members of Class III have their renewal buds exactly at the surface of the ground and are thus one step further in the scale of protection than the chamaephytes. Raunkiaer distinguished three subclasses: (1) the rosette type, with all leaves at the base of the stem; (2) the subrosette type, with both basal and cauline leaves; and (3) the nonrosette type or protohemicryptophyte, without basal leaves. These groups may or may not produce stolons. The hemicryptophytes are a large and complex group of life forms that are usually lumped together in most statistical treatments.

CLASS IV, CRYPTOPHYTES (CR).   Members of Class IV have their buds beneath the soil, in water, or in soil under water. The *geophytes* (G) have more or less tuberous subterranean organs filled with food and able to make a quick growth when favorable conditions return. All above-ground parts die back and the perennating buds are associated with bulbs *(Allium)*, corms *(Arisaema)*, rhizomes *(Podophyllum)*, stem tubers *(Solanum)*, root tubers *(Orchis)*, or rootstocks *(Cirsium)*. The latter type is somewhat transitional with hemicryptophytes, but the buds at the base of the stem (rootstock) are definitely subterranean. The subclass *hydrophytes* (Hy) includes both free-floating forms *(Lemna, Utricularia)* and those with submersed stems *(Potamogeton)*. Helophytes (He) are marsh plants in which the perennating bud is in soil under the water. When hydrophytes and helophytes are lumped together, the symbol (HH) is used.

Dansereau (150) has developed a new classification of the biological forms of hydrophytes that is compared with the systems of Braun-Blanquet (58), Fassett (196), and Wilson (421) in Table 57 and illustrated in Figure 41. This is a sensitive system that has the very important ecological attribute of correlating well with the zonation of communities along streams and shores of lakes.

CLASS V, THEROPHYTES (TH).   Class V includes all the annuals. Their only perennating buds are those of the embryos in seeds, all

TABLE 57. Dansereau's classification of the biological forms of aquatic plants compared with the systems of Braun-Blanquet and Fassett and Wilson

	Braun-Blanquet	Fassett-Wilson
HELOPHYTA—Plants paludous:		
Lythrum salicaria		
Butomus umbellatus		
HYDROPHYTA—Plants aquatic		
1. NATANTIA—Not fixed to the substratum:	Hydrophyta natantia	Type 5
Lemna minor		
Ceratophyllum demersum		
RADICANTIA—Fixed to the substratum		
EMERSA—At least partially emerged		
2. FOLIACEA—With a grand leaf development:		Type 4
Sagittaria latifolia		
Pontedera cordata		
3. JUNCIFORMIA—Reduced leaf development:		Type 4
Scirpus validus		
Juncus effusus		
4. NYMPHOIDEA—leaves floating:		Type 3
Nymphaea odorata		
Nymphoides lacunosum		
SUBMERSA—Having none or a few leaves floating		
5. VITTATA—With a long stem or leaves soft:		Type 1
Potamogeton richardsonii		
Vallisneria americana		
6. ROSULATA—Leaves reduced, basal:	Hydro-hemi-crypto-phyta	Type 2
Isoëtes braunii		
Lobelia dortmanna		
7. ANNUA—Therophytes:	Hydro-thero-phyta	Type 1
Najas flexilis		
Potamogeton pusillus		
8. ADNATA—Fixed on rocks, debris, or plants:	Hydrophyta adnata	
Fontinalis spp.		
Podostemon ceratophyllum		

(Braun-Blanquet column: items 2–7 bracketed as "Hydrophyta radicanta"; items 2–5 further bracketed as "Hydrogeophyta")

other organs of the plants having died. Maximum protection against unfavorable conditions is normally provided for the buds of seeds. This is the ultimate of Raunkiaer's series of life forms.

Raunkiaer's normal spectrum, according to his calculations of 1916, is shown in Table 58. In comparative studies of the biological spectra

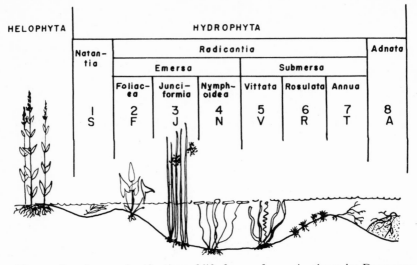

HELOPHYTA	HYDROPHYTA							
	Natantia	Radicantia						Adnata
		Emersa			Submersa			
		Foliacea	Junciformia	Nymphoidea	Vittata	Rosulata	Annua	
	1 S	2 F	3 J	4 N	5 V	6 R	7 T	8 A

FIGURE 41.   A new classification of life forms of aquatic plants by Dansereau (150). The following species are used to illustrate the types: Helophyta—*Lythrum salicaria;* Natantia—*Ceratophyllum demersum;* Foliacea—*Sagittaria latifolia;* Junciformia—*Scirpus validus;* Nymphoidea—*Nymphaea tuberosa;* Vittata—*Vallisneria americana;* Rosulata—*Isoetes* sp.; Annua—*Najas flexilis;* Adnata—*Fontinalis* sp.

of different regions or different communities the actual percentages are not considered as important as the divergence of the various life-form classes from the "normal" or standard. When one class or another is relatively large, one can speak, for example, of the phanerophytic climate of humid tropics, the therophytic climate of deserts, the geophytic climate of the Mediterranean, the chamaephytic climate of high latitudes and high altitudes, etc.

Because of the easily accessible review of life forms and phytoclimates by Cain (97), we will not elaborate the matter here but will only point out certain major correlations that have been established. Table 59 illustrates some phytoclimates according to Raunkiaer (333) that are named after the significant life-form class, as measured by their departure from the normal spectrum. Other spectra, arranged according to the prevailing vegetation of the areas, are shown in Table 60. The dramatic increase of chamaephytes with increasing altitude is shown in several studies. At Clova, Scotland (Raunkiaer, 333), chamaephytes increase from 7 to 27 percent in passing from the zone below 300 m. to that above 1000 m. altitude. Raunkiaer also shows a shift from 5 to 35 percent for the zones from below 850 to above 2850 m. in the Alps at Poschiavo. In the nival zone of the Alps, from 2400

TABLE 58.   The "normal" biological spectrum of Raunkiaer (333)

Symbols		Classes	Class Percentages		
(S)		Stem succulents	2		
(E)		Epiphytes	3		
(MM)		Mega- and Mesophanerophytes	8		
(Mi)		Microphanerophytes	18		
(N)		Nanophanerophytes	15		
	(Ph)	Total phanerophytes		**46**	
	(Ch)	Chamaephytes	9	**9**	
		Total epigeal forms			55
	(H)	Hemicryptophytes	26	**26**	
(G)		Geophytes	4		
(HH)		Hydrophytes and Helophytes	2		
	(Cr)	Total cryptophytes		**6**	
		Total hypogeal forms			32
	(Th)	Therophytes	13	**13**	13
			100	100	100

TABLE 59.   Life-form spectra for four major phytoclimates, according to Raunkiaer (333)

Locality and Phytoclimate	Number of Species	Life-Form Classes				
		Ph	Ch	H	Cr	Th
Phanerophytic climate						
St. Thomas and St. Jan	904	**61**	12	9	4	14
Seychelles	258	**61**	6	12	5	16
Therophytic climate						
Death Valley, California	294	26	7	18	7	**42**
Argentario, Italy	866	12	6	29	11	**42**
Hemicryptophytic climate						
Altamaha, Georgia	717	23	4	**55**	10	8
Denmark	1084	7	3	**50**	22	18
Chamaephytic climate						
Spitzbergen	110	1	**22**	**60**	15	2
St. Laurence Island, Alaska	126	0	**23**	**61**	15	1
Normal spectrum	1000	46	9	26	6	13

TABLE 60. Selected life-form spectra arranged according to the prevailing vegetation type

Vegetation Type and Locality	Author	Number of Species	Ph	Ch	H	Cr	Th
Rainforest							
Queensland	Cromer & Pryor (142)	141	96	2	0	2	0
Subtropical evergreen							
Matheran, India	Bharucha & Ferreira (39)	361	63	17	2	5	10
Desert							
Transcaspia	Paulsen (310)	768	11	7	27	14	41
Mediterranean							
Crete	Turrill (396)	1571	9	13	27	10	38
Steppe							
Akron, Colorado	Paulsen (311)	79	0	19	58	8	15
Deciduous broad leaf							
Connecticut	Ennis (186)	1453	15	2	49	22	12
Tundra							
Spitzbergen	Raunkiaer (333)	110	1	22	60	15	2
Normal spectrum	Raunkiaer (333)	1000	46	9	26	6	13

to plus 3600 m., the increase is from 24 to 67 percent. At Mt. Cook, New Zealand, Allan (10) reports a change from 31 to 64 percent chamaephytes between 500 and plus 2000 m. altitude. On Clavering Island, Greenland, Gelting (208) records a shift from 31 to 67 percent chamaephytes between sea level and 1250 m. Contrary to the change in chamaephytes with increasing altitude, there is a regular diminution in the proportion of therophytes. Some of the same authors have shown similar changes in biological spectra in both hemispheres with increasing latitude. Table 61 (Cain, 97) shows a series of biological spectra correlated with the dry climatic classes of the Köppen system. The same review has a table of 18 biological spectra for regions in which the principal vegetation is that of the temperate broad-leaf forest; another table assembles spectra for 12 local studies of different forest types of the deciduous broad-leaf formation, of which all but three examples are from the United States. For the regional spectra of the United States the phanerophytes range from 14 to 22 percent, being generally of smaller proportion toward the north. In the European spectra for this formation the proportion of phanerophytes is definitely lower—7 to 10 percent—as would be expected from the more impoverished woody flora; whereas in Japan it is 27 percent, as would be expected from the richer deciduous woody flora of southeast Asia. In all cases the phanerophytes are much less abundant in the broad-leaf deciduous forest formation than they are in the normal spectrum, even though this is the dominant life form in the structure of the vegetation. On the other hand, hemicryptophytes range from 33 to 55 percent, being in most cases about 50 percent, or nearly double that of the normal spectrum. The formation belongs definitely to the hemicryptophytic climate, according to Raunkiaer. In studies of specific forest types of the formation, the variability among these life-form classes is somewhat greater, but the relationships are of the same order.

Buell and Wilbur (72) studied the hardwood forests in Minnesota. They found that the stands of the prairie margin had a pronounced shift toward the more protected life forms, in comparison with those of the hardwood-conifer tension zone. Also, in comparing their Minnesota data with those of Oosting (302) for the Piedmont climax in North Carolina, they found an even stronger shift toward protection (Table 62).

Schimper and Faber (361) have organized world vegetation in 15 formation types that have been arranged in a bioclimatic diagram by Dansereau (152, 153). This diagram (see Figure 42) is arranged so that the principal contacts among the types are apparent and so that extreme warmth and moisture are at the upper right-hand angle of the diagram, extreme warmth and dryness at the upper left-hand angle, and extreme coldness and dryness at the lower angle of the diagram. The lower part of Figure 42 (from Dansereau, 153) shows that these bioclimatic areas and formations can be characterized by the principal life-form classes of each formation. The system of formations, as shown in the illustration, is: (1) tropical rain forest, (2) subtropical rain forest, (3) moonsoon forest, (4) temperate rain forest, (5) summergreen deciduous forest, (6) needle-leaf forest, (7) evergreen hardwood forest, (8) savana woodland, (9) thorn forest and scrub, (10) savana, (11) steppe and half desert, (12) heath, (13) dry desert, (14) tundra and cold woodland, and (15) cold desert.

We have seen that the biological spectra show that there is no single adaptation which meets the exigencies of a situation; no climatic type has vegetation of a single life-form type, or even of two or three classes. On the other hand, no life-form class is confined to a single climatic type. What we find is a relatively great departure from the normal spectrum of certain life-form classes—either more or less—in certain climatic regions. This is to be expected because the dominant synusia of vegetation is the only one normally bearing the full force of the general climate, and it, in its adaptive development, modifies the general climate and produces a series of microclimates in which other life forms

TABLE 61. Some life-form spectra for dry climates compared with the Köppen types

Type, Locality, Source	Köppen Class	Number of Species	Life-Form Classes						
			S	MM	N	Ch	H	Cr	Th
Tropical monsoon climate: dry summer									
Madras, India (Bharucha & Ferreira, 39)	Am	689	0	(34	)	23	10	5	15
Tuticorim, India (Bergesen, 50)	Am	35	0	3	20	28	8	3	37
Hot desert climate									
Death Valley, California (Raunkiaer, 333)	BWh	294	3	2	21	7	18	7	42
Salton Sink, California (Paulsen, 311)	BWh	81	0	0	33	6	(14	)	47
El Golea, Sahara (Raunkiaer, 333)	BWh	169	0	0	9	13	15	7	56
Ghardaia, N. Africa (Raunkiaer, 333)	BWh	300	0.3	0	3	16	20	3	58
Libyan Desert (Raunkiaer, 333)	BWh	194	0	3	9	21	20	5	42
Oudjda Desert (Braun-Blanquet, 60)	BWh	49	0	0	0	4	17	6	73
Oudjda semi-desert (Braun-Blanquet, 60)	BWh	32	0	0	0	59	14	0	27
Canary Islands, lowlands (Bergesen, 50)	BWh	176	0	2	17	19	10	4	47
Aden (Raunkiaer, 333)	BWh	176	0	7	26	27	19	3	17
Ooldea, Australia (Adamson & Osborn, 5)	BWh	188	4	19	23	14	4	1	35
Cold desert climate									
Transcaspian lowlands (Paulsen, 310)	BWk	768	0	0	11	7	27	14	41
Hot steppe climate									
Tucson, Arizona (Paulsen, 311)	BS	266	0	0	18	11	(24	)	47
Whitehill, S. Africa (Adamson, 4)	BSh	428	1	1	8	42	2	18	23
Timbuctu, Africa (Hagerup, 227)	BSh	138	1	11	12	36	9	6	25
Tripoli, N. Africa (Raunkiaer, 333)	BSh	369	0	0.3	6	13	19	11	51
Cyrenaica, N. Africa (Raunkiaer, 333)	BSh	375	0	1	7	14	19	8	50
Madeira Islands, lowlands (Raunkiaer, 333)	BSh	213	0	1	14	7	24	3	51

Cool steppe climate									
Akron, Colorado (Paulsen, 311)	BSk	379	0	0	0	19	58	8	15
Toole, Utah (Paulsen, 311)	BSk	116	0	0	2	23	46	3	14
Danube, SE Europe (Bojko, 47)	BSk	?	0	0	7	5	55	10	23
Yekatornoslaw, Near East (Paulsen, 311)	BSk	1046	0	0	5	3	55	13	24
Pamir Mts. steppe (Paulsen, 311)	BSk	514	0	0	1	12	63	10	14
Mediterranean: hot dry summer									
Argentario, Italy (Raunkiaer, 333)	Csa	866	0	6	6	6	29	2	42
Southern France (Braun-Blanquet, 57)	Csa	?	0	0	7	13	29	8	43
Crete (Turrill, 396)	Csa	1571	0	4	5	13	27	12	38
Samos, Greece (Raunkiaer, 333)	Csa	400	0	5	4	13	32	13	33
Mediterranean: warm dry summer									
Table Mt., S. Africa (Adamson, 2)	Csb	93	0	4	37	14	18	19	7
Normal spectrum (Raunkiaer, 333)		1000	2	26	15	9	26	6	13

TABLE 62.   Life-form spectra based on species list for forests from different regions (Buell and Wilbur, 72)

	Number of Species	Life Forms				
		Ph	Ch	H	Cr	Th
A						
Five Minnesota hardwood forest stands in the conifer-hardwood forest tension zone	91	38.5	4.4	41.7	15.4	0
Five Minnesota hardwood forest stands along the prairie margin	125	35.2	3.2	45.6	16.0	0
B						
North Carolina Piedmont forest climax. Oosting (302)	89	59.6	0	36.0	4.5	0
Ten Minnesota hardwood stands, the same as A above	145	35.9	2.8	44.1	17.2	0

A, two groups of hardwood forest stands in the Itasca region; B, from the ten Minnesota stands included in A, compared with those of a similar study on the North Carolina Piedmont. The arrows indicate the direction of shift in emphasis when the second spectrum of each group is compared with the one just above it.

have adaptive roles to play. We have found, then, that biological spectra based on the flora of climatic regions and vegetation formations help analyze and describe the vegetation. Furthermore, within a formation, spectra for whole floras of associations can help in the differentiation and description of the associations.

Because in the analysis of vegetation we are confronted with composition and structure, and because life form is one of the leading characteristics of structure, we turn now to a more efficient use of life form than statistics based solely on the species. In the spectra we have considered so far, a rare species enters the statistics with the same weight as an abundant or dominant species. It was logical that students of vegetation approached the problem of correlating quantitative data (density, frequency, coverage, etc.) and life-form data.

Raunkiaer (338) compared for different communities the biological spectra obtained from species lists with those obtained from frequency points (Table 63). In Community B the spectra based on species and those based on frequency points are remarkably similar, but in Com-

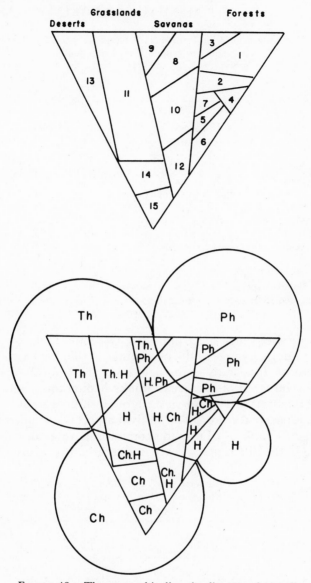

Figure 42. The upper bioclimatic diagram shows the major types of Schimper and Faber (361), their principal contacts with each other, and their climatic relations (Dansereau, 152, 153). Extreme warmth and moisture are at the upper right-hand corner, extreme warmth and dryness at the upper left-hand corner, and extreme cold and dryness at the lower angle. The lower diagram has imposed on the same base the predominant or characteristic life forms according to Raunkiaer's system, revealing a general consistency between climate and life forms in the great world systems of vegetation.

TABLE 63.   A comparison of life-form spectra based on species, with spectra based on frequency points (Raunkiaer, 338)

Field Layer	Life-Form Classes			
	Ch	H	G	Th
Community A				
Spectrum based on species: 18 species	11.1	66.7	22.7	. . .
Spectrum based on frequency points: 504 points	17.5	42.0	40.5	. . .
Community B				
Spectrum based on species: 42 species	4.8	83.3	9.5	2.4
Spectrum based on frequency points: 1848 points	4.1	83.8	8.5	3.2
Community C				
Spectrum based on species: 16 species	12.5	68.4	19.3	. . .
Spectrum based on frequency points: 456 points	12.3	75.0	12.5	. . .
Community D				
Spectrum based on species: 31 species	9.7	80.6	9.7	. . .
Spectrum based on frequency points: 848 points	15.5	56.5	27.8	. . .

munity A the frequency spectrum shows the importance of geophytes in the community by raising the percentage of that life form from 22.7 to 40.5 percent. In a study of the field layer (herb-shrub layer) of the cove hardwood forest of the Great Smoky Mountains, Cain (95) employed 10 quadrats of 1 sq. m. at each of 10 stations in an analysis of the vernal aspect of the flora. The aestival aspect was studied by quadrats of 6 sq. m. (Table 64). From this comparison we see that the spectra calculated in the different ways are not greatly divergent. This is un-

TABLE 64.   A comparison of life-form spectra of the field layer of the cove hardwood forests of the Great Smoky Mountains based on species and on frequency points (Cain, 95)

Field Layer Only	Life-Form Classes			
	Ch	H	Cr	Th
Vernal aspect				
Spectrum based on species: 72 species	7.0	47.2	40.3	5.5
Spectrum based on frequency points: 1309 points	11.0	43.3	41.9	3.8
Aestival aspect				
Spectrum based on species: 75 species	6.6	61.3	29.3	2.6
Spectrum based on frequency points: 1258 points	14.2	58.6	23.9	3.3
Raunkiaerian class percentages recalculated by omitting phanerophytes	17.0	48.0	11.0	24.0

doubtedly due to the fact that the herbaceous flora of these forests is comparatively rich in species and without pronounced dominance of one or a few species. Comparison of the vernal and aestival aspects of the same flora shows the relatively greater importance of cryptophytes (all geophytes) in the vernal aspect and of hemicryptophytes in the aestival aspect of this synusia. Also in this table we have included a "normal" spectrum that results from a recalculation of the life-form classes with phanerophytes omitted, as they are in a study of only the field layer of a forest. Comparison of this spectrum with those of the field layer of the cove hardwoods shows the relatively great role of geophytes in the latter vegetation, and the great paucity of therophytes.

Buell and Wilbur (72) used frequency points as well as species lists in constructing life-form spectra in the Itasca region of Minnesota. Their data are shown in Table 65, along with comparable ones from Cain (95) and Oosting (302). The use of frequency points as well as species lists in the construction of life-form spectra reveals a shift toward the more protected forms in the northwestern margin of the hardwood forest that is absent from the North Carolina and Tennessee studies a thousand miles to the southeast.

The use of quantitative data needs further exploration in relation to life-form spectra. As we have shown elsewhere, frequency statistics are strongly influenced by the size of the sample unit. This is not true of density data; therefore the use of density points in calculating life-form spectra would not be influenced by quadrat size but would suffer from the great disparity in size and role of different species—numbers of trees and numbers of herbs are scarcely comparable. The use of dominance data (coverage) would seem to be a satisfactory basis for calculating spectra in describing associations, but in this case equal-size coverage classes or direct measures should be used rather than the customary unequal-size classes of the plant sociologists.

The data in Tables 64 and 65 are satisfactory for the purpose of illustrating the great difference that may exist between life-form spectra based on species and those based on satisfactory quantitative data. The field layer of *Acer-Fagus* forest, Haven Hill, Oakland County, Michigan, was studied by Cain at the time of full development of the spring flora, May 26, 1956. Coverage data were obtained by two sampling methods: (1) by using 20 quadrats each 1 sq. m. (2000 sq. dm.), and (2) by using 100 m. of line intercept. In the first sample the coverage of each species was estimated for each quadrat in which it occurred. The coverage of each species was totaled and expressed in square decimeters and as relative coverage, or the percentage that a species coverage is of the coverage of all species. In the second sample the

TABLE 65.   Life-form spectra showing, by means of arrows, the direction in which the emphasis shifts when frequency points rather than species lists are used as a basis (Table from Buell and Wilbur, 72). Phanerophytes omitted

	Life Forms			
	Ch	H	Cr	Th
Aestival aspect, cove hardwoods, Great Smoky Mountains, Tennessee (Cain, 95)				
Spectrum based on species	6.6	61.3	29.3	2.6
Spectrum based on frequency points	14.2	58.6	23.9	3.3
Autumnal aspect, Piedmont climax, North Carolina (Oosting, 302)				
Spectrum based on species	0	88.9	11.1	0
Spectrum based on frequency points	0	92.3	7.7	0
Itasca region, Minnesota (Buell and Wilbur, 72)				
Spectrum based on species	4.3	68.8	26.9	0
Spectrum based on frequency points	3.6	60.4	36.0	0

intercept of each species was measured to the nearest centimeter in each segment of the total line. The intercept was accumulated for each species and again expressed as relative coverage (or dominance). The base data in Table 66 show that each method is satisfactory, since the leading species come out in approximately the same order of magnitude. Although the two samples were taken in the same part of the forest, they did not and could not cover exactly the same ground, so some of the species do not occur on both lists. As a matter of fact, both samples are extremely small fractions of 1 percent of the total field vegetation of the stand, so such differences are to be expected. Not only are there close agreements between the measures by the two methods, considering the small sizes of the samples, but the bare ground also has very close percentages: 70.45 and 69.17, respectively.

Table 67 shows the life-form spectra calculated from the preceding data. As would be expected, the spectra are rather similar for each method of sampling, and the main point is made very clear. Although it is generally known that cryptophytes (geophytes) are important in the spring flora under deciduous broad-leaf forest, as shown by the species-based spectra, their real importance in the structure of the synusia is very evident in the dominance or coverage-based spectra,

TABLE 66. Comparative coverage (dominance) data for the vernal aspect of the field layer of *Acer-Fagus* forest, Oakland County, Michigan, determined by two methods

Species and Life Form	20 1 sq. m. Quadrats (2000 sq. dm.)		100 m. Line Intercept (10,000 cm.)	
	Sq. dm.	Rel. Cover	Cm.	Rel. Cover
Cr Podophyllum peltatum	320	54.16	1563	50.70
Cr Carex pensylvanica	67	11.34	248	8.04
Cr Smilacina racemosa	52	8.80	187	6.07
Cr Trillium grandiflorum	31	5.25	295	9.57
Cr Polygonatum biflorum	27	4.57	84	2.72
Cr Claytonia virginica	13	2.20	150	4.87
H Hystrix patula	11	1.86	132	4.28
Cr Panax trifolia	20	3.38	187	6.07
Ph Acer saccharum	12	2.03	68	2.21
H Solidago caesia	6	1.02	36	1.17
Ch Euonymus obovatus	6	1.02	18	0.58
H Carex sp.?	6	1.02	14	0.45
Ph Tilia americana	3	0.51	32	1.04
Cr Osmorhiza claytoni	2	0.34	13	0.42
Cr Uvularia perfoliata	3	0.51	28	0.91
H Prenanthes alba	1	0.17	24	0.78
Ph Prunus serotina	1	0.17	5	0.16
Cr Dentaria diphylla	6	1.02	...	...
Ph Ribes cynosbati	1	0.17	...	...
Ph Carya cordiformis	1	0.17	...	...
H Viola rostrata	1	0.17	...	...
H Galium circaezans	1	0.17	...	...
Ph Ulmus americana	Trace		19	0.62
Cr Ranunculus abortivus	Trace		1	0.03
Th Impatiens biflora	Trace		...	...
H Viola pubescens	Trace		...	...
H Viola papilionacea	Trace		...	...
Cr Geranium maculatum	Trace		...	...
Ph Acer rubrum	Trace		...	...
H Galium concinnum	Trace		...	...
Cr Caulophyllum thalictroides	...		51	1.65
Ph Carpinus caroliniana	...		14	0.45
Cr Botrychium virginianum	...		6	0.19
Ph Viburnum acerifolium	...		4	0.13
Ph Quercus rubra	...		1	0.03
Ch Psedera quinquefolia	...		1	0.03
Bare ground	1409	70.45%	6917	69.17%

TABLE 67.   Life-form spectra of the vernal aspect of the field layer
of *Acer-Fagus* forest, Oakland County, Michigan, based on species
and on coverage as determined by quadrats and by line interception

Life-Form Class	Species spectra		Coverage spectra	
	No. spp.	Percent	Area	Percent
Quadrat survey (area in sq. dm.)				
Ph	7	23.3	18	3.05
Ch	1	3.3	6	1.02
H	9	30.0	26	4.41
Cr (G)	12	40.0	541	91.57
Th	1	3.3	. . .	. . .
	30		591	
Line interception survey (in cm.)				
Ph	7	28.0	143	4.50
Ch	2	8.0	19	0.61
H	4	16.0	206	6.47
Cr	12	48.0	2813	88.42
Th	. . .	. . .	. . .	. . .
	25		3181	

where they are found to be 88.42 percent by the line-intercept method
and 91.57 percent by the quadrat method. It should be pointed out that
regional life-form spectra for the deciduous forest formation show high
percentages of hemicryptophytes (Tables 59, 60, 62, 63). The very
strong departure revealed here shows the advantage of using quantita-
tive-based life-form spectra in describing communities (phytocoenoses
and even separate synusiae composing them).

Another illustration is found in the recent study by Kilburn (256).
Using the line-intercept method, he has determined the actual coverage of each species (proportion of line intercepted by each one) sampled in the field layer of six stands each of three forest types in Cheybogan County, Michigan. The sample at each of the 18 stations consisted of 10 scattered lines 30 ft. in length, or a total of 300 ft. These
data were then handled as relative coverage, or the percentage the
cover of each species is of the total cover of all species.

Table 68 is adapted from Kilburn's Table 30. Although the forest
types are floristically very closely related, except for the dominant tree
of each type, important differences among the spectra are apparent
on a species basis, but even stronger differences are shown by the
coverage-based spectra. Perhaps the outstanding differences are the
very great importance in the structure of the field layer of geophytes

TABLE 68. Comparison of life-form spectra percentages of the field
layer, based on species and on relative coverage, of three forest types
in Cheybogan County, Michigan, each sampled at six stations.
(Abstracted from Kilburn, 256, Table 30)

Life-Form Class	Species Spectra	Coverage Spectra
	Aspen type	
Ph	39.3 (4.3)[a]	14.0 (9.2)[a]
Ch	23.2 (15.5)[b]	5.7 (2.7)[b]
H	22.2	10.3
Cr (G)	12.0	69.3
Th	2.3	...
	Jack pine type	
Ph	28.0 (6.0)	5.8 (3.5)
Ch	37.6 (24.3)	47.1 (10.8)
H	13.3	5.5
Cr (G)	15.2	40.2
Th	3.3	1.3
	Oak type	
Ph	27.3 (5.8)	21.8 (13.5)
Ch	34.7 (27.7)	40.9 (32.7)
H	25.2	5.3
Cr (G)	12.7	31.7
Th	3.8	0.8

[a] The first figure in parentheses is the nanophanerophytic percentage.
[b] The second figure in parentheses is the percentage of bryoid chamaephytes.

in the aspen forest type, of woody chamaephytes in the jack pine type,
and of chamaephytes collectively, but especially bryoid chamaephytes,
in the oak type. Hemicryptophytes are shown to be low in all three
types, again a result not to be expected from earlier work dealing with
entire floras.

LEAF-SIZE CLASSES

There is a general observation that leaves are large in moist tropical
vegetation (as in equatorial rain forest), medium sized in temperate
forests, and small in drier conditions (tundra, heath, grassland). In
general, leaves tend to be small in vegetation of dry or cold conditions.
Actually there are very few quantitative data, especially data based
on all the species of a community.

Raunkiaer established a limited number of leaf-size classes to facilitate statistical treatment of that aspect of vegetation. (See Raunkiaer, 337, for a compendium of his earlier works; see also Fuller and Bakke, 202; Cain, 81.) After studying a large series of species of many regions of the world, he set size-class limits for six classes that seemed to form more or less natural groups, and had a number of botanists also consider the problem and the size classes he had suggested. The result caused him to set the upper limit of the smallest leaf-size class at 25 sq. mm. Five successive multiplications by 9 determined the boundaries of the other classes, as follows:

Class 1   Leptophyll—up to 25 sq. mm.
Class 2   Nanophyll—$9 \times 25 = 225$ sq. mm. (2.25 sq. cm.)
Class 3   Microphyll—$9^2 \times 25 = 2025$ sq. mm. (20.25 sq. cm.)
Class 4   Mesophyll—$9^3 \times 25 = 18{,}225$ sq. mm. (182.25 sq. cm.)
Class 5   Macrophyll—$9^4 \times 25 = 164{,}025$ sq. mm. (1640.25 sq. cm.)
Class 6   Megaphyll—larger than Class 5

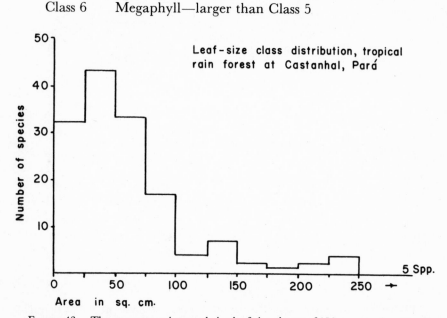

FIGURE 43.   The occurrence in equal-size leaf-size classes of 150 tree species of tropical rain forest of terra firme, Castanhal, Pará, Brazil.

Leaf-size spectra of floras and communities are not widely available the way life-form spectra are, so we will examine the system on the basis of original work in Brazil. Pires, Dobzhansky, and Black (320) published a list of tree species observed on a 3.5-ha. plot in luxuriant virgin, terra firme rain forest near the village of Três de Outubro, between Castanhal and the River Guamá, about 120 km. from Belém, Pará. Cain was able to study herbarium sheets of 150 of these tree species at the Instituto Agrônomico do Norte, Belém, through the courtesy of the late Dr. G. A. Black, and he computed the areas of typical leaves of mature trees. All the tree species of Castanhal were included so far as they were represented in the herbarium; and where possible, material from Castanhal was used.

The results of this study are expressed in two ways. First the species were assigned leaf-size classes on an arithmetic base, each class increasing in size by 25 sq. cm. Figure 43 shows a strongly skewed curve with a mode in the 26 to 50 sq. cm. class. This is in the range of the mesophyll class of Raunkiaer. The next step was to assign the species

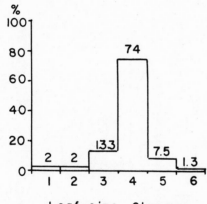

Leaf-size Classes

FIGURE 44. Occurrence in Raunkiaerian leaf-size classes of 150 tree species of tropical rain forest of terra firme, Castanhal, Pará, Brazil.

to the Raunkiaerian classes (Figure 44). On a log base the data produced an apparently normal curve, with 74 percent of the species in the mesophyll class and 13 percent in the next smaller microphyll class.

It may be that the paucity of leaf-size data in statistical biogeography has been due to the tediousness of the measurements recommended by Raunkiaer—making leaf tracings on cross-section paper and counting the squares, or cutting out the outline and weighing the paper to establish a weight-area relationship in some desired unit.

In the study under discussion a simpler procedure was used. The

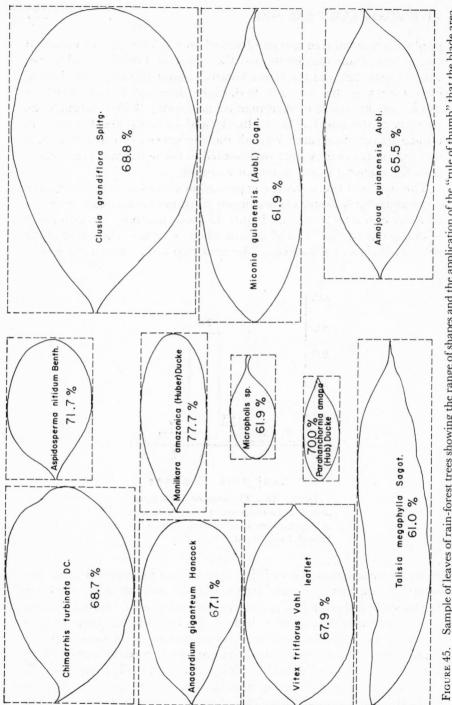

Clusia grandiflora Splitg. 68.8 %

Miconia guianensis (Aubl.) Cogn. 61.9 %

Amajoua guianensis Aubl. 65.5 %

Aspidosperma nitidum Benth. 71.7 %

Manilkara amazonica (Huber)Ducke 77.7 %

Micropholis sp. 61.9 %

Parahancornia amapa (Hub.) Ducke 70.0 %

Chimarrhis turbinata DC. 68.7 %

Anacardium giganteum Hancock 67.1 %

Vitex triflorus Vahl. leaflet 67.9 %

Talisia megaphylla Sagot. 61.0 %

FIGURE 45.   Sample of leaves of rain-forest trees showing the range of shapes and the application of the "rule of thumb" that the blade area is approximately ⅔ of the length-breadth rectangular area.

length and maximum breadth of leaf blades (or leaflets of compound leaves) were measured to the nearest millimeter for small leaves and to the nearest centimeter for larger ones. More care needs to be taken with leaves near the boundary of a class than with those obviously well within a common class, the general size of which one soon becomes familiar with. The area of a blade was assumed to be $\frac{2}{3}$ of the recorded rectangular area of length $\times$ breadth. The justification of this short cut lies in the fact that several leaves of different sizes and shapes that were carefully analyzed showed that tracings of the blade areas averaged 67.4 percent of the length-breadth rectangles that included the blades, as shown in the following list and in Figure 45.

Talisia megaphylla Sagot.	61.0%
Micropholis sp.? (Pires, Black, & Dobzhansky Coll. 4113)	61.9%
Miconia guianensis (Aubl.) Cogn.	61.9%
Amajoua guianensis Aubl.	65.5%
Anacardium giganteum Hancock	67.1%
Vitex triflorus Vahl. (lateral leaflet)	67.9%
Chimarrhis turbinata DC.	68.7%
Clusia grandiflora Splitg.	68.8%
Parahanchornia amapa (Huber) Ducke	70.0%
Aspidosperma nitidum Benth.	71.7%
Manilkara amazonica (Huber) Ducke	77.7%
Average	67.4%

General observations showed that leaves with crooked or curved blades, such as *Talisia megaphylla,* or with long acuminations on an otherwise broad leaf, such as *Miconia guianensis,* gave low ratios, and that elliptical leaves approaching rectangular shapes, such as *Manilkara amazonica,* gave high ratios. The vast majority of leaves of oval, ovate, and obovate shape, which are commonest in the forest of Castanhal, have ratios very close to $\frac{2}{3}$ of the overall rectangle. Therefore, for the purpose of classifying leaves into Raunkiaerian leaf-size classes no significant error is introduced by this quick method.

The excellent book, *The Tropical Rain Forest,* by Richards (344), shows the predominance of mesophyll leaves in rain forest. In the wet evergreen forest of the Shasta Reserve, Nigeria, 84 percent of the leaves are mesophyll. In the evergreen seasonal forest of Trinidad the emergent trees are 86 percent mesophyll, and the trees of the lower story have 80 percent in the mesophyll leaf-size class. Data from Brown (68) show that in the Philippine Islands the dipterocarp tropical rain forest of Mt. Maquiling has 86 percent mesophyll leaves, the submontane rain forest has 87 percent, and the montane mossy rain forest has 50 percent mesophyll leaves. Our results with virgin rain-forest trees of terra firme at Castanhal (74 percent) are lower than what is to be expected from Richards' generalization, ". . . that in normal Tropical Rain Forest at least 80% of the species (and individuals) of trees have leaves of the mesophyll size-class," but the departure is not great.

Further analysis of the leaves of trees in the Castanhal study showed that 69.3 percent are simple, 24.7 percent are once-pinnate, 3.3 percent are bi- or tripinnate, and 2.6 percent are deeply palmate-lobed or divided. Only 29.4 percent of the leaves were not acuminate. It is more or less arbitrary to classify some of the acuminate leaves as having drip points; but among the 70.6 percent of the leaves with acuminate tips, 28.0 percent of the 150 species studied had abruptly more or less long tips of the drip-point type. Good examples of leaves with drip points from this community include *Protium sagotianum* Marsh., *Brosimum paraense* Huber, *Minquartia guianensis* Aubl., *Guatteria elongata* Benth., *Inga heterophylla* Willd., *Qualea albiflora* Warm., *Lacunaria crenata* (Tul.) A. C. Smith, and *Pouteria glomerata* Radlk.

On the basis of only the nonsimple leaves in the Castanhal flora, it was found that compound leaves tend to have smaller leaflets than simple leaves do blades. This is shown in Table 69. There are 64.9 percent mesophyll (74 percent for the entire list) and 29.7 percent microphyll (13.3 percent for the entire list) among pinnate-leaved species. The small number of decompound species have leaflets in the two smallest size classes; but the palmate leaves, at least in the few cases available, are larger than pinnate leaves.

For the evergreen seasonal forest of Trinidad, Beard (34; Richards, 344) showed that the emergent trees have a higher percentage of species with mesophyll leaves than do the trees of the canopy (Table 70). From the Castanhal data we find that 60 species that have trees over 40 cm. in diameter have leaves a little smaller than do the 90 species that do not have trees reaching this diameter on the sample plot (Table 71). From the data available it is not possible to assign the species to definite layers or to Raunkiaerian height classes.

Cain, Castro, *et al.* (103) studied the leaf sizes of plants on a 2-ha. sample plot of rain forest at Mucambo, Belém, about 120 km. from Castanhal. The results are shown in Table 72, which combines life-form and leaf-size data. Here it is seen that for all phanerophytes only 75.9 percent of the leaves are mesophyll; but on the basis of height subclasses, 75.5 percent of the megaphanerophytes and 75.6 percent of the mesophanerophytes are of the mesophyll leaf-size class. The smaller leaf-size classes, however, are better represented among

TABLE 69.   Leaf-size classes of nonsimple leaves in the Castanhal rain forest

Class	Pinnate Number	Percent	Decompound Number	Palmate Number
Leptophyll	0	. . .	3	0
Nanophyll	0	. . .	2	0
Microphyll	11	29.7	0	0
Mesophyll	24	64.9	0	2
Macrophyll	2	5.3	0	2
Megaphyll	0	. . .	0	0

TABLE 70.   Raunkiaerian leaf-size classes in the evergreen seasonal forest of Trinidad
(After Beard, 34)

	Emergent Trees		Canopy Layer		Lower Story	
	Species %	Indi-viduals %	Species %	Indi-viduals %	Species %	Indi-viduals %
Leptophyll	. . .	. . .	2.2	43.3	. . .	. . .
Nanophyll	2.4	. . .	. . .	. . .	. . .	. . .
Microphyll	4.8	20.5	17.4	8.5	11.8	16.4
Mesophyll	85.7	63.5	76.1	55.2	80.4	71.5
Macrophyll	7.1	16.0	4.3	1.9	7.8	12.1
Megaphyll	. . .	. . .	. . .	. . .	. . .	. . .

TABLE 71.   Raunkiaerian leaf-size classes of tree species as Castanhal, Pará, based
on measurements by S. A. Cain. Virgin rain forest of terra firme

	All Species with Trunks Attaining Diameters of Over 40 Cm. %	All Species not Attaining Diameters of 40 Cm. %	All Species Attaining Diameters Over 10 Cm. %
Leptophyll	3.3	1.1	2.0
Nanophyll	3.3	1.1	2.0
Microphyll	16.6	10.0	13.3
Mesophyll	71.1	74.4	74.0
Macrophyll	3.3	12.2	7.3
Megaphyll	1.7	1.1	1.3
Number of species	60	90	150

the taller trees; the larger size (macrophyll) is very poorly represented
among the tallest trees.

The same authors have reported on life-form and leaf-size classification of the Brazilian rain forest from a variety of types. Table 73,

TABLE 72.   Occurrence in Raunkiaerian life-form and leaf-size classes of the species on a 2-ha. sample plot, Mucambo, Belém, Pará

Life-Form Classes	Leptophyll	Nanophyll	Microphyll	Mesophyll	Macrophyll	Total: percent	Number
Total Phanerophytes: Lianas and Epiphytes excluded	2.47	0.62	12.35	75.92	8.64	74.31	162
Megaphanerophytes	4.08	2.04	16.33	75.51	2.04	22.48	49
Mesophanerophytes	2.33		10.46	75.58	11.63	39.45	86
Microphanerophytes				66.7	33.3	1.38	3
Nanophanerophytes			12.50	79.17	8.33	11.01	24
Lianas		3.58	17.85	67.85	10.72	12.84	28
Epiphytes		16.67	38.89	16.67	27.77	8.25	18
Chamaephytes	50.0			50.0		0.92	2
Hemicryptophytes		33.33	16.67	33.33	16.67	2.75	6
Geophytes				50.0	50.0	0.92	2
Therophytes						0.0	0
Total: percent	2.29	3.21	15.14	68.35	11.01	100.00	
number	5	7	33	149	24		218

from the southernmost extension of the rain-forest formation near Pelotas, Rio Grande do Sul, shows the effects of climatic change. Mesophylls have dropped from 75.9 to 31.9 percent for true phaneorophytes, and microphylls have increased from 12.35 to 48.6 percent. For the group of trees in the mesophanerophytic size class, the change in mesophylls is from 75.6 to 39.3 percent, and the change in microphylls is from 10.46 to 60.7 percent, in the comparison of Mucambo in the Amazon region with Pelotas in the south. The latter is gallery rain forest in a grassland region.

When one places the total flora of a region or a community in leaf-size classes, there appear certain problems that require special consideration. As we mentioned earlier, and as Raunkiaer emphasized, the leaflet of the compound leaf is to be compared with the blade of the simple leaf because they seem to be comparable physiological units, at least in respect to adaptation to the environment. Moderately lobed leaves offer no difficulty, but deeply divided ones call for a rather arbitrary decision by the investigator as to what constitutes the unit that is to be measured as the basis for leaf-size classification.

The exact area of a leaf seldom is of significance in assignment to classes because of the wide range of sizes within the classes. Nevertheless, the investigator should attempt to work with "typical" leaves of each species, certainly not with the largest or smallest leaves available. For example, in most cases an average-sized sun leaf should be used for trees typical of the forest canopy, rather than a shade leaf which is usually larger—sometimes very much larger. In the canopy the sun leaf has the most significance for general climate; but for species of the undergrowth, the shade leaf is typical. Here as elsewhere, rules can't be made that obviate the need for common sense.

As in the case of life-form classification, there would seem to be a very definite gain from relating leaf-size spectra to frequency points, density points, or some other measure than mere presence of a species on the community lists, for in this case a rare species counts as much as a prevalent one. In a study of the rain forest at Mucambo, near Belém, we computed the importance value index for each of the tree species 1 dm.

TABLE 73. Occurrence in Raunkiaerian life-form and leaf-size classes of the species of the natural forest of Horto Botânico do Instituto Agrônomico do Sul, Pelotas, Rio Grande do Sul (Data from Cain, Castro, and Sacco, 101)

Life-Form Classes	Aphyllus	Leptophyll	Nanophyll	Microphyll	Mesophyll	Macrophyll	Total: percent	Number
All phanerophytes	6.9	5.5	5.5	48.6	31.9	1.4	51.4	72
Mesophanerophytes				60.7	39.3		20.0	28
Microphanerophytes	6.7		6.7	66.7	20.0		10.7	15
Nanophanerophytes	13.8	13.8	10.3	27.6	31.0	3.7	20.7	29
Lianas		6.7	6.7	60.0	26.6		10.7	15
Epiphytes	27.3	9.1	9.1	36.4	18.2		7.9	11
Chamaephytes				80.0		20.0	3.6	5
Hemicryptophytes			26.1	60.9	13.0		16.4	23
Cryptophytes (Geo-)				71.4	28.6		5.0	7
Therophytes			28.6	71.4			5.0	7
Stem succulents[a]	(2)							
Total: per cent	5.7	4.3	10.0	54.3	24.3	1.4	100.0	
number	8	6	14	76	34	2		140

[a] Stem succulents counted in their height classes.

Note the absence of the megaphanerophyte life-form class and the megaphyll leaf-size class.

or more in diameter on a 2-ha. sample plot. This quantitative measure can then be used for computing a leaf-size class spectrum. Table 74 shows the difference between the class percentages computed on the basis of species and on the basis of the indexes computed for each species as the sum of the relative density, relative basal area (dominance),

TABLE 74.   Leaf-size class percentages computed on the basis of tree species only and on the basis of their importance value indexes, equatorial rain forest at Mucambo, Belém, Pará

Leaf-Size Class	Number of Species	%	Sum of the Importance Values	%
Leptophyll	4	3.2	10.04	3.7
Nanophyll	1	0.8	0.60	0.2
Microphyll	15	12.1	31.86	11.7
Mesophyll	93	75.0	216.36	79.6
Macrophyll	11	8.9	12.81	4.7
Unclassified	28		28.33	
Total	152 (124)		300.00 (271.67)	

and relative frequency. The fact that the percentages are not very different results from the large number of species involved and the lack of clear dominance by a small number of them. However, the mesophyll leaf-size class is shown to be somewhat more important in the vegetation that is determined by species alone, and the macrophyll size is shown to be of lesser importance. Life-form spectra computed on the basis of the importance value index would be very desirable, but we do not have the requisite quantitative data except for trees.

Dansereau (152) has devised a system for the description and recording of vegetation that is based on structure with six sets of characteristics considered: (1) life form, (2) size, (3) function, (4) leaf shape and size, (5) leaf texture, and (6) coverage. His series of leaf sizes and shapes consists of six broad categories:

n   Needle, scale, or spine leaves as in *Juniperus oxycedrus, Thuja occidentalis,* and *Opuntia vulgaris*

g   Graminoid leaves as in *Desylirion graminifolium, Festuca elatior, Tillandsia usneoides,* and *Scirpus atrovirens*

a   Medium or small leaves as in *Ilex opaca* and *Solidago canadensis*

h   Broad leaves as in *Rhododendron maximum* and *Liriodendron tulipifera*

v   Compound leaves as in *Roupala heterophylla* and *Dennstaedtia punctilobula*

q   Thalloid vegetative parts as in masses of algae, in fungi, and in
        liverworts

Dansereau says that his Class n includes Raunkiaer's leptophylls and
nanophylls, his Class a includes Raunkiaer's microphylls and mesophylls, and his Class h includes Raunkiaer's macrophylls and mega-
phylls.

Dansereau's fifth series of characteristics is leaf texture, of which
there are four principal types:

f   Filmy as in *Hymenophyllum rarum, Adiantum pedatum, Muium cuspi-
        datum,* and in fact many ferns and mosses
z   Membranous as in *Corylus cornuta, Aster novae-angliae,* and in fact
        the bulk of the flowering plants
x   Sclerophyll as in *Rhododendron maximum, Ilex opaca, Picea pungens,*
        and many other woody plants
k   Succulent or fungoid as in *Othonna crassifolia, Iresine portulaccoides,
        Marchantia* spp., and many spermatophytes and thallophytes

Dansereau gives applications of his system to various types of vegetation, but there are no statistical summaries of, for example, his leaf
classes for the species of a community.

GLOSSARY

THE GLOSSARY includes technical terms in plant sociology and geography, especially those that have been given precise meanings that sometimes differ from common usage. It omits most of the common terms of biology.

Abundance. Number of individuals of a species in a sample plot, estimated (not counted) according to a limited number of classes; rarely, the average number of individuals of a species computed on the basis of occupied quadrats.

Aciculilignosa. Narrow-leaf sclerophyll forest and bush.

Action. The effects of environmental factors on organisms.

Aestilignosa. Broad-leaf summer-green forest and bush; deciduous with cold.

Aggregation. The process resulting in the grouping of organisms either through active movement or as a result of dissemination of propagules.

Alliance. A group of related associations showing floristic and sociological affinities.

Allogenous flora. Relic plants of an earlier prevailing flora and environment; epibiotic plants.

Area. (1) A geographical unit smaller than a region. (2) The total range of a taxonomic unit, such as species, a genus, or a community.

Areography. The geography of areas of species and associations, or other units of flora and vegetation; chorology.

Aspect. The seasonal impress on a community, such as the vernal aspect in deciduous forest produced by geoghytic herbs, or the winter, leafless aspect.

Aspection. The phenomenon of changing (cyclical) physiognomy of vegetation because of coincident rhythms of periodicity of species.

Association. (1) A climax community that is the largest subdivision of a climax, biome, or formation. (2) Loosely, any stable community.

Association fragment. A stand of a community type that does not have characteristic composition and structure, presumably because it occupies less than the minimal area for the community.

Association-individual. A stand; a concrete example of an association.

Association-segregate. An association that has differentiated out of a mixed association under the historical influence of climatic differentiation.

Associes. Any seral community below the climax association.

Autecology. The study of the ecological relations of individuals or kinds, in contradistinction to synecology, the study of communities; the ecology of the individual.

Barrier. A topographic, climatic, edaphic, or biological condition which separates a form from an area with a suitable environment for the form, the breadth of the barrier being greater than the normal dispersal capacity of the form.

Basal area. In trees, the cross-section area of the trunk at 4.5 ft. above the ground. In grasses, the cross-section area of a bunch grass measured at cropping height, about 1 in. above the ground.

Biological spectrum. The array of life-form class percentages of the flora of an area or a community.

Biomass. The quantity of organic substance produced on a given area, as in the weight of vegetable matter removed by clipping a quadrat, or the plankton of a given volume of water.

Biome. A major climax community composed of plants and animals; equivalent to climax or formation.

Biota. The fauna and flora of an area.

Biotic province. A territory based on a correspondence between the distribution of particular animals with vegetation which consequently has a certain amount of ecological homogeneity.

Biotope. The smallest natural area or space characterized by a particular environment. *See* Niche.

Bisect. A representation of a vertical section of a community showing the roots and shoots in their natural positions.

Buffer zone. An area provided around a sample plot (usually a permanent quadrat) to eliminate any marginal effects on the sample taken within the plot.

Buttress. Planklike outgrowth at the base of a tree trunk.

Canopy. The uppermost essentially continuous layer in forests.

Cauliflory. The adventitious production of flowers and fruits on leafless woody stems, sometimes on the main trunk of trees.

Center of origin. The more or less local area where a phylogenetic stock arose. The concept is applicable to associations.

Chamaephyte. A life-form class with perennating buds definitely above ground but less than ¼ m. high; usually woody or semi-woody perennials.

Characteristic species. Species of high fidelity to a community type; fidelity classes 3 to 5 according to Braun-Blanquet.

Chart quadrat. Representation of a sample plot in which the location of each plant is shown in its proper place.

Chorology. The science of areas and their development.

Climax. The terminal community of a sere which is in dynamic equilibrium with the prevailing climate. The major world climaxes are equivalent to formations and biomes. The term is also used in connection with any subdivision, such as a climax association, and with modifying adjectives.

Climax adaptation number. A number (representing one of a limited number of classes) assigned to a species to show its relative position in succession, or its "relative degree of climaxness." *See* Ecological sequence number.

Cline. A series of form changes; a gradient of biotypes along an environmental transition.

Clip quadrat. A sample plot from which the vegetation is removed for counting or determination of biomass.

Clisere. A series of climaxes following one another in any given area as a result of climatic change. Contiguous climaxes move together in a common direction because of a widespread climatic change that induces regional parallelism.

Coaction. The interaction of organisms; the reciprocal effects of plants and animals.

Codominant. (1) In ecology, the few species that together dominate or control a community (phytocoenosis or synusia). (2) In forestry, trees that share the space in the canopy of the forest.

Combined frequency. Frequency being a concept concerning occurrence of plants of a species in sample plots of a single stand, combined frequency is the total figure resulting when several stands of the same type are studied.

Combining stand. A layer community common to two or more phytocoenoses. The other layers are different, or alternating.

Community. An organized group of plants or animals, or both. The term is employed when it is not necessary or desirable to use a more specific designation such as association, associes, etc. It is an organized complex having a typical composition and structure that result from interactions through time.

Compensation. The condition when one or a group of environmental factors, usually limiting to the life of an organism, is counteracted by an excess or difference of other factors.

Competition. The struggle for existence that results when two or more organisms have similar requirements in excess of the supply.

Congenors. Closely related species, as in members of the same genus.

Consociation. A community with a single dominant species.

Constancy. A relative expression of the presence and absence of plants of a species in different stands of a community type, based on equal-area samples.

Constant-dominants.   Species constantly occurring as dominants in a series of samples of a community

Contagious distribution.   A distribution of individuals of a population in which the ratio to the average spacing expected for a random dispersion is less than unity; i.e., the plants are more or less clumped.

Continuum.   The sequence of communities of a formation showing gradual changes in composition (and sometimes structure) over distance in a major vegetation type.

Corticolous.   Living on bark, as in the case of bryophytic communities on the trunks and branches of trees.

Count quadrat.   A sample plot on which density is determined.

Cover quadrat.   A sample plot on which area of coverage, or shading, is determined.

Cover type.   The type of vegetation at present occupying an area.

Coverage.   The area covered (or volume of space occupied) by individuals of a species, usually computed on a sample area by vertical projection onto the ground; often determined for trees from basal area.

Cryptophytes.   A life-form class whose plants have their perennating buds under the surface of the substratum.

d.b.h.   Diameter of a tree, measured at 4.5 ft. above the ground, i.e., diameter breast high.

Density.   The number of individuals of a species (counted, not estimated) on a unit of area

Deserta.   Dry desert and tundra or cold desert.

DFD index.   The sum of percentage density, percentage frequency, and percentage dominance (or coverage).

Diaspore.   Any spore, seed, fruit, bud, or other portion of a plant that consists of its active dispersal phase and is capable of reproducing a new plant.

Differential species.   Species that can be used to distinguish subassociations.

Disclimax.   A long-enduring subclimax stage that is prevented from attaining the true climatic climax condition by human, animal, or other interference.

Disjunct area.   An area of occurrence of a species separated from other areas of it by a distance greater than the normal dispersal capacity of the species and consequently having some historical explanation; applicable also to stands of a community type.

Dispersal.   The transport of diaspores. It does not constitute migration, but is a necessary antecedent to it.

Dominance.   The term used to refer to the extent of area covered, space occupied, or degree of control of a community by one or more species.

Dominant.   A form that has a high degree of dominance or control over a community.

Drip point. An attenuated, acuminate leaf tip, common among rain-forest trees.

Durilignosa. Broad-leaf sclerophyll forest and bush.

Dynamic behavior (of species). The function of a species with respect to the integrity of a community, i.e., whether in its life process a species is constructive, consolidating, or conserving of the community, or disintegrative and destructive. In succession, a single species may be destructive of one community and initiating and constructive of the succeeding community.

Ecad. A habitat form, a modification, a change or difference that is purely somatic and not heritable; resulting from adaptation, not genetic difference.

Ecological amplitude. Breadth of tolerance to specific factors or environmental factor complexes.

Ecological sequence number. A synonym of "climax adaptation number" that avoids the implication of the relationship of a species to a single climax.

Ecology. The study of the complex interrelations between organisms and their environments; more broadly, the term used to include much of the fields of biogeography and phytosociology.

Ecosystem. The interacting system comprising living things, together with their nonliving habitat. The term was applied originally to such units as the community and biome, but is equally applicable to other levels of organization.

Ecotone. The transition region between two communities which contains characteristic species of each and presumably is intermediate in environment.

Edaphic. Pertaining to the soil, especially its influence on organisms; edaphic factors may be physical, chemical, or biological.

Edaphic climax. A relatively stable, long-enduring community under the immediate control of soil factors.

Element. Plants or animals characteristic of a certain natural area, whether growing within that area or extraneously, as costal plain element.

Enclosure. A fenced area in which sample plots are located and from which the coaction of certain animals is excluded.

Endemic. (1) Forms that are confined to a single natural area. (2) Forms that are confined to a single area, whether natural or not, large or small, isolated or continuous.

Environment. The sum total of effective external factors to which an organism responds; the living conditions of a community.

Epibiotic. Relics; survivors of a former prevailing flora.

Epiphyte. A plant growing upon another plant without direct connection with the soil, but not parasitic.

Equiformal progressive areas. Areas of species that have radiated (migrated) from the same center of origin or survival and consequently have more or less concentric or equiformal areas of different sizes.

Ericilignosa.   True health vegetation.

Exposure.   The direction a slope faces, such as northern exposure.

Extraneous.   An occurrence of plants nearer the periphery than the center of area. At any given station a plant is extraneous if it is near its margin of range and its main area of occurrence is elsewhere.

Faciation (Facies).   A portion of an association (climax) characterized by a particular combination of dominants of the association and having an areal basis related to climatic difference within the general climatic type controlling the association.

Fauna.   The animals of an area considered as kinds rather than as composing communities.

Fidelity.   The degree to which species are confined to certain communities; exclusiveness.

Field layer.   The herbaceous layer or synusia of a phytocoenosis; not the lower *Bodenschicht* of mosses, lichens, etc.

Flora.   The plants of an area considered as kinds rather than as composing communities.

Floristic area.   An area resulting from similarity in the individual areas of several species.

Floristic element.   Plants characteristic in a certain territory but occurring elsewhere as a foreign element. For example, "coastal plain species" occurring also in mountains constitute a coastal plain element in the mountain flora.

Floristic territory.   A territory resulting from the occurrence of a series of plants common to and more or less confined within a given region, although other species occur within it, more or less extending through or beyond it.

Forest type.   Any type of tree-dominated community that covers considerable area.

Formation.   The largest subdivision of world vegetation; equivalent to climax and biome.

Fragmentary association.   A stand (concrete community) of a size smaller than minimal area and not having the typical composition and structure of the association.

Frequency (Raunkiaer).   A statistical expression of the representation (presence or absence) of individuals of a species in a series of subsamples; i.e., the ratio between the number of sample areas that contains a species and the total number of sample areas.

Frequency class (Raunkiaer).   One of a small series of classes based on the range of possible frequencies from zero to 100 percent.

Frequency index.   The number of subsamples, in the analysis of a stand, that contain a given species is the frequency index, such as 16/25, in which 16 out of 25 subsamples are found to contain the given species. It is more common to convert the index to a percentage, as different surveys may have different numbers of subsamples.

Frigorideserta. Cold desert or tundra.

Gallery forest (galleria). A narrow forest extending into grassland, savanna, etc., along watercourses; a fringing forest.

Gaussian curve. A probability curve.

Genecology. The ecology of organisms or taxonomic units; the combination of genetic and ecological methods and concepts, particularly in the study of species and species groups.

Geophyte. A life-form class whose plants have their perennating buds underground associated with rhizomes, bulbs, corms, etc.

Growth form. *See* Life form.

Habitat. The environment of a particular station occupied by an organism, species, or community.

Helophyte. A life-form class composed of marsh plants whose perennating buds are in soil under water.

Hemicryptophyte. A life-form class whose plants have their perennating buds at the surface of the ground.

Hemiparasite. A form transitional between epiphytes that receive only support from their substrata, and true parasites that lack chlorophyll.

Herbosa. Vegetation dominated by nonwoody plants.

Hiemilignosa. Monsoon or rain-green forest and bush.

Holocoenotic. The nature of the action of the environment, i.e., the simultaneous action and interaction of the many factors in the environment.

Homologous series (communities). Series of twin associations arranged according to ecological as well as phytosociological characteristics.

Hydathode. A leaf structure from which liquid is extruded under root pressure.

Hydrophyte. (1) An organism living under conditions of high environmental moisture; usually aquatic. (2) A life-form class whose plants have their perennating buds under water.

Hygrophilous. Living in or having the structure of plants of areas with high atmospheric moisture.

Hyperdispersion. A pattern of occurrence of individuals of a species that is more aggregated (clumped) than they would be in a random (normal) distribution.

Hypodispersion. A pattern of occurrence of individuals of a species that is more regularly (evenly) spaced than would be the case in a random (normal) distribution.

Inclosure. A fenced research area.

Indicators. Species or communities that indicate ecological conditions or processes because of their high fidelity or dominance, etc.

Intraneous. The occurrence of organisms well within the total area of their distribution. A species is intraneous if at a given station its area extends in all directions. *See* Extraneous.

IVI, importance value index. The sum of relative density, relative frequence, and relative dominance of species. These indexes, for all the species of a stand studied, must total 300 as each factor is a percentage.

Laurilignosa. Laurel forest and bush.

Law of frequency (Raunkiaer). Distribution of frequency percentages of a community in five classes, A to E, as follows:

$$A > B > C \gtreqless D < E$$

Layer. A stratum of vegetation, as an herb layer, shrub layer, etc.

Leaf-size class. An arbitrary size class of leaf-blade area, introduced by Raunkiaer for statistical comparisons of vegetation.

Leptophyll. A leaf-size class in which the blade area is not more than 25 sq. mm.

Liana. A climbing vine; panerophytia scandentia.

Life form. The vegetative form of the plant body, thought usually to be a hereditary adjustment to environment; growth form.

Life-form class. One of a series of classificatory groups based on vegetative form, introduced by Raunkiaer for statistical comparisons of vegetation.

Life zone. Latitudinal and altitudinal belts characterized by biota correlated with certain climatic factors.

Lignosa. Any formation dominated by woody plants.

Line-intercept method. A method of sampling vegetation based on the interception of plants by a measured line at ground level, or the vertical projection of plants onto the line.

Line-plot method. A system in which sample plots are spaced regularly along a line.

List quadrat. A sample plot on which each species is listed.

Local abundance. A combination estimate of the occurrence of a species on a sample plot involving sociability and local abundance and coverage.

Lociation (Locies). A local variant of a climax association which may not differ from the rest of the association or faciation with respect to dominants, but which is characterized by its own subdominants in the inferior layers of the community; usually correlated with microclimatic or edaphic conditions.

Macrophyll. A leaf-size class in which the blade area is between 18,225 and 164,025 sq. mm. ($9^4 \times 25$).

Megaphanerophyte. Trees (phanerophytes) over 30 m. tall; also lianas and vascular epiphytes in the same height range.

Megaphyll. A leaf-size class in which the blade area is larger than 164,025 sq. mm.

Mesophanerophytes. Trees (phanerophytes) between 8 and 30 m. tall; also lianas and vascular epiphytes in the same height range.

Mesophyll. A leaf-size class in which the blade area is between 2025 and 18,225 sq. mm. ($9^3 \times 25$).

Mesophyte. An organism living under moderate moisture conditions; intermediate between hydrophyte and xerophyte.

Microphanerophytes. Trees and shrubs between 2 and 8 m. tall; also lianas and vascular epiphytes in the same height range.

Microphyll. A leaf-size class in which the blade area is between 225 and 2025 sq. mm. ($9^2 \times 25$).

Migration. The culmination of dissemination in ecesis; establishment in a new area.

Migratory highway. A sufficiently continuous series of habitats suitable for the species under question.

Minimal area (of a community). The least area on which the community can develop its characteristic composition and structure.

Monoclimax hypothesis. The theory that, given sufficient time, within a regional climatic type there will develop a single climax.

Monotopic. Having a single area of occurrence; used for species that do not have discontinuous areas.

Monsoon forest. A tropical and subtropical formation that is deciduous with drought.

Multiple-plot method. A system of sampling vegetation by means of numerous subsamples within a stand, with any manner of spacing.

Myrmecophilous. Plants with which ants or termites are associated; often with special adaptive structures.

Nanophanerophytes. Shrubs between 25 cm. and 2 m. tall; also perennial herbs, lianas, and vascular epiphytes with perennating buds in the same height range.

Nanophyll. A leaf-size class in which the blade area is between 25 and 225 sq. mm. (9×25).

Nested plots. A system of sample plots in which several plots of different sizes are so arranged that each larger plot contains the smaller ones.

Niche. A place suitable for an organism or, by extension, a synusia. The biotope or smallest unit of habitat.

Normal distribution. A pattern of occurrence of individuals of a species that is random.

Normal spectrum. The array of life-form class percentages used as a standard for comparison, based on a selected sample of the world flora.

Octave of frequency. In statistics, an interval of 2 to 1, as in the number series: 1, 2, 4, 8, 16, 32, 64. . . .

Perennating bud. The meristematic or embryonic tissues responsible for renewing growth, often of bud form surrounded by scales.

Periodicity. In plant sociology, commonly the periods of the year during which a plant is vegetative, flowering, fruiting, etc. *See* Aspection.

Phanerophyte. One of the Raunkiaerian life-form classes composed of all woody perennials taller than 25 cm., and consisting of a series of subclasses according to height.

Physiognomy. The form and structure of vegetation; the appearance of vegetation that results from the life forms of predominant plants.

Phytocoenosis. The total assemblage of plants living at a particular station; the community as a whole, including all its synusiae.

Phytograph. A polygonal figure resulting from the graphing of sociological data on four equiangular radii.

Phytosociology.   In particular, the study of the composition and structure of communities, and their classification; sometimes extended to include pertinent ecological phenomena.

Pluviilignosa.   Rain forest (Pluviisilvae) and rain bush (Pluviifruticeta).

Point-contact method.   A system of sampling vegetation by means of a moving point or set of points making contact with plants.

Poisson distribution.   A normal distribution.

Polster.   A cushion plant; a low, compact, shrubby perennial.

Polyclimax hypothesis.   The theory that within a regional climatic type there will develop more than one climax because the climatic and biological factors cannot completely subordinate the edaphic factors.

Polytopic.   Having more than one area of occurrence; used in reference to species with disjunct subareas.

Postclimax.   A climax community requiring more favorable moisture conditions than prevail generally in an area; usually a relic that has survived because of moisture compensation.

Preclimax.   A climax community requiring less favorable moisture conditions than prevail generally in an area; usually a relic that has survived in suitable edaphic or microclimatic situations.

Preferential species.   In the sense of Curtis, species of 50 percent or more presence in one association and at least 10 percent greater presence in the type than in any closely related association.

In the sense of Braun-Blanquet, species of Class 3 fidelity—species more or less abundantly in several communities but predominantly in one certain community.

Presence.   The degree to which a species is represented in a series of stands of a community type. In any given stand a species is counted present if it occurs at all within the stand.

Profile.   A diagrammatic or naturalistic representation of the vertical structure of vegetation.

Propagule.   Diaspore; seed, spore, gemma, or other reproductive-disseminative structure.

Quadrat.   A square sample plot; loosely, any sample plot, whether or not it is square.

Rain forest.   A world formation type found in equatorial regions of high rainfall without a dry period; a tall, evergreen forest type.

Random sample.   In vegetation analysis, a sample in which each spatial unit of the entire stand of size equal to the size of the sample unit (quadrat) should have an equal and independent chance of being examined (drawn).

Reaction.   The effects that organisms living in an area have upon the environment of that area.

Refugium.   An area that has not been as drastically altered as a region as a whole and consequently harbors relic species.

Relative abundance.   (1) An index determined for a species by multiplying the number of plants per unit of area by the number of lists (subsamples) in which it occurs and dividing by the total number of lists. (2) The number of individuals per occupied quadrat.

Relative density. The percentage the number of individuals is of the total number of individuals of all species in a sample.

Relative dominance (coverage). The percentage which the coverage of a species in a sample is of the total coverage of all species in the sample.

Relative frequency. The percentage which the frequency of a species in a sample is of the total frequency of all species in the sample.

Relevé. A floristic list based on a single stand of a community, usually with assignment to each species of various types of sociological data, such as total estimate, sociability, etc.

Relic. A surviving organism, population, or community characteristic of an earlier time and usually a different condition.

Saturation deficit. The vapor pressure deficit which is the difference between the actual vapor pressure of the atmosphere and the vapor pressure of a saturated atmosphere at the same temperature, measured in mm. of Hg.

Savanna. A formation of grassland with scattered trees, either as individuals or clumps; often a transitional type between true grassland and forest.

Saxicolous. Growing on rocks.

Sclerophyll. Plants with hard evergreen leaves, either broad (Durilignosa) or narrow and conifer-like (Aciculignosa).

Sere. The several stages in a succession of communities from pioneer to climax.

Siccideserta. Dry desert.

Single-plot method. A method of sampling vegetation in which a single plot (at least of minimal area) is taken in each stand of a community type.

Site. The quality of the environment at a particular location, usually measured by growth of a dominant species.

Site type (index). A classification of site usually based on height growth of dominant trees in a given number of years.

Sociability. The degree to which plants are normally aggregated. The concept of sociability, in the sense of Braun-Blanquet, applies to a species and is usually expressed by a limited number of classes ranging from isolated to highly gregarious patterns of occurrence.

Species-area relationship. The relationship between number of species on an area and the size of the area.

Stand. A concrete example of a community, as a stand of beech-maple trees; an association-individual.

Station. The geographical locality of occurrence of an organism or a community.

Steppe. A formation of treeless grasslands, especially short grasses of warm temperate and subtropical regions.

Stratum. A layer of vegetation; a horizontally distributed synusia.

Strip sample. A long rectangular sample area.

Subclimax. A long-enduring, late associes.

Subplot. A portion of a plot; a smaller area laid out within a large plot.

Subsample. One of a series of plots taken in the same statistical universe; a unit of a sample.

Succession. The development of a sere; the replacement of one community by another.

Synecology. The study of communities, especially their environmental relations and structure.

Synusia. A minor community within a phytocoenosis characterized by relative uniformity of life form, floristic composition, and ecology.

Taxon. Any classificatory unit of any rank, such as subspecies, species, or genus.

Terriherbosa. Prairie and steppe vegetation.

Therophyte. An annual plant; a life-form class whose only perennating buds are those of the embryos in seeds.

Thorn forest. A formation rich in thorny trees, shrubs, and vines and with a xerophilous cast; usually without vascular epiphytes and poor in herbs, especially grass.

Tolerance. The range of intensity of factors of the environment within which an organism can function or endure.

Total estimate. Combination of estimates of abundance and coverage in one scale; sometimes also combined with vigor.

Transect. A cross section of vegetation; a strip sample.

Transgressive. Seedlings or other young plants encountered in a low layer of vegetation but destined, when mature, to occupy a higher layer (stratum).

Tundra. A world formation of high latitudes and altitudes; cold desert.

Twin formations. Pairs of communities with a combining stand (layer) and two or more alternating stands (layers).

Union. A vegetational classificatory unit based on unistratal communities, or synusiae.

Unistratal community. A community consisting of a single synusia.

Varzea. A term for flood plain, used in Brazil.

Vegetation. The plants of an area considered in general or especially in relation to the communities they form, but never solely taxonomically as in floristics.

Vegetation continuum index. The product of the climax adaptation number times the importance value index. The maximum value of the vegetation continuum index is 3000.

Velamen. A cortical water-absorbing tissue of the aerial roots of certain tropical epiphytes and lianas.

Vitality. An expression of vigor attained by a species; the extent to which it completes its life cycle, flowering, fruiting, etc.

Xeromorph. An organism whose morphology is usually associated with dry conditions, but not necessarily a xerophyte.

Xerophyte. An organism that characteristically lives under dry conditions.

LITERATURE CITED

1. Acocks, J. P. H.   Veld types of South Africa. *Union of South Africa, Dept. Agric., Div. Bot., Bot. Surv. Mem.,* 1953, 28:1–192.
2. Adamson, R. S.   The plant communities of Table Mountain. I. Preliminary account. *Jour. Ecol.,* 1927, 15:278–309.
3. Adamson, R. S.   The plant communities of Table Mountain. II. Lifeform dominance and succession. *Jour. Ecol.,* 1931, 19:304–320.
4. Adamson, R. S.   The classification of life-forms of plants. *Bot. Rev.,* 1939, 5:546–561.
5. Adamson, R. S., and T. G. B. Osborn.   On the ecology of the Ooldea district. *Trans. Roy. Soc. S. Aust.,* 1922, 46:539–564.
6. Alechin, W. W.   Ist die Pflanzengesellschaft eine Abstraktion oder eine Realität? *Engler's Bot. Jahrb.,* 1925, 60 (Beibl. 135): 17–25.
7. Alechin, W. W.   Was ist eine Pflanzengesellschaft? *Fedde Repert. spec. nov. reg. veg.,* 1926, Beih. 37:1–50.
8. Alechin, W. W.   Die altere russische Steppenforschung mit besonderer Berücksichtung der quantitativen Methoden. *Beitr. Biol. Pflanz. (Conn),* 1932, 20:25–58.
9. Allan, H. H.   Notes on the study of open communities of high mountain areas in New Zealand. In A. G. Tansley and T. F. Chipp, *Aims and Methods in the Study of Vegetation.* London, Brit. Empire Veg. Comm., 1926.
10. Allan, H. H.   A consideration of the "biological spectra" of New Zealand. *Jour. Ecol.,* 1937, 25:116–152.
11. Allard, H. A.   Length of day in relation to the natural and artificial distribution of plants. *Ecol.,* 1932, 13:221–234.
12. Allee, W. C.   Measurements of environmental factors in the tropical rain forest of Panama. *Ecol.,* 1926, 7:273–302.
13. Allee, W. C., *et al.   Principles of Animal Ecology.* Philadelphia, Saunders, 1949.

14. Anderson, E.   The species problem in *Iris*. *Ann. Missouri Bot. Gard.*, 1936, 23:494–496.

15. Anderson, K. L.   A comparison of line transect and permanent quadrats in evaluating composition and density of pasture vegetation of the tall grass prairie type. *Jour. Amer. Soc. Agron.*, 1942, 34:805–822.

16. Archibald, E. A. A.   The specific character of plant communities. I. Herbaceous communities. II. A quantitative approach. *Jour. Ecol.*, 1949, 37:260–273, 274–288.

17. Arny, A. C.   Alfalfa and grass percentage determinations with the inclined point apparatus at different stages of development of the mixture. *Jour. Amer. Soc. Agron.*, 1944, 36:996–998.

18. Arny, A. C., and A. R. Schmid.   A study of the inclined point quadrat method of botanical analysis of pasture mixtures. *Jour. Amer. Soc. Agron.*, 1942, 34:238–247.

19. Ashby, E.   The quantitative analysis of vegetation. *Ann. Bot.*, 1935, 49:779–802.

20. Ashby, E.   Statistical ecology. *Bot. Rev.*, 1936, 2:221–235.

21. Aubreville, A. M. A.   La forêt coloniale: les forêts de l'Afrique occidentals française. *Ann. Acad. Sci. colon., Paris*, 1938, 9:1–245.

22. Aubreville, A. M. A.   Tropical Africa. In S. Haden-Guest (ed.), *A World Geography of Forest Resources*. New York, Ronald, 1956, 353–384.

23. Baker, F. S.   A revised tolerance table. *Jour. For.*, 1949, 47:179–181.

24. Barbour, W. R.   Forest types of tropical America. *Caribbean For.*, 1942, 3:137–150.

25. Barbour, W. R.   South America. In S. Haden-Guest (ed.), *A World Geography of Forest Resources*. New York, Ronald, 1956, 201–230.

26. Barnes, R. D.   The ecological distribution of spiders in non-forest communities at Beaufort, North Carolina. *Ecol. Monogr.*, 1952, 23:315–337.

27. Bates, H. W.   *The Naturalist on the River Amazon*. London, Murray, 1863.

28. Bates, Marston.   *The Natural History of Mosquitoes*. New York, Macmillan, 1949.

29. Bauer, H. L.   Moisture relations in the chaparral of the Santa Monica Mountains, California. *Ecol. Monogr.*, 1936, 6:409–454.

30. Bauer, H. L.   The statistical analysis of chaparral and other plant communities by means of transect samples. *Ecol.*, 1943, 24:45–60.

31. Beard, J. S.   Montane vegetation in the Antilles. *Caribbean For.*, 1942, 3:61–74.

32. Beard, J. S.   Climax vegetation in tropical America. *Ecol.*, 1944, 25:127–158.

33. Beard, J. S.   The natural vegetation of the Island of Tobago, British West Indies. *Ecol. Monogr.*, 1944, 14:135–163.

34. Beard, J. S.   The natural vegetation of Trinidad. *Oxford For. Mem.*, 1946, 20:1–155.

35. Beard, J. S. The savanna vegetation of Northern Tropical America. *Ecol. Monogr.*, 1953, 23:149–215.
36. Belt, T. *The Naturalist in Nicaragua.* London, Bumpus, 1888.
37. Benoist, R. La végétation de la Guiane française. *Bull. Soc. Bot. France*, 1924, 71:1169–1177.
38. Bertsch, K. *Lehrbuch der Pollenanalyse.* Handb. der prakt. Vorgeschichtsforschung, Bd. 3, Stuttgart, Enke, 1942.
39. Bharucha, F. R., and D. B. Ferreira. The biological spectrum of the Madras flora. *Jour. Univ. Bombay*, 1941, 9:93–100.
40. Bitterlick, W. Die Winkelzählprobe. *Allg. Forst- u. Holzw. Zgt.*, 1948, 59:4–5.
41. Black, G. A., and S. A. Cain, 1955. Field notes are in possession of the author.
42. Black, G. A., T. Dobzhansky, and C. Pavan. Some attempts to estimate species diversity and population density of trees in Amazonian forests. *Bot. Gaz.*, 1950, 111:413–425.
43. Blackman, G. E. A study by statistical methods of the distribution of species in grassland associations. *Ann. Bot.*, 1935, 49:749–777.
44. Blackman, G. E. Statistical and ecological studies on the distribution of species in plant communities. *Ann. Bot.*, 1942, 56:351–366.
45. Blair, W. F. The biotic provinces of Texas. *Texas Jour. Sci.*, 1950, 2:93–117.
46. Böcher, T. W. Phytogeographical studies of the Greenland flora. *Meddl. om Grønland*, 1933, 104 (3):1–56.
47. Bojko, H. Die vegetationsverhältnisse im Seewinkel. *Beih. Bot. Centralbl.*, 1934, 51:600–747.
48. Booberg, G. Grondvormen etages, en phytocoenosen van Java's vegetatie. *Hand. 6de ned. -ind. naturw. Congr., 1931*, 1932, 329–346.
49. Børgesen, F. Contribution to the knowledge of the vegetation of the Canary Islands. *D. Kgl. Dansk Vidensk. Selsk. Schrift., Naturvidensk og Mathern*, 1924, 8 (VI) 3:285–398.
50. Børgesen, F. Fra en Rejse i Indien 1927–28. *Bot. Tidsskr.*, 1930, 41: 113–154.
51. Bormann, F. H. The statistical efficiency of sample plot size and shape in forest ecology. *Ecol.*, 1953, 34:474–487.
52. Bourdeau, P. F. A test of random versus systematic ecological sampling. *Ecol.*, 1953, 34:499–511.
53. Braun, E. L. The undifferentiated deciduous forest climax and the association segregate. *Ecol.*, 1935, 16:514–519.
54. Braun, E. L. *Deciduous Forests of Eastern North America.* Philadelphia, Blakiston, 1950.
55. Braun-Blanquet, J. Essai sur les notions de "élement" et de "territoire" phytogéographiques. *Arch. sci. phys. et nat. Genève*, 1919, 124, Vol. 1.
56. Braun-Blanquet, J. *L'origine et le dévelopement des flores dans le Massif Central de France.* Paris, L'homme, 1923.

57. Braun-Blanquet, J.   Die *Brachypodium ramosum-Phlomis lychnis*-association der Rolerdeboden Süd-Frankreichs. *Veröffentl. Géobot. Inst. Rübel Zürich,* 1925, 3:304–320.

58. Braun-Blanquet, J.   *Plant Sociology* (transl. G. D. Fuller and H. S. Conard). New York, McGraw-Hill, 1932.

59. Braun-Blanquet, J., and H. Jenny.   Vegetationsentwicklung und Bodenbildung in der alpinen Stufe der Zentralalpen. *Neue Denkschr. Schweiz. Naturf. Ges.,* 1926, 63:175–349.

60. Braun-Blanquet, J., and R. Marie.   Études sur la végétation et la flore Marocaines. *Mém. Soc. Sci. Nat. de Maroc,* 1924, 8:1–244.

61. Brenner, W.   Växtgeografiska studier i Barösunds skärgard. *Acta Soc. Fauna Flora Fennica,* 1924, 49 (5).

62. Briquet, J.   Caractères résumés des principaux groupes de formations végétales étudiés dans un cours de géographie botanique. *Ann. cons. jard. bot. Genève,* 1920, 21:389–404.

63. Brockmann-Jerosch, H.   *Die Flora des Puschlav und ihre Pflanzengesellschaften.* Leipzig, Engelmann, 1907.

64. Brockmann-Jerosch, H., and W. Rübel.   Eine Einteilung der Pflanzengesellschaften nach ökologisch-physiognomischen Gesichtpunkten. Leipzig, Engelmann, 1912.

65. Brown, D.   Methods of surveying and measuring vegetation. *Commonwealth Bur. Pastures and Field Corps, Bull. 42,* 1954, 1–223.

66. Brown, R. T., and J. T. Curtis.   The upland conifer-hardwood forests of Northern Wisconsin. *Ecol. Monogr.,* 1952, 22:217–234.

67. Brown, W. H.   Evaporation and plant habitats in Jamaica. *Pl. World,* 1910, 13:268–272.

68. Brown, W. H.   Vegetation of Philippine mountains. *Dept. Agric. Nat. Res. Bur. Sci., Bull. 13,* 1919.

69. Buck, L. J.   Association of plants and minerals. *Jour. N.Y. Bot. Gard.,* 1949, 50:265–269.

70. Buell, M. F., and J. E. Cantlon.   A study of two committees of the New Jersey pine barrens and a comparison of methods. *Ecol.,* 1950, 31:567–586.

71. Buell, M. F., and J. E. Cantlon.   A study of two forest stands in Minnesota with an interpretation of the prairie-forest margin. *Ecol.,* 1951, 32:294–316.

72. Buell, M. F., and R. L. Wilbur.   Life-form spectra of the hardwood forests of the Itasca Park region, Minnesota. *Ecol.,* 1948, 29:352–359.

73. Burt, W. H.   Faunal relationships and geographic distribution of mammals in Sonora, Mexico. *Miscl. Publ. Mus. Zoo. Univ. Mich.,* 1938, 39:1–77.

74. Burtt-Davy, J.   *Transvaal Flowering Plants and Ferns,* Parts I and II, London, Longmans, Green, 1926, 1932.

75. Burtt-Davy, J.   The forest vegetation of south central tropical Africa. *Empire For. Jour.,* 1931, 10:73–85.

76. Burtt-Davy, J. A sketch of the forest vegetation and flora of tropical Africa. *Empire For. Jour.,* 1935, 14:191–201.
77. Burtt-Davy, J. The classification of tropical woody vegetation types. *Imperial For. Inst.,* 1938, Paper 13.
78. Cabrera, A., and J. Yepes. *Mamiferos Sud-Americanos.* Buenos Aires, Co. Ed. Argentina, 1940.
79. Cain, S. A. Certain floristic affinities of the trees and shrubs of the Great Smoky Mountains and vicinity. *Butler Univ. Bot. Stud.,* 1930, 1:129–150.
80. Cain, S. A. An ecological study of the heath balds of the Great Smoky Mountains. *Butler Univ. Bot. Stud.,* 1930, 1:176–208.
81. Cain, S. A. Concerning certain phytosociological concepts. *Ecol. Monogr.,* 1932, 2:475–508.
82. Cain, S. A. Density and frequency of the woody plants of Donaldson's Woods, Lawrence County, Indiana. *Proc. Ind. Acad. Sci.,* 1932, 41:105–122.
83. Cain, S. A. A comparison of quadrat sizes in a quantitative phytosociological study of Nash's Woods, Posey County, Indiana. *Amer. Midl. Nat.,* 1934, 15:529–566.
84. Cain, S. A. Bald cypress, *Taxodium distichum* (L.) Rich., at Hovey Lake, Posey County, Indiana. *Amer. Midl. Nat.,* 1935, 16:72–82.
85. Cain, S. A. Ecological studies of the vegetation of the Great Smoky Mountains. II. The quadrat method applied to sampling spruce and fir forest types. *Amer. Midl. Nat.,* 1935, 16:566–584.
86. Cain, S. A. Studies on virgin hardwood forest. III. Warren's Woods, a beech-maple climax forest in Berrien County, Michigan. *Ecol.,* 1935, 16:500–513.
87. Cain, S. A. Synusiae as a basis in plant sociological field work. *Amer. Midl. Nat.,* 1936, 17:665–672.
88. Cain, S. A. The species-area curve. *Amer. Midl. Nat.,* 1938, 19:573–581.
89. Cain, S. A. The climax and its complexities. *Amer. Midl. Nat.,* 1939, 21:146–181.
90. Cain, S. A. Some observations on the concept of species senescence. *Ecol.,* 1940, 21:213–215.
91. Cain, S. A. An interesting behavior of yellow birch in the Great Smoky Mountains. *Chicago Nat.,* 1940, 3:20–21.
92. Cain, S. A. Sample-plot technique applied to alpine vegetation in Wyoming. *Amer. Jour. Bot.,* 1943, 30:240–247.
93. Cain, S. A. *Foundations of Plant Geography.* New York, Harper, 1944.
94. Cain, S. A. The place of pollen analysis in paleoecology. *Chron. Botan.,* 1945, 9:106–114.
95. Cain, S. A. A biological spectrum of the flora of the Great Smoky Mountains National Park. *Butler Univ. Bot. Stud.,* 1945, 7:1–14.

96. Cain, S. A.   Characteristics of natural areas and factors in their development. *Ecol. Monogr.*, 1947, 17:185–200.

97. Cain, S. A.   Life-forms and phytoclimates. *Bot. Rev.*, 1950, 16:1–32.

98. Cain, S. A., and F. C. Evans.   The distribution patterns of three plant species in an old-field community in southeastern Michigan. *Contrib. Lab. Vert. Biol. Univ. Mich.*, 1952, 52:1–11.

99. Cain, S. A., and W. T. Penfound.   *Aceretum rubri:* The red maple swamp forest of Central Long Island. *Amer. Midl. Nat.*, 1938, 19:390–416.

100. Cain, S. A., and A. J. Sharp.   Bryophytic unions of certain forest types of the Great Smoky Mountains. *Amer. Midl. Nat.*, 1938, 20:249–301.

101. Cain, S. A., G. M. de Oliviera Castro, and José da Costa Sacco, *Amer. Jour. Bot.*, 1955, 43:936–939.

102. Cain, S. A., M. Nelson, and W. McLean.   *Andropogonetum Hempsteadi:* A Long Island grassland vegetation type. *Amer. Midl. Nat.*, 1937, 18:334–350.

103. Cain, S. A., G. M. de Oliveira Castro, J. Murca Pires, and N. T. da Silva.   Application of some phytosociological techniques to Brazilian rain forest. *Amer. Jour. Bot.*, 1956, 43:911–941. Also in W. C. Steere (ed.), *Fifty Years of Botany*, New York, McGraw-Hill, 1958.

104. Cajander, A. K.   Beiträge zur Kenntnis der Vegetation der Hochgebirge zwischen Kittilä und Muonio. *Fennica*, 1904, 20:9.

105. Cajander, A. K.   Über Waldtypen. *Acta Forest. Fennica*, 1909, 1.

106. Cajander, A. K.   The theory of forest types. *Acta Forest. Fennica*, 1926, 31.

107. Canfield, R. H.   Application of the line interception method in sampling range vegetation. *Jour. For.*, 1941, 39:388–394.

108. Canfield, R. H.   Sampling range vegetation by the line interception method. Plant cover-composition-density-degree of forage use. *U.S. Dept. Agric. Southwestern For. Range Exp. Sta. Res. Rept.*, 1942, 4:1–28.

109. Canfield, R. H.   Measurement of grazing use by the line interception method. *Jour. For.*, 1944, 42:192–194.

110. Canfield, R. H.   Sampling range by the line interception method. *U.S. Dept. Agric. Southwestern For. Range Exp. Sta. Res. Rept.*, 1950, 4:1–28.

111. Carpenter, C. A. G., and O. Saarela.   The point quadrat method of Levy and its use in the investigation of vegetation on pastures. *Valt. Maatalousk Julk.*, 1941, 108:1–31.

112. Carpenter, J. R.   *An Ecological Glossary*. Norman, Univ. Oklahoma Press, 1938.

113. Charter, C. F.   *A Reconnaissance of the Soils of British Honduras*. Trinidad, Government Print. Office, 1941.

114. Chaturvedi, M. D.   India. In S. Haden-Guest (ed.), *A World Geography of Forest Resources*. New York, Ronald, 1956.

115. Chevalier, A. *La forêt et les bois du Gabon. Les végétaux utiles d'Africa tropical française.* Fasc. 9. Paris, 1909.

116. Chipp, T. F. Aims and methods of study in tropical countries with special reference to West Africa. In A. G. Tansley and T. F. Chipp, *Aims and Methods in the Study of Vegetation,* London, Brit. Empire Veg. Comm., 1926.

117. Christ, H. Über die Verbreitung der Pflanzen der alpinen Region der europäischen Alpenkette. *Neue Denkschr. Schweiz. Naturf. Ges.,* 1867, 22.

118. Clapham, A. R. The form of the observational unit in quantitative ecology. *Jour. Ecol.,* 1932, 20:192–197.

119. Clark, P. J., and F. C. Evans. Distance to nearest neighbor as a measure of spatial relationships in populations. *Ecol.,* 1954, 35:445–453.

120. Clarke, G. L. *Elements of Ecology.* New York, Wiley, 1954.

121. Clarke, S. E., J. A. Campbell, and J. B. Campbell. An ecological and grazing study of the native grass pastures in southern Alberta, Saskatchewan and Manitoba. *Dom. Canada Dept. Agric. Tech. Bull.,* 1942, 44:1–31.

122. Clausen, J., D. D. Keck, and W. M. Hiesey. Experimental studies on the nature of species. I. Effect of varied environments on western Amrican plants. *Carnegie Inst. Wash. Publ. 520,* 1940, 1–452.

123. Clements, F. E. *The Development and Structure of Vegetation.* Lincoln, Woodruff-Collins, 1904.

124. Clements, F. E. *Research Methods in Ecology.* Lincoln, Woodruff-Collins, 1905.

125. Clements, F. E. Plant succession. *Carnegie Inst. Wash. Publ. 242,* 1916.

126. Clements, F. E. Plant indicators. *Carnegie Inst. Wash. Publ. 290,* 1920.

127. Clements, F. E. *Plant Succession and Indicators.* New York, Wilson, 1928.

128. Clements, F. E. Nature and structure of the climax. *Jour. Ecol.,* 1936, 24:252–284.

129. Clements, F. E., and G. W. Goldsmith. The phytometer method in ecology. *Carnegie Inst. Wash. Publ. 356,* 1924.

130. Clements, F. E., and V. E. Shelford. *Bio-Ecology.* New York, Wiley, 1939.

131. Cole, L. C. A theory for analysing contagiously distributed populations. *Ecol.,* 1946, 27:329–341.

132. Costello, D. F., and R. Price. Weather and plant development data as determinants of grazing periods on mountain range. *U.S. Dept. Agric. Tech. Bull.,* 1939, 686:1–30.

133. Cottam, G. A point method for making rapid surveys of woodlands. *Bull. Ecol. Soc. Amer.,* 1947, 28:60.

134. Cottam, G. The phytosociology of an oak woods in southwestern Wisconsin. *Ecol.,* 1949, 30:271–287.

135. Cottam, G., and J. T. Curtis. A method of making rapid surveys of

woodlands by means of randomly selected trees. *Ecol.*, 1949, 30:101–104.

136. Cottam, G., and J. T. Curtis. Correction for various exclusion angles in the random pairs method. *Ecol.*, 1955, 36:767.

137. Cottam, G., and J. T. Curtis. The use of distance measures in phytosociological sampling. *Ecol.*, 1956, 37:451–460.

138. Cottam, G., J. T. Curtis, and B. W. Hale. Some sampling characteristics of randomly dispersed individuals. *Ecol.*, 1953, 34:741–757.

139. Coupland, R. T. Ecology of mixed prairie in Canada. *Ecol. Monogr.*, 1950, 20:271–315.

140. Cowles, H. C. The succession point of view in floristics. *Proc. Intern. Congr. Pl. Sci. Ithaca 1926*, 1929, 1:687–691.

141. Crocker, R. L., and N. S. Tiver. Survey methods in grassland ecology. *Jour. Brit. Grassl. Soc.*, 1948, 3:1–26.

142. Cromer, D. A. N., and L. D. Pryor. A contribution to rain forest ecology. *Proc. Linn. Soc. New S. Wales*, 1942, 67:249–268.

143. Curtis, J. T. Nutrient supply of epiphytic orchids in the mountains of Haiti. *Ecol.*, 1946, 27:264–266.

144. Curtis, J. T. The palo verde forest type near Gonivaves, Haiti, and its relation to the surrounding vegetation. *Caribbean For.*, 1947, 8:1–26.

145. Curtis, J. T., and H. C. Greene. A study of relic Wisconsin prairies by the species-presence method. *Ecol.*, 1949, 30:83–92.

146. Curtis, J. T., and R. P. McIntosh. The inter-relations of certain analytic and synthetic phytosociological characters. *Ecol.*, 1950, 31:434–455.

147. Curtis, J. T., and R. P. McIntosh. An upland forest continuum in the prairie-forest border region of Wisconsin. *Ecol.*, 1951, 32:476–496.

148. Cushing, D. H. The vertical migration of planktonic Crustacea. *Biol. Revs. Cambridge Phil. Soc.*, 1951, 26:158–192.

149. Dansereau, P. L'érablière laurentienne. I. Valeur d'indice des espèces. *Can. Jour. Res.*, 1943, 21:66–93.

150. Dansereau, P. Essai de corrélation sociologique entre les plantes supérieures et les poissons de la beine du Lac Saint-Louis. *Can. Biol.*, 1945, 4:369–417.

151. Dansereau, P. Os planos da Biogeografia. *Rev. Brasil. Geograf.*, 1946, 8:189–211.

152. Dansereau, P. Description and recording of vegetation on a structural basis. *Ecol.*, 1951, 32:172–229.

153. Dansereau, P. The varieties of evolutionary opportunity. *Rev. Can. Biol.*, 1952, 11:305–388.

154. Dansereau, P. A preliminary note on the structure variations of temperate rainforests. *Proc. VIII Pacific Sci. Congr.*, 1956, 4B.

155. Dansereau, P. *Biogeography: An Ecological Perspective*. New York, Ronald, 1957.

156. Darling, F. F. History of Scottish forests. *Scot. Geogr. Mag.*, 1949, 65:132–137.

157. Darlington, P. J., Jr. *Zoögeography: The Geographical Distribution of Animals.* New York, Wiley, 1957.
158. Daubenmire, R. F. The "Big Woods" of Minnesota, its structure and relation to climate, fire, and soils. *Ecol. Monogr.,* 1936, 6:233–268.
159. Davis, T. A. W., and P. W. Richards. The vegetation of Moraballi Creek, British Guiana; an ecological study of a limited area of tropican rain forest. *Jour. Ecol.,* 1933, 21:350–385; 1934, 22:106–155.
160. Dice, L. R. The Canadian biotic province with special reference to the mammals. *Ecol.,* 1938, 19:503–514.
161. Dice, L. R. *The Biotic Provinces of North America.* Ann Arbor, Univ. Mich. Press, 1943.
162. Dice, L. R. Relationship between frequency index and population density. *Ecol.,* 1948, 29:389–391.
163. Dice, L. R. *Natural Communities.* Ann Arbor, Univ. Mich. Press, 1952.
164. Dice, L. R. Measure of the spacing between individuals within a population. *Contrib. Lab. Vert. Biol. Univ. Mich.,* 1952, 55:1–23.
165. Diels, L. *Pflanzengeographie,* Nr. 389, 2 Aufl. Leipzig, Samml. Goschen, 1918.
166. Domin, K. *Problemy a metody rostlinne sociologie.* Praha, 1923.
167. Drew, W. B. Studies on the use of the point-quadrat method of botanical analysis of mixed pasture vegetation. *Jour. Agric. Res.,* 1944, 69:289–297.
168. Drude, O. *Die Florenreiche der Erde.* Petermanns Mitteil., 1884, Erganzungsh. 74.
169. Drude, O. *Handbuch der Pflanzengeographie.* Stuttgart, J. Engelhorn (transl. G. Poirault as *Manual de Géographie Botanique*), Paris, Lib. Sci. Nat., 1897.
170. Drude, O. *Die Ökologie der Pflanzen.* Brunswick, Vieweg, 1913.
171. Ducke, A., and G. A. Black. Phytogeographical notes on the Brazilian Amazon. *Ann. Acad. Brasileira Ciencias,* 1953, 25:1–46.
172. DuRietz, G. E. *Zur methodologischen Grundlage der modernen Pflanzensoziologie.* Uppsala, Akad. Abh., 1921.
173. DuRietz, G. E. The fundamental units of biological taxonomy. *Svensk. Bot. Tidskr.,* 1930, 24:333–428.
174. DuRietz, G. E. Life-forms of terrestrial flowering plants. *Acta Phytogeogr. Suecica,* 1931, 3:1–95.
175. Eden, T., and T. E. T. Bond. The effects of manurial treatment on the growth of weeds in tea. *Empire Jour. Exp. Agric.,* 1945, 13:141–157.
176. Eggler, W. A. The maple-basswood forest type in Washburn County, Wisconsin. *Ecol.,* 1938, 19:243–263.
177. Egler, F. E. Arid southwest Oahu vegetation, Hawaii. *Ecol. Monogr.,* 1947, 17:383–435.
178. Ellison, L. A comparison of methods of quadratting short-grass vegetation. *Jour. Agric. Res.,* 1942, 64:595–613.

179. Ellison, L. Subalpine vegetation of the Wasatch Plateau, Utah. *Ecol. Monogr.,* 1954, 24:89–184.

180. Engler, A. *Versuch einer Entwicklungsgeschichte der Pflanzenwelt, inbesondere der Florengebiete, seit der Tertiarperiode.* Leipzig, Engelmann, 1879.

181. Engler, A. Übersicht über die Florenreiche und Florengebiete der Erde. *Syllabus d. Pflanzenf.,* Berlin, Borntraeger, 1903.

182. Engler, A. Grundzüge der Entwicklung der Flora seit der Tertiärzeit. *Result. Sci. Congr. Intern. de Bot. Vienna,* 1905.

183. Engler, A. *Die Pflanzenwelt Afrikas, I.* Leipzig, Engelmann, 1908.

184. Engler, A. *Syllabus der Pflanzenfamilien,* 9–10 Aufl. Berlin, Borntraeger, 1924.

185. Engler, A., and L. Diels. *Syllabus der Pflanzenfamilien,* 11. ergänzte Aufl. Berlin, Borntraeger, 1936.

186. Ennis, B. The life-forms of Connecticut plants and their significance in relation to climate. *Conn. St. Geol. Nat. Hist. Surv.,* 1928, 43:1–100.

187. Erdtman, G. *An Introduction to Pollen Analysis.* Waltham, Chron. Botan., 1943.

188. Evans, F. C. The influence of size of quadrat on the distributional patterns of plant populations. *Contr. Lab. Vert. Biol. Univ. Mich.,* 1952, 54:1–15.

189. Evans, F. C. Ecosystem as the basic unit in ecology. *Sci.,* 1956, 123: 1127–1128.

190. Evans, F. C., and S. A. Cain. Preliminary studies on the vegetation of an old-field community in southeastern Michigan. *Contrib. Lab. Vert. Biol. Univ. Mich.,* 1952, 51:1–17.

191. Evans, F. C., and E. Dahl. The vegetational structure of an abandoned field in southeastern Michigan and its relation to environmental factors. *Ecol.,* 1955, 36:685–705.

192. Evans, F. C., P. J. Clark, and R. H. Brand. Estimation of the number of species present on a given area. *Ecol.,* 1955, 36:342–343.

193. Faegri, K., and J. Iversen. *Textbook of Modern Pollen Analysis.* Copenhagen, E. Munksgaard, 1950.

194. Fanshawe, D. B. The vegetation of British Guiana. *Imperial For. Inst.,* 1952, Paper 29.

195. Fanshawe, D. B. Forest types of British Guiana. *Caribbean For.,* 1954, 15:73–111.

196. Fassett, N. C. The plants of some northeastern Wisconsin lakes. *Trans. Wis. Acad. Sci.,* 1930, 25:157–160.

197. Fisher, R. A. *Statistical Methods for Research Workers.* London, Oliver and Boyd, 1941.

198. Flahault, C., and C. Schröter. Phytogeographische Nomenklatur. *IIIᵉ Congr. Intern. Brussels,* 1910.

199. Fracker, S. B., and H. A. Brischle. Measuring local distribution of *Ribes. Ecol.,* 1944, 25:283–303.

200. Francis, W. D. The development of buttresses in Queensland trees. *Proc. Roy. Soc. Queensl.,* 1925, 36:277–285.

201. Fuller, G. D.   Evaporation and soil moisture in relation to the succession of plant associations. *Bot. Gaz.*, 1914, 58:193–234.

202. Fuller, G. D., and A. L. Bakke.   Raunkiaer's "life-forms," "leaf-size" classes, and statistical methods. *Pl. World*, 1918, 21:25–37, 57–63.

203. Gachot, R., M. N. Gallant, and P. K. McGrath.   Report to the Government of Brazil on forest development in the Amazon Valley. *U.N. Food and Agric. Rept.*, 1953, 171:1–152.

204. Gams, H.   Prinzipienfragen der Vegetationsforschung. *Vierteljahrschr. d. Naturf. Gesell. Zürich.*, 1918, 63:293–493.

205. Garner, W. W.   Recent work on photoperiodism. *Bot. Rev.*, 1937, 3: 259–275.

206. Garner, W. W., and H. A. Allard.   Effect of the relative length of day and night and other factors of the environment on growth and reproduction in plants. *Jour. Agric. Res.*, 1920, 18:553–606.

207. Gaussen, H.   *Géographie des Plantes*. Paris, Colin, 1933.

208. Gelting, P.   Studies on the vascular plants of East Greenland between Franz Joseph Fjord and Dove Bay. *Meddl. om Grønland*, 1934, 101:1–337.

209. Gleason, H. A.   Some applications of the quadrat method. *Bull. Torrey Bot. Club*, 1920, 47:21–33.

210. Gleason, H. A.   On the relation between species and area. *Ecol.*, 1922, 3:158–162.

211. Gleason, H. A.   The vegetational history of the Middle West. *Ann. Assoc. Amer. Geogr.*, 1923, 12:39–85.

212. Gleason, H. A.   The individualistic concept of the plant association. *Bull. Torrey Bot. Club*, 1926, 53:7–26.

213. Gleason, H. A.   The significance of Raunkiaer's law of frequence. *Ecol.*, 1929, 10:406–408.

214. Gleason, H. A.   Is the synusia an association? *Ecol.*, 1936, 17:444–451.

215. Gleason, H. A., and M. T. Cook.   Plant ecology of Porto Rico. In *Scientific Study of Porto Rico and Virgin Islands*, N.Y. Acad. Sci., 1926, Vol. 7.

216. Gomes, P., and H. Fernandes.   Florestas amazonicas. *Caribbean For.*, 1951, 12:141–152. (English, pp. 153–155.)

217. Good, R.   A theory of plant geography. *New Phytol.*, 1931, 30:149–171.

218. Good, R.   *The Geography of Flowering Plants*. London, Longmans, Green, 1947, 1953.

219. Goodall, D. W.   Some considerations in the use of point quadrats for the analysis of vegetation. *Aust. Jour. Sci. Res.*, Ser. B, 1952, 5:1–41.

220. Goodall, D. W.   Quantitative aspects of plant distribution. *Biol. Rev.*, 1952, 27:194–245.

221. Greig-Smith, P.   *Quantitative Plant Ecology*. New York, Academic Press, 1957.

222. Grisebach, A. *Die Vegetation der Erde nach ihrer klimatischen Anordnung.*
Leipzig, Engelmann, 1872.

223. Grosenbaugh, L. R.   Plotless timber estimates—new, fast, easy. *Jour.
For.*, 1952, 50:32–37.

224. Grosenbaugh, L. R.   Shortcuts for cruisers and scalers. *Occ. Papers
So. For. Exp. Sta.*, 1952, 126:1–24.

225. Haberlandt, H.   Anatomisch-physiologische Untersuchungen über
das tropische Laubblatt. *Sitzungsber. Wiener Akad.*, 1892, 51, 53, 54.

226. Haden-Guest, S. (ed.).   *A World Geography of Forest Resources.* New
York, Ronald, 1956.

227. Hagerup, O.   Études des types biologiques de Raunkiaer dans la
flora autour de Tombouctou. *Kgl. Dansk. Vidensk. Selsk. Biol. Meddl.*,
1930, 9:1–116.

228. Hanson, H. C.   A comparison of methods of botanical analysis of the
native prairie in western North Dakota. *Jour. Agric. Res.*, 1934, 49:
815–842.

229. Hanson, H. C., and L. D. Love.   Size of list quadrat for use in determining effects of different systems of grazing on *Agropyron smithii*
mixed prairie. *Jour. Agric. Res.*, 1930, 41:549–560.

230. Harris, J. A.   *The physico-chemical properties of plant saps in relation to
phytogeography.* Minneapolis, Univ. Minn. Press, 1934.

231. Hasel, A. A.   Sampling errors in timber surveys. *Jour. Agric. Res.*,
1938, 57:713–736.

232. Haurwitz, B., and J. M. Austin.   *Climatology.* New York, McGraw-
Hill, 1944.

233. Hawley, R. C., *et al.   Forest Cover Types of the Eastern United States.*
Washington, Soc. Amer. For., 1940.

234. Hayek, A.   *Allgemeine Pflanzengeographie.* Berlin, Borntraeger, 1926.

235. Heer, O.   Die Vegetationsverhältnisse des sudöstlichen Teiles des
Kantons Glarus. *Mitt. Geb. Theoret. Erdkunde, Zürich,* 1835.

236. Heimans, J.   Plantengeographische elemente in de Nederlandsche
flora. *Nederl. Kruidkundig Archief.*, 1939, 49:416–436.

237. Heinsdijk, D.   Inventários florestais nas regiões tropicais. *Anuário
Brasil. Econ. Florestal,* 1954, 7:1–10.

238. Henkel, J. S.   Types of vegetation in Southern Rhodesia. *Proc. Rhod.
Sci. Assoc.*, 1930, 30:1–23.

239. Holdridge, L. R.   Middle America. In S. Haden-Guest (ed.), *A
World Geography of Forest Resources.* New York, Ronald, 1956.

240. Hope-Simpson, J. F.   On the errors in the ordinary use of subjective
frequency estimations in grassland. *Jour. Ecol.*, 1940, 28:193–209.

241. Hormay, A. L.   Getting better records of vegetation changes with the
line interception method. *Jour. Range Mgt.*, 1949, 2:67–69.

242. Hult, R.   Försök till analytisk behandling af Växtformationerna.
Meddl. soc. pro fauna et flora Fennica, 1881, 8.

243. Hultén, E.   *Outline of the History of Arctic and Boreal Biota During the
Quaternary Period.* Stockholm, Bokför lag aktiebolaget Thule, 1937.

244. Humboldt, A.   *Ideen zu einer Physiognomik der Gewächse.* Tubingen, 1806.
245. Humboldt, A.   *Essai sur la géographie des plantes, accompagné d'un tableau physique des régions équinoxiales.* Paris, Levrault, 1805.
246. Ilvessalo, Y.   Vegetationsstatistische Untersuchungen über die Waldtypen. *Acta Forest. Fennica,* 1922, 20.
247. Jaccard, P.   The distribution of flora in the alpine zone. *New Phytol.,* 1912, 11:37–50.
248. Jaccard, P.   Die statistisch-floristische Methode als Grundlage der Pflanzensoziologie. *Handb. Biol. Arbietsm. Abderhalden,* 1928, XI, 5: 165–202.
249. Johnston, I. M.   Gypsophily among Mexican desert plants. *Jour. Arnold Arb.,* 1941, 22:145–170.
250. Justesen, H. S.   Influence of size and shape of plots on the precision of field experiments with potatoes. *Jour. Agric. Res.,* 1932, 22:365–372.
251. Kalamkar, R. J.   Experimental error and the field plot technique with potatoes. *Jour. Agric. Res.,* 1932, 22:373–383.
252. Katz, N.   Die Zwillingsassoziationen und die homologen Reihen in der Phytosoziologie. *Ber. deutsch. botan. Ges.,* 1929, 47:154–164.
253. Keller, B. A.   Distribution of vegetation on the plains of European Russia. *Jour. Ecol.,* 1927, 15:189–233.
254. Kenoyer, L. A.   A study of Raunkiaer's law of frequence. *Ecol.,* 1927, 8:341–349.
255. Kerner von Marilaun, A.   *Das Pflanzenleben der Donauländer.* 2. anastatische Aufl., Innsbruck, Wagner, 1929. (Eng. transl. H. S. Conard, Iowa State College Press, 1949.)
256. Kilburn, P. D.   Historical development and structure of the aspen, Jack pine and oak vegetation types on sandy soils in Northern Lower Michigan. Ann Arbor, Univ. Mich. thesis, 1957.
257. Klages, K. H. W.   *Ecological Crop Geography.* New York, Macmillan, 1942.
258. Köppen, W.   Klassifikation der Klimate nach Temperatur, Niederschlag, und Jahrslauf. *Petermanns Mitteil.,* 1918, 64:193.
259. Köppen, W.   *Die Klimate der Erde.* Berlin, de Gruyte, 1923.
260. Köppen, W.   Das geographische System der Klimate. *Handb. der Klimatologie,* Berlin, 1936.
261. Korstian, C. F., and P. W. Stickel.   Natural replacement of blight-killed chestnut in the hardwood forests of the Northeast. *Jour. Agric. Res.,* 1927, 34:631–648.
262. Küchler, A. W.   A geographic system of vegetation. *Geogr. Rev.,* 1947, 37:233–240.
263. Küchler, A. W.   A new vegetation map of Manchuria. *Ecol.,* 1948, 29:513–516.
264. Küchler, A. W.   A physiognomic classification of vegetation. *Ann. Assoc. Amer. Geogr.,* 1949, 39:201–210.
265. Küchler, A. W.   Die physiognomische Kartierung der Vegetation. *Petermanns Geogr. Mitteil.,* 1950, 96:1–6.

312 LITERATURE CITED

266. Kylin, H. Uber Begriffsbildung und Statistik in der Pflanzenso-ziologie. *Bot. Notiser,* 1926, 81–180.
267. Lam, H. J. Fragmenta papuana (Observations of a Naturalist in Netherlands New Guinea, transl. L. M. Perry). *Sargentia,* 1945, 5:1–196.
268. Lam, H. J. Notes on the historical phytogeography of the Celebes. *Blumea,* 1945, 5:600–640.
269. LeCointe, P. *O Estado do Pará: A Terra, A Agua e o Ar; A Faune e A Flora Mineraes.* São Paulo, Co. Ed. Nacional, 1945.
270. LeCointe, P. *Amazonia Brasileira III: Avires e Plantas Uteis.* São Paulo, Co. Ed. Nacional, 1947.
271. Levy, E. B., and E. A. Madden. The point method of pasture analysis. *New Zealand Jour. Agric.,* 1933, 46:267–279.
272. Lippmaa, T. La méthode des associations unistrates et la système écologique des associations. *Acta Inst. Horti Botan. Univ. Tartu.,* 1934, 4 (1–2):1–6.
273. Lippmaa, T. Une analyse des forêts de l'île estonienne d'Abruka (Abro) sur la bade des associations unistrates. *Acta Inst. Horti Botan. Univ. Tartu,* 1935, 4 (1–2):1–97.
274. Lippmaa, T. Areal und Altersbestimmung einer Union sowie das Problem der Charakterarten und der Konstanten. *Acta Inst. Horti Botan. Univ. Tartu,* 1938, 6 (2):1–152.
275. Lippmaa, T. The unistratal concept of plant communities (The Unions). *Amer. Midl. Nat.,* 1939, 21:111–145.
276. Lorenz, J. R. Allgemeine Resultate aus der pflanzengeographischen und genetischen Untersuchung der Moore im präalpinen Hügelland Salzburgs. *Flora,* 1858, 16:209–221.
277. Lüdi, W. Der Assoziationsbegriff in der Pflanzensoziologie. *Biblio. Bot.,* 1928, 96.
278. Luis, T., and A. Bertels. *Guia dos Visitantes.* Pelotas, Horto Botanico do Instituto Agronômico do Sul, 1951.
279. Lundegardh, H. G. *Environment and Plant Development.* London, Edward Arnold, 1931.
280. Lutz, A. Waldmosquitos und Waldmalaria. *Centralbl. Bakteriol. Parasit. Infektionskr.,* 1903, 33:282–292.
281. Lutz, H. J. The vegetation of Heart's Content, a virgin forest in northwestern Pennsylvania. *Ecol.,* 1930, 11:1–29.
282. MacMillan, C. *The Metaspermae of the Minnesota Valley.* Geol. Nat. Hist. Surv. Minn., 1892, Ser. I.
283. Magnanini, A. Contribuicão ao estudo das zonas de vegetacão do praia de Sernambetiba, D. F., Brasil. *Arq. Serv. Florestal,* 1954, 8:147–232.
284. Marshall, R. C. Physiography and vegetation of Trinidad and Tobago. *Oxford For. Mem.,* 1934, 17.
285. von Martius, C. *Flora Brasiliensis,* 15 vol. Leipzig, Oldenburg, 1840–1906.

286. Mason, H. L. The principles of geographic distribution as applied to floral analysis. *Madroño*, 1936, 3:181–190.

287. McGinnies, W. G. The relation between frequency index and abundance as applied to plant populations in a semiarid region. *Ecol.*, 1934, 15:263–282.

288. McLean, R. C., and W. R. I. Cook. *Practical Field Ecology*. London, George Allen & Unwin, 1946.

289. Mello-Leitão, C. Los alacranes y la zoogeografia de Sudamerica. *Rev. Argentina de Zoogeogr.*, 1942, 2:125–131.

290. Merkle, J. An analysis of the plant communities of Mary's Peak, Western Oregon. *Ecol.*, 1951, 32:618–640.

291. Merrill, E. D. Malaysian phytogeography in relation to the Polynesian flora. In *Essays in Geobotany*, Berkeley, Univ. Calif. Press, 1936.

292. Meyen, F. J. F. *Grundriss der Pflanzengeographie* (transl. M. Johnston as *Outlines of the Geography of Plants*. London, Ray Soc., 1846.)

293. Mildbraed, J. *Wissenschaftliche Ergbnisse der zweiten deutschen Zentral-Afrika-Expedition 1910–1911 unter Führung Adolph Friedrichs, Herzog zu Mecklenburg*. Leipzig, 1922.

294. Mildbraed, J. Probeflachen-Aufnahme aus den Kameruner Regenwald. *Notizbl. Bot. Gard. Mus. Berlin-Dahlem*, 1930, 10:951–976. (See transl. *Empire For. Jour.*, 1930, 9:242–266.)

295. Moore, P. G. Spacing in plant populations. *Ecol.*, 1954, 35:222–227.

296. Moreau, R. E. A synecological study of Usambara, Tanganyika Territory. *Jour. Ecol.*, 1935, 23:1–43.

297. Morisita, M. Estimation of population density by spacing method. *Mem. Fac. Sci. Kyushu Univ.*, Ser. E, 1954, 1:187–197.

298. Navez, A. La foret equatoriale brésilienne, I. *Bull. Soc. Bot. Belg.*, 1924, 57:7–17.

299. Navez, A. On the distribution of tabular roots in *Ceiba* (Bombacaceae). *Proc. Nat. Acad. Sci. Wash.*, 1930, 16:339–344.

300. Neyman, J. On a new class of "contagious" distributions applicable in entomology and bacteriology. *Ann. Math. Statistics*, 1939, 10:35–37.

301. Odum, E. P. *Fundamentals of Ecology*. Philadelphia, Saunders, 1953.

302. Oosting, H. J. An ecological analysis of the plant communities of the Piedmont, North Carolina. *Amer. Midl. Nat.*, 1942, 28:1–126.

303. Oosting, H. J. *The Study of Plant Communities*. San Francisco, Freeman, 1948.

304. Oosting, H. J., and W. D. Billings. A comparison of virgin sprucefir forest in the northern and southern Appalachian system. *Ecol.*, 1951, 32:84–103.

305. Oosting, H. J., and J. F. Reed. Virgin spruce-fir forest in the Medicine Bow Mountains, Wyoming. *Ecol. Monogr.*, 1952, 22:69–91.

306. Osborn, T. G. B., J. G. Wood, and T. B. Paltridge. The climate and vegetation of Koonamore Vegetation Reserve. *Proc. Linn. Soc. New S. Wales*, 1935, 60:392–427.

314   LITERATURE CITED

307. Palmgren, A.   Studier öfver Löfängsimradena pa Aland, III. *Acta Soc. Fauna Flora Fennica*, 1917, 42.
308. Park, O.   Nocturnalism—the development of a problem. *Ecol. Monogr.*, 1940, 10:485–536.
309. Parker, K. W., and D. A. Savage.   Reliability of the line interception method in measuring vegetation on the Southern Great Plains. *Jour. Amer. Soc. Agron.*, 1944, 36:97–110.
310. Paulsen, O.   The second Danish Pamir expedition. Studies on the vegetation of the Transcaspian lowland. *Arbejder fra den bot. Have i København*, 1912, 90:1–279.
311. Paulsen, O.   Some remarks on the desert vegetation of America. *Pl. World*, 1915, 18:155–161.
312. Pechanec, J. F., and G. Stewart.   Sagebrush-grass range sampling studies: size and structure of sampling units. *Jour. Amer. Soc. Agron.*, 1940, 32:669–682.
313. Penfound, W. T.   A study of phytosociological relationships by means of aggregations of colored cards. *Ecol.*, 1945, 26:38–57.
314. Penfound, W. T., and A. G. Watkins.   Phytosociological studies in the pinelands of southeastern Louisiana. *Amer. Midl. Nat.*, 1937, 18:661–682.
315. Petch, T.   Buttress roots. *Ann. Roy. Soc. Gard. Poradeniya*, 1930, 11:277–286.
316. Peters, J. A.   Use and misuse of the biotic province concept. *Amer. Nat.*, 1955, 89:21–28.
317. Phillips, J.   Some important vegetation communities in the central province of Tanganyika Territory. *Jour. Ecol*, 1930, 18:193–234.
318. Phillips, J.   A sketch of the floral regions of Tanganyika Territory. *Trans. Roy. Soc. S. Africa*, 1931, 19:363–372.
319. Picado, C.   Les Bromeliacées epiphytis, considerées comme milieu biologique. *Bull. Sci. France et Belgique*, 1913, 47:215–360.
320. Pires, J. M., T. Dobzhansky, and G. A. Black.   An estimate of the number of species of trees in an Amazonian forest community. *Bot. Gaz.*, 1953, 114:467–477.
321. Pittendrigh, C. S.   The bromelian-Anopheles-malaria complex in Trinidad. I. The bromeliad flora. *Evolution*, 1948, 2:58–89.
322. Pittendrigh, C. S.   The ecoclimatic divergence of *Anopheles bellator* and *A. homunculus*. *Evolution*, 1950, 4:43–63.
323. Pittendrigh, C. S.   The ecotypic specialization of *Anopheles homunculus* and its relation to competition with *A. bellator*. *Evolution*, 1950, 4:64–78.
324. Pittier, H.   Our present knowledge of the forest formations of the Isthmus of Panama. *Jour. For.*, 1918, 16:76–84.
325. Pittier, H.   *Suplemento a las Plantas Usuales de Venezuela*. Caracas, Ed. Elite, 1939.
326. Pitt-Schenkel, C. J. W.   Some important communities of warm tem-

perate rain forest at Magamba, West Isambara, Tanganyika Territory. *Jour. Ecol.*, 1938, 26:50–81.

327. Poore, M. E. D. The use of phytosociological methods in ecological investigations. *Jour. Ecol.*, 1955, 43:226–269, 606–651; 1956, 44:28–50.

328. Pound, R., and F. E. Clements. *Phytogeography of Nebraska*. Lincoln, North, 1898.

329. Pound, R., and F. E. Clements. A method of determining the abundance of secondary species. *Minn. Bot. Stud.*, 1898, 2:19–24.

330. Preston, F. W. The commonness and rarity of species. *Ecol.*, 1948, 29:254–283.

331. Raunkiaer, C. Types biologiques pour la géographie botanique. *Bull. Acad. Roy. Soc. Sci. Denmark*, 1905, 5.

332. Raunkiaer, C. Investigations and statistics of plant formations (Danish). *Bot. Tidsskr.*, 1909, 30.

333. Raunkiaer, C. Über das biologische Normalspektrum. *Kgl. Dansk. Vidensk. Selsk. Biol. Meddl.*, 1918, i. (4).

334. Raunkiaer, C. Om Blodstørrelsens Anvendelae i den biologiske Plantegeografi. *Bot. Tidsskr.*, 1916, 34.

335. Raunkiaer, C. Recherches statistique sur les formations végétales. *Kgl. Dansk. Vidensk. Selsk. Biol. Meddl.*, 1918, 1 (3):1–80.

336. Raunkiaer, C. The area of dominance, species density, and formation dominants. *Kgl. Dansk. Vidensk. Selsk. Biol. Meddl.*, 1928, 7 (1).

337. Raunkiaer, C. *The Life Forms of Plants and Statistical Plant Geography*. Oxford, Clarendon Press, 1934.

338. Raunkiaer, C. Allindelille Fredskov. Statistical investigations of the plant formations. *Arbejder fra den bot. Have i København*, 1935, 123:165–226.

339. Raup, H. M. Some natural floristic areas in Boreal America. *Ecol. Monogr.*, 1947, 17:221–234.

340. Rea, R. J. A. The forest types of vegetation in Tanganyika Territory. *Empire For. Jour.*, 1935, 14:202–208.

341. Rice, E. L., and W. T. Penfound. An evaluation of variable-radius and paired-tree methods in the black jack-post oak forest. *Ecol.*, 1955, 35:315–320.

342. Richards, P. W. Ecological observations on the rain forest of Mount Dulit, Sarawak. *Jour. Ecol.*, 1936, 24:1–37, 340–360.

343. Richards, P. W. Ecological studies on the rain forest of Southern Nigeria. I. The structure and floristic composition of the primary forest. *Jour. Ecol.*, 1939, 27:1–61.

344. Richards, P. W. *The Tropical Rain Forest*. Cambridge, Univ. Press, 1952.

345. Richards, P. W., A. G. Tansley, and A. S. Watt. The recording of structure, life-form and flora of tropical forest communities as a basis for their classification. *Imperial For. Inst.*, 1939, 19. (Also in *Jour. Ecol.*, 1940, 28:224–239).

346. Rikli, M.   Die Florenreiche. *Handworterb. Naturwiss.* 4, Jena, 1913.

347. Roach, A. W.   Phytosociology of the Nash Crater lava flows, Linn County, Oregon. *Ecol. Monogr.,* 1952, 22:169–193.

348. Roe, R.   Preliminary survey of the natural pastures of the New England district of New South Wales and a general discussion of their problems. *Council Sci. Industr. Res. Bull.,* 1947, 210:1–26.

349. Rogers, L. J.   Report to the Government of Brazil on silvicultural problems of *Araucaria angustifolia. U.N. Food and Agric. Rept.,* 1953, 206:1–64.

350. Romell, L. G.   L'influence de la structure des groupements végétaux sur les rélévés de la statistique phytosociologie. *Bot. Notiser,* 1925, 299–308.

351. Romell, L. G.   Comments on Raunkiaer's and similar methods of vegetation analysis and the law of frequency. *Ecol.,* 1930, 11:589–596.

352. Rübel, E.   *Geobotanische Untersuchungsmethoden.* Berlin, Borntraeger, 1922.

353. Rübel, E.   *Pflanzengesellschaften der Erde.* Bern-Berlin, Hans Huber, 1930.

354. Salisbury, E. J.   The structure of woodlands. *Veröff. Géobot. Inst. Rübel Zürich,* 1925, 3:334–354.

355. Sampson, A. W.   Plant succession in relation to range management. *U.S. Dept. Agric. Bull.,* 1919, 791:1–76.

356. Sampson, H. C.   The mixed mesophytic forest community of Northeastern Ohio. *Ohio Jour. Sci.,* 1930, 30:358–367.

357. Schenck, H.   Beiträge zur Biologie und Anatomie der Lianen, im Besonderer der im Brasïlien anheimischen Arten. I, II. *Bot. Mitt. aus den Tropen.* Jena, Fischer, 1892, 4, 5.

358. Schennikov, A. P.   *Pflanzensoziologie.* Berlin, Braunverlag, 1953.

359. Schimper, A. F. W.   Epiphytische Vegetation Amerikas. *Bott. Mitt. aus den Tropen.* Jena, Fischer, 1888, 2.

360. Schimper, A. F. W.   *Pflanzengeographie auf physiologischer Grundlage.* 1898. (Transl. P. Groom and I. B. Balfour as *Plant-geography upon a Physiological Basis.* Oxford, Clarendon Press, 1903.)

361. Schimper, A. F. W., and F. C. von Faber.   *Pflanzengeographie auf physiologischer Grundlage.* Jena, Fischer, 1935.

362. Schouw, F.   *Grundzüge einer allegemeinen Pflanzengeographie.* Berlin, G. Reimer, 1823.

363. Schumacher, F. X., and R. A. Chapman.   Sampling methods in forestry and range management. *Duke Univ. School For. Bull.,* 1948, 7.

364. Sewandono, R.   Southeast Asia. In S. Haden-Guest (ed.), *A World Geography of Forest Resources.* New York, Ronald, 1956.

365. Shanks, R. E.   Plotless sampling trials in Appalachian forest types. *Ecol.,* 1954, 35:237–244.

366. Shantz, H. L., and C. F. Marbut.   The vegetation and soils of Africa. *Amer. Geogr. Soc. Res. Ser.,* 1923, 13:1–242.

367. Shreve, F.   A montane rain forest. *Carnegie Inst. Wash.,* 1914, 199.

368. Sirgo, V.   Plant unions of the swamps at the mouth of the river Emajogi. *Acta Inst. Horti Botan. Univ. Tartu,* 1935, 4 (3–4):1–64.

369. Smith, A. D.   A study of the reliability of range vegetation estimates. *Ecol.,* 1944, 25:441–448.

370. Smith, R.   Botanical survey of Scotland, Edinburgh District. II. North Perthshire. *Scot. Geogr. Mag.,* 1900.

371. Smith, W. G.   Botanical survey of Scotland. III, IV. Forfar and Fife. *Scot. Geogr. Mag.,* 1904–1905.

372. Snowden, J. D.   A study in altitudinal zonation in South Kigezi and on Mountains Muhavara and Mgahinga, Uganda. *Jour. Ecol.,* 1933, 21:7–27.

373. Spruce, R.   *Notes of a Botanist on the Amazon and Andes.* London, Macmillan, 1908.

374. Stamp, L. D.   *The Vegetation of Burma.* Rangoon, Univ. Press Monogr. 1, 1924.

375. Stamp, L. D.   Some aspects of vegetational survey in the tropics. In A. G. Tansley and T. F. Chipp, *Aims and Methods in the Study of Vegetation.* London, Brit. Empire Veg. Comm., 1926.

376. Stehlé, H.   *Essai d'écologie et de géographie botanique: Flore de la Guadeloupe. Basse-terre.* Guadeloupe, 1935.

377. Stehlé, H.   Esquisse de associations végétales de la Martinique. *Bull. Agric. Martinique,* 1938.

378. Stehlé, H.   Conditions éco-sociologiques et évolution des forêts des Antilles françaises. *Caribbean For.,* 1941, 2:154–259.

379. Steiger, T. L.   The structure of prairie vegetation. *Ecol.,* 1930, 11:170–217.

380. Sukachev, V. N.   Principles of classification of the spruce communities of European Russia. *Jour. Ecol.,* 1928, 16:1–18.

381. Svedberg, T.   Ett bidrag till de statistika metodernas anvandning inom vaxtbiologien. *Svensk. Bot. Tidskr.,* 1922, 16:1–8.

382. Talbot, M. W.   Indicators of southwestern range conditions. *U.S. Dept. Agric. Farmer's Bull.,* 1937, 1782:1–34.

383. Tansley, A. G.   The use and abuse of vegetational concepts and terms. *Ecol.,* 1935, 16:284–307.

384. Tansley, A. G.   *Introduction to Plant Ecology.* London, George Allen & Unwin, 1946.

385. Tansley, A. G.   *The British Islands and Their Vegetation.* Cambridge, Univ. Press, 1949.

386. Tansley, A. G., and T. F. Chipp.   *Aims and Methods in the Study of Vegetation.* London, Brit. Empire Veg. Comm., 1926.

387. Thomson, G. W.   Measures of plant aggregation based on contagious distributions. *Contr. Lab. Vert. Biol. Univ. Mich.,* 1952, 53:1–16.

388. Tinney, F. W., O. S. Aamodt, and H. L. Ahlgren.   Preliminary report of a study on methods in botanical analysis of pasture swards. *Jour. Amer. Soc. Agron.,* 1937, 29:835–846.

389. Tiver, N. S., and R. S. Crocker.   The grasslands of southeast South

Australia in relation to climate, soils, and developmental history. *Jour. Brit. Grassl. Soc.*, 1951, 6:29–80.

390. Todd, V.　The habits and ecology of British harvestmen (*Arachnida opiliones*) with special reference to those of the Oxford District. *Jour. Animal Ecol.*, 1949, 18:209–216.

391. Tropical Forest Experiment Station.　Tenth Annual Report. *Caribbean For.*, 1950, 11:59–80.

392. Tropical Forest Experiment Station. Eleventh Annual Report. *Caribbean For.*, 1951, 12:1–16.

393. Troup, R. S.　*Report on Forestry in Kenya Colony.* London, Crown Agents, 1922.

394. Turesson, G.　The plant species in relation to habitat and climate. *Hereditas*, 1925, 6:147–236.

395. Turesson, G.　Zur Natur und Begrenzung der Arteinheiten. *Hereditas*, 1929, 12:323–334.

396. Turrill, W. B.　*The Plant Life of the Balkan Peninsula: A Phytographical Study.* London, Clarendon Press, 1929.

397. Ule, E.　Epiphyten des Amazonasgebietes. *Vegetationsbilder*, 1904, Ser. 2, Fasc. 1.

398. U.S. Soil Conservation Service.　*Range Management Handbook.* Washington, S.C.S. Region 9, 1938.

399. Vahl, M.　The growth-forms of some plant formations of Swedish Lapland. *Dansk. Bot. Ark.*, 1913, 1:1–18.

400. Vaughn, R. E., and P. O. Wiehe.　Studies on the vegetation of Mauritius. III. The structure and development of the upland climax forest. *Jour. Ecol.*, 1941, 29:127–160.

401. Vavilov, N. I.　The new systematics of cultivated plants. In J. Huxley (ed.), *The New Systematics.* Oxford, Clarendon Press, 1940.

402. Vestal, A. G.　Unequal scales for rating species in communities. *Amer. Jour. Bot.*, 1943, 30:305–310.

403. Vestal, A. G.　Internal relations of terrestrial associations. *Amer. Midl. Nat.*, 1954, 48:413–445.

404. Vierhapper, F.　Eine neue Einteilung der Pflanzengesellschaften. *Natur. Wissenschf.*, 1921, 20.

405. Voth, P.　Conduction of rainfall by plant stems in a tropical rain forest. *Bot. Gaz.*, 1939, 101:328–340.

406. Wallace, A. R.　*Tropical Nature and Other Essays.* London, Macmillan, 1878.

407. Wangerin, W.　Beiträge zur pflanzensociologischen Begriffsbildung und Terminology. I. Die Assoziation. *Fedde Repert. Spec. nov. reg. veg.*, 1925, Beih. 36:3–59.

408. Warming, E.　Lagoa Santa. *Naturvidensk. og math afdel. 1890–92*, 1892, 6:153–488.

409. Warming, E.　*Plantesamfund.* (Transl. P. Groom and I. B. Balfour, *Oecology of Plants.* Oxford, Univ. Press, 1909.)

410. Warming, E., and P. Graebner. *Lehrbuch der Ökologischen Pflanzengeographie.* Berlin, Borntraeger, 1933.

411. Wells, B. W.   Plant communities of the coastal plain of North Carolina and their successional relations. *Ecol.,* 1928, 9:230–242.

412. West, O.   An investigation of the methods of botanical analysis of pasture. *So. African Jour. Sci.,* 1937, 33:501–559.

413. Whitford, H. N.   The vegetation of the Lamao Forest Reserve. *Philippine Jour. Sci.,* 1906, 1:373–431, 637–682.

414. Whitford, P. B.   Distribution of woodland plants in relation to succession and clonal growth. *Ecol.,* 1949, 30:199–208.

415. Whitford, P. B.   Estimation of the ages of forest stands in the prairie-forest border region. *Ecol.,* 1951, 32:143–147.

416. Whitman, W. C., and E. I. Siggeirsson.   Comparison of line interception and point contact methods of mixed grass range vegetation. *Ecol.,* 1954, 35:431–436.

417. Whittaker, R. H.   A study of summer foliage insect communities in the Great Smoky Mountains. *Ecol. Monogr.,* 1952, 22:1–44.

418. Willdenow, C.   Allgemeine Bemerkungen über die Unterschied der Vegetation. *Mag. naturf. Freunde,* 1811.

419. Williams, C. B.   The application of the logarithmic series to the frequency of occurrence of plant species in quadrats. *Jour. Ecol.,* 1950, 38:107–138.

420. Willis, J. C.   *Age and Area.* Cambridge, Univ. Press, 1922.

421. Wilson, L. R.   Rooted aquatic plants and their relation to the limnology of freshwater lakes. *Amer. Assoc. Adv. Sci.,* 1939, 10:107–122.

422. Winch, N. J.   *An essay on the geographical distribution of plants through the counties of Northumberland, Cumberland, and Durham.* Newcastle, Hodgson, 1819.

423. Wood, B. R.   The vegetation of forests of the Bartica-Kaburi area. *Rept. Conserv. For. Brit. Guiana Court, 2nd Sp. Ses.* Georgetown, 1926.

424. Woodin, H. E., and A. A. Lindsey.   Juniper-pinon east of the continental divide, as analyzed by the line-strip method. *Ecol.,* 1954, 35:473–489.

425. Wulff, E. V.   *An Introduction to Historical Plant Geography.* Waltham, Chron. Bot., 1943.

INDEX